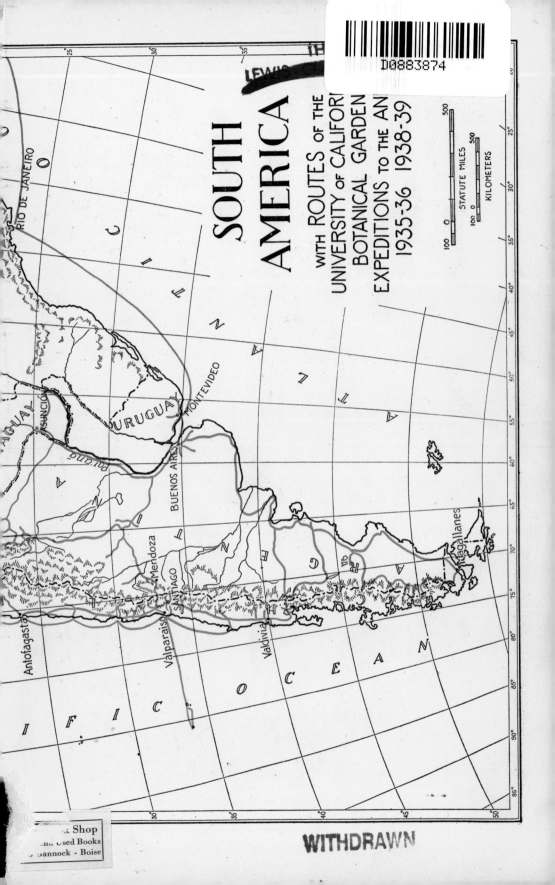

SOUTH AMERICA

WITH ROUTES of THE
UNIVERSITY of CALIFORNIA
BOTANICAL GARDEN
EXPEDITIONS to THE ANDES
1935-36   1938-39

STATUTE MILES

KILOMETERS

RIO DE JANEIRO

CHILE

URUGUAY

MONTEVIDEO

ASUNCION

Paraná

BUENOS AIRES

ARGENTINA

Mendoza

SANTIAGO

Valparaiso

Valdivia

Magallanes

Antofagasta

PACIFIC OCEAN

ATLANTIC

PLANT HUNTERS
IN THE ANDES

The massive flower stalk of a pineapple relative (*Puya caerulea*) silhouetted against the dry coastal mountains of central Chile

PLANT HUNTERS
IN THE ANDES

By

T. HARPER GOODSPEED

Illustrated with Photographs

FARRAR AND RINEHART, INC.

NEW YORK   TORONTO

TO

LORA J. KNIGHT

WITH AFFECTION AND GRATITUDE

ACKNOWLEDGMENTS

In this book some of the Peruvian and Chilean accomplishments and experiences of members of two plant hunting expeditions sent out by the University of California Botanical Garden are described. These expeditions were made possible by grants-in-aid from the American Academy of Arts and Sciences (Boston), American Philosophical Society (Philadelphia), California Garden Clubs, Incorporated, California Spring Garden Show, Inc. (Oakland, California), Huntington Botanical Garden (San Marino, California), Instituto de Botanica Darwinion (Buenos Aires), Royal Horticultural Society (London), and by many private individuals who made contributions to the expedition fund set up by the University of California. During the first expedition the author was assisted by renewal of a Fellowship grant by the John Simon Guggenheim Memorial Foundation of New York. W. R. Grace & Co., McCormick Steamship Co., and Pan American Airways granted reductions in passenger fares and the cost of transporting equipment and collections. Without the co-operation of the governments of the Republics of Argentina, Bolivia, Chile, and Peru, their scientific institutions, a large number of their citizens, and of the missions of the United States in those republics, our work in South America could not have been accomplished. The author and a number of members of the expeditions were appointed collaborators of the United States Department of Agriculture, Bureau of Plant Industry, and Division of Plant Exploration and Introduction.

For assistance in the preparation of this book I am under obligation to Dr. Harvey E. Stork. He not only made contributions to the subject matter, but also put at my disposal his knowledge of the refinements of photographic technique to which is due such excellence as the illustrative material possesses. To my wife I am indebted for constructive criticism of the manuscript. Her sympathetic, yet discerning, reaction to

South American life is reflected in the descriptions of intimate scenes and experiences. Other members of the expeditions and the staff of the University of California Botanical Garden have assisted in many ways. A Work Projects Administration project, providing clerical and gardening assistance, has been in part responsible for the rapidity with which our South American plant collections have yielded the botanical information which has been included.

The photographs reproduced were, with one exception, taken by expedition members and in most cases by Dr. Stork, Prinz Egon von Ratibor (James West), and Dr. John L. Morrison. Mr. Bennett Greig, a member of the British Legation in Lima, has kindly permitted me to reproduce his photograph of Peruvian Indian women which appears between pages 192 and 193.

CONTENTS

ILLUSTRATIONS

PLANT HUNTERS
IN THE ANDES

Chapter I

WHY, WHO, AND WHERE?

The squash grew from the earth above Earth-Mother's navel, the beans from the earth above her feet, and tobacco from above her head—thus it soothes the mind and sobers thought. —*Iroquois tradition*

THE SENIOR class stood in broken ranks on College Hill waiting to begin the march to the First Baptist Meeting House where we would receive our last official gift from Brown University—that short roll of white paper tied with a knot of brown ribbon. Relatives and friends pressed upon us with greetings and congratulations. In the crowd I saw one of my freshman fraternity brothers. Hailed and instructed, he left for the Chapter House in search of any mail that might have come that morning for me. Perhaps there would be a letter, or more than one, to bring the written equivalents of those encouraging words which on every side were being spoken to my classmates fortunate enough to have their families with them at Commencement. However brave the look and sophisticated the attitude, the senior on that last day discovers the world, a formidable and complex place, for the first time, and a word of encouragement is more heartening than he permits it to appear.

Among my letters was something that I had given up hope of receiving—notice of my appointment as Assistant in the Department of Botany at the University of California. That was more than thirty years ago, and, although from time to time I have wandered far afield, my connection with the University of California has been continuous and my regard for it increasing. Quantitatively it was a small institution in those days, but in things of the mind and spirit it had already reached a plane which in the intervening years it has been difficult to elevate.

When I came to California I had little idea that I was taking the first positive step in the life of a plant hunter. There was no way of telling that ahead of me lay adventures on the eaves of the world and on the Pacific shelf of the Southern

3

continent below them. For my plant hunting in the Andes really began with an introduction to *Nicotiana* on the second day after my arrival. That introduction was to lead eventually to the two South American expeditions which this book describes.

I recall now hours of earthquake and shipwreck, of experienced or imagined dangers and privations in deserts, jungles, and snowfields, of sickness, loneliness, and the depression that follows long contact with primitive ways of life in uncongenial climates. Extended over a total of more than a year these experiences furnish me with an example, not the first and not the best, of how sustaining scientific curiosity can become. I sometimes wonder at my temerity in having assumed responsibility for the well-being of my wife and the other ten members of the two expeditions to the Andes; for we spent a total of eighty man months there, many of them in territory where I knew in advance that distress of body and mind might lie in wait at any point, at any time.

When we ask the why and the where of this story we come back to the plants which led us on. *Nicotiana* is the name given to an aggregation or genus of flowering plants which belongs to the Solanaceae or Nightshade family. To this large and cosmopolitan plant family also belongs the potato, tomato, the pepper (but not the one in the pepper shaker), and many less known plants. So far as *Nicotiana* itself is concerned its chief claim to fame is the species *tabacum,* the tobacco plant, one of the most commercially valuable crop plants in the world. But in addition to *tabacum* there are some sixty other species classified under *Nicotiana,* of which one or two have some agricultural, a few considerable horticultural, and the remainder botanical, importance.

My introduction to *Nicotiana tabacum* as a living plant (for my smoking began long before) was arranged by Dr. W. A. Setchell, one of the world's foremost botanists, at that time and for many years thereafter Chairman of the Department of Botany at the University in Berkeley. The size of his pipe and the volume of his smoke had awed the undergraduate long before my advent on the campus. It was in part his enthusiasm as a smoker but far more his scientific curiosity and a keen collector's instinct that led him to make, first, a collection of tobacco pipes from near and far; second, a collection of the early literature on and broadsides against smoking; and, finally, a living collection in the University's Botanical Garden of the many cultivated varieties of the tobacco plant and its numerous wild relatives.

That first morning in the Botanical Garden the professor showed me plants of "Havana," "Maryland Broadleaf," "White Burley," and many other tobacco varieties, most of which were of lesser agricultural and greater botanical interest. Some were low-growing but many were over six feet in height and portly. There were white, red, pink, larger and smaller flowered races. One of them bore peculiar double flowers of a sort sometimes called "hose in hose," and on the same order as the "cup and saucer" flowered *Campanula* of old-fashioned gardens. Some varieties bore stalked or petiolate leaves, others unstalked or sessile ones; some leaves were slender and sharp-pointed, others blunt at the apex and wide behind it. The professor showed me why shape is one of the things important in the selection of tobacco leaves for making cigar wrappers, because one shape will cut more wrappers without excessive waste than another. He pulled down an old branch, long out of flower, and from the dry, open capsules at its end, poured into my hand thousands of the minute dark-brown seeds which the tobacco plant produces.

Nearby was another species of *Nicotiana* called *rustica*. It was actually the first sort of tobacco cultivated in the Colony of Virginia, where the white man obtained the seeds from the little gardens in which the Indians were growing it along with their corn and beans and squashes. It was not long, however, before the colonists replaced *rustica* with the far more desirable species, *tabacum*, which probably came to them from Indian cultivation in the West Indies and has ever since been the tobacco of commerce. Of late years *rustica* is beginning to have some agricultural importance as a high-yielding source of nicotine sulfate for use in insecticides.

Then the professor showed me his collection of "wild" species of *Nicotiana*, those which had no importance agriculturally but were allied in form and structure to those which had. First I saw the native North American species. They came from the Great Plains, the Southwest, and the Pacific slopes, and almost all of them had been smoked, on ceremonial occasions at least, by the Blackfoot, Crow, Navajo, Comanche, and other tribes. Then there were species from Australia, Tasmania, and New Caledonia, all of them small plants as compared with tobacco and bearing fragrant, white flowers. I have always wondered why they are not more frequently grown in gardens.

Because of man's intervention it is today hard to say just what were the original areas of distribution of the various Australian species of *Nicotiana*. Many years ago in Australia, cattle were driven over long distances to market or to seasonal pasturage, and the minute seeds of trailside Nicotianas were caught in their rough coats and carried far away from their native homes, to grow and mingle and cross with cousins that were originally distant both geographically and botanically.

Finally the professor and I came to the garden beds in which he was growing the Nicotianas from South America. Towering high above its relatives from other continents was the great "tree tobacco" (*N. tomentosa*) of the Andes. We shall come across it in a later chapter growing to a height of forty feet where the jungle disappears and the Peruvian Cordilleras rise to their supreme altitudes. What I saw on that first day in the Botanical Garden was a monstrous bush twenty feet high with many stems from the base, all clothed with large coarse leaves and bearing at their tips pyramids of pinkish white flowers. It had been growing happily and vigorously in the Berkeley climate for a number of years and lived as long again until finally killed by an unusually heavy frost.

Near the base of this giant *Nicotiana* were lower but still sizable plants of another species, which produced flat-topped heads of long, slender, white tubular flowers, very fragrant. It is a native of Andean foothills in northwestern Argentina. Sometimes under its own name, *Nicotiana sylvestris,* or under that of some other species, it is listed in seedsmen's catalogues and may be seen now and then in gardens other than botanical ones.

There were many other Nicotianas from the Andes and from the east and west coasts of our sister continent. We shall

come across them, as well as others not known to exist until
we discovered them, in the pages that follow, and they had best
be described in their own native setting and with the comic or
tragic experiences of the plant hunters who collected them.

My introduction, thirty years ago, to *Nicotiana* resulted
in a permanent alliance, and my study of her and her relatives
will apparently be lifelong. This study has already taken me to
many pleasant places and put me into touch with colleagues
all around the world. It sent me to Sweden when the demorali-
zation of German science that immediately followed the first
World War had made Botaniska Institutet of the University of
Stockholm the most famous headquarters in the world for research in the anatomy of the cell; to botanical centers in England, France, and Germany in 1930 and 1931. With my family
I lived most of that year in Berlin-Dahlem to be near the research institutes of the Kaiser Wilhelm Gesellschaft and the
Botanical Garden and Museum of the University of Berlin.

How vividly I remember my first Nazi salutes! By special
dispensation my fifteen-year-old son was admitted as a full-
fledged student in the Arndt Gymnasium; there he lived in
one of the villa dormitories originally built by Wilhelm in
order that the sons of his provincial ministers might live and be
educated in the capital. For the spring holiday he was invited to
go home with a schoolmate whose family owned one of the
great estates in East Prussia. I went to the school to see the two
boys off on their train for the country. From the school gate
the young Germans were pouring out loaded with bags and
rucksacks and filling Königin-Luise Strasse with their noisy holiday exuberance and shouted good-byes to classmates and teachers. But many of these good-byes were not spoken ones only but
ended in an arm-raised, palm-fronted salute. It was new to me
and seemed very foreign to a Germany that had shown only
evidence of glorying in its freedom from military etiquette as
well as Verboten signs. How little I realized on that spring
morning more than ten years ago that the raised arms I saw
represented outward allegiance by German schoolboys and their
teachers to a formula designed to breed the ultimate in man's
inhumanity to man!

Still on the trail of *Nicotiana* I was in Europe again in

1938 and in Germany six weeks before "Munich." I have just been listening on the radio to Hendrik van Loon. He was telling how history repeats illustrations of what he called the "fact blindness" of men and nations. He defined it as an inability or unwillingness, inconceivable in retrospect, of human beings and their leaders to interpret the evidence before their eyes in terms of the result which it so clearly indicated, and then to formulate their plans and direct their activities in accordance with the facts. Berlin in the summer of 1938 was full of facts. Not alone sidewalks crowded with soldiers equipped to fight and camouflaged motor transport for troops and guns on many streets but, more disturbing, an all-pervading atmosphere of expectation among the young and anxiety among the old, which you felt almost like the hush that immediately precedes the storm. How could the world have been so blind?

The culmination of my pursuit and study of *Nicotiana* came in an expedition to South America in 1935-1936 which was followed by another in 1938-1939. Distillation of the fruits, material and otherwise, of a part of those South American journeys is the substance of this book.

My scientific addiction to *Nicotiana* has had a single underlying purpose. I hope to produce a picture of the way in which in past time the species of a typical genus of flowering plants— and *Nicotiana* is one—have originated; of how and to what extent they are today related, and of the various avenues along which their evolution will in the future be directed. To this end we have assembled from near and far in the University of California Botanical Garden the world's largest living collection of *Nicotiana* species. Growing side by side under equivalent conditions their likenesses and distinctions in form and structure can be estimated. Hybridization between species and varieties and study of the breeding behavior of hybrid progenies have extracted from the living plants evidence concerning their origins and relationships. More fundamental and precise is our evidence from the cell itself and the microscopical revelation of the character and behavior of the nucleus, bearer of the hereditary potentialities, in species and hybrids. Finally, and in the desire that the picture should be not only most complete and accurate but also most realistic, I went to South America where I could see growing in their native state the most numerous and the most important of the species of *Nicotiana*. In the foothills and on the higher slopes of the Andes from near the Equator almost to Cape Horn, along the coasts of all of Peru and Argentina and of part of Brazil and Chile they were reported to be growing. I believed that if I could know them on their native heaths and not alone as dried specimens in the museum or as expatriates growing in a California Botanical Garden, they might reveal secrets concerning their lives and relationships which would not otherwise be revealed. My expectation was abundantly fulfilled.

There was no dollar sign at the end of our search for the wild relatives of the tobacco plant, not even the desire to add something to the quality of the five-cent cigar. Why then, you may ask, spend time and money, subject yourself and others to danger and privation in a far-off land, on such a thoroughly "impractical" quest? There is only one reply, the one that fortunately has been valid since man began to think—the pursuit of knowledge can become an end in itself.

Actually our plant hunting for *Nicotiana* in the Andes *had* practical significance. For the Bureau of Plant Exploration and Introduction of the United States Department of Agriculture we collected many strains of the tobacco plant, either cultivated ones or those that had escaped from cultivation and become naturalized in the wilderness. In addition, duplicates of all the new or little-known wild species of *Nicotiana* went to Washington. There, in the experimental plots, greenhouses, and laboratories, the government's tobacco experts are working, among other things, on the problem of finding disease-resistant races of tobacco. This problem has a big dollar sign attached to it, because the losses from fungus diseases alone in the tobacco-growing areas of the Southern states may amount to many millions of dollars annually. To reduction in these losses, some of our collections of *Nicotiana* may make a contribution.

Some years ago we proved that the tobacco plant is a hybrid originally produced in past, perhaps very distant past, time by the natural crossing of the ancestors of *Nicotiana* species which today grow in the Andes of Peru, Bolivia, and Argentina. These descendants are vigorous wild plants and some of them may prove to be disease resistant. This means that by artifically crossing them with our highly bred and selected, and thus less vigorous and more susceptible, tobacco varieties, the original virtues of the wild ancestors that produced the first tobacco plants may be reintroduced into our fields. We found in the Andes these descendants in great number and variety, indeed some that had never before been known to exist; and they have all gone to the tobacco breeders. Perhaps after all we may, indirectly, have a hand in the creation of that better five-cent cigar!

I was brought up at the extremity of our family's mid-Victorianism and New Englandism. As the only child in a clan that included a number of quite young to very adult aunts and uncles, it was difficult for me to resist the frequent admonitions to turn out my toes, and I became ingenious in lightening the severity of strict Sunday observances. In general I managed to be something of a thorn in the family flesh. Less easy to resist was the insistence upon doubling up on things. It became a matter of conscience never to do one thing at a time if more than one could be accomplished, and remarks were made about "letting your head save your heels." It got to the stage where you hated to go up or down the stairs unless there was something to carry in addition to yourself. There is no limit to the ramifications of this tendency not to let well enough alone. I believe that it all must have been an oblique application of the New England hatred of idleness. At any rate I am still afflicted with a passion for pyramiding my activities. I lightheartedly make commitments, like writing this book, in the face of clear and positive evidence that commitments already made represent a full day's work.

It will, therefore, be no surprise to learn that my Andean plant hunting had more than one objective. Study of the wide geographic distribution of *Nicotiana* and particularly the search for previously unknown species were its primary objectives, and the areas and seasons in which we collected were determined solely in favor of them. In addition, however, I accepted commissions from botanists at home and abroad to do a little private hunting for the South American plants they needed; from the

United States Department of Agriculture to collect wild potatoes, corn, cotton and tomatoes as well as tobacco; and from garden clubs and others to bring home as many plants of proved
or potential ornamental importance as we could find. As if this
were not enough of a program I decided (with the result that
no member of the two expeditions could feel that he had a free
moment) to make four or more dried and pressed specimens of
all the various kinds of plants in addition to *Nicotiana* that we
came across. Certainly the shades of my ancestors had no reason
to complain.

I needed help to carry out successfully the plant-hunting
program just described. Not ordinary people to go with me to
South America but trained collectors or at least those who had
a botanical background and some experience in adjusting themselves to foreign and unfavorable environments. A minimum of
newspaper publicity concerning our plans for South American
plant hunting was enough to bring out the volunteers.

From all over the United States young and old, male and
female, wrote to me intimately about their physiques, moral
character, adventurous spirit, love of flowers, and burning desire to see South America. All this they would freely and willingly devote to the success of the expeditions in return for
traveling expenses and a reasonable salary. Some of them gave
me their advance picture of what we would be doing in South
America. It was apparently to be a glorious safari—native porters in a straggling line winding through the untrodden wilderness, flanked with swarms of bronzed and hardy botanists gathering in the rare and beautiful vegetation. One volunteer, employed at the moment in a lumber camp, saw himself chopping
down the tall and stately forest trees of the high Andes so that
we might gather their topmost blossoms. A young lady, expert
in the manipulation of business machines of all sorts, was to
make a charming picture seated at the door of her tent on the
mountainside running her fingers rapidly over a battery of cal-
culators. Otherwise, she predicted serious errors in our accounts.
By their letters, these and many more volunteers demonstrated
that the pioneer spirit is with us yet—we still long to "live ad-
venturously."

One volunteer called upon me personally. He was an

amazingly versatile gentleman. First, he told me that he was a construction expert. Before I could stop him he had built me quite a village, which he said would be essential as headquarters in the Andean fastnesses for the dozens of collectors, packers, cooks, and body servants we would be taking along. His opinion of the importance of our expedition suffered visibly when I finally had a chance to explain that not more than two or three of us were likely to be in any one part of the Andes at any one time. He then revealed the fact that he was an embalmer. Pointing an accusing finger at me, he said, "Have you considered death and what you would do about it?" Before he gave me time to ponder this sobering question he poured forth such a flood of statistics on the causes and incidence of accidental death as would deter the stoutest heart from venturing any distance from his hearthstone. Before I recovered from this gloomy prospect he took me into the mortician's confidence concerning rates of decay in cadavers, with special reference to cause of death, temperature relations, and other depressing details.

In other words, it appeared that each member of the expedition should, like the immortal Sarah, travel with a coffin, our friend, the volunteer, being on hand to counteract decay and dissolution as one after another of us died an unnatural death. I never thought to ask him what would happen at the end when he found himself alone with his coffin. But this was not all. Our combined construction expert and embalmer was also an airplane pilot and thus was able to add the capstone to the arch—he would fly each product of his handiwork to civilization, thence to start its journey home to its relatives. He explained that for legal as well as sentimental reasons the relatives probably would insist upon receiving the remains. I cannot understand why such a versatile man, so serious minded, so conscientious, with so picturesque an imagination, should have been on government relief!

From my point of view the most important member of our two South American expeditions was my wife. Her acquaintance with *Nicotiana* is almost as old as mine. For twenty-five years, in dusty museums, on muddy experimental fields, and along Andean coasts and mountainsides, Florence has made drawings and helped me in taking notes and photographs. Her amiability is without limit and her confidence in the ultimate triumph of the good, the true, and the beautiful, is unshakable. She is a joyful traveler, anticipating only pleasure, entertainment, and profit, and therefore finding them always awaiting her. She acted as artist and secretary of the two expeditions and assisted in the care and preparation as well as the collecting of plant material.

During the comparatively brief expedition of 1935-1936, Mrs. Ynes Mexia and Prince Egon von Ratibor were with us as assistants and collectors. Mrs. Mexia was a remarkable woman. Relatively late in life she began her travels in Mexico, Alaska, and South America, which had as principal objective the collecting of plants in remote and inaccessible regions. She had already had almost three years of plant collecting in Brazil, Ecuador, and Peru before she joined the 1935 expedition; and the advice and information she gave us concerning primitive life in the Andes and how to become adjusted to it was invaluable. During the three months that Mrs. Mexia was with us she covered a large amount of territory and collected intensively, particularly in Peru and the foothills of the Argentinean Andes. The dried and pressed specimens she prepared were uniformly models of their kind and were annotated very fully and effectively. She was the true explorer type and happiest when independent and far from civilization. She always made light of the privations and dangers which, at sixty-five years of age and alone except for native helpers, she endured for long periods in exceedingly out-of-the-way parts of temperate and tropical South America and Mexico. Her death in 1938, following an expedition to the mountains in the state of Oaxaco, Mexico, was a great loss to botanists who had learned so much that was new about the vegetation of the territories in which she had collected.

During her work in Ecuador, Mrs. Mexia had acquired a devoted servant and assistant. Palma was a short, stout, jolly young Ecuadorian. He looked upon his position with pride and took his duties seriously. On collecting trips he ranged far and wide to gather in armloads of miscellaneous vegetation which he would triumphantly deposit at Mrs. Mexia's feet. She would immediately sort it out, call his attention to those species of which she wanted more specimens, and then they would put the plants into the presses.

We were all together in Lima for a week in October, 1935, and Palma insisted upon valeting me. My shoes were his particular passion and he always managed to seize them on the doorstep of my room in the hotel before the sleepy porters had begun their early morning shoe-shining operations. Unfortunately he was afflicted with a settled conviction that my oil shoe polish required the addition of saliva, and as a result the effect of his ministrations was a somewhat foggy and not at all lasting variety of shine. For this reason and also because bad blood began to develop between Palma and the official hotel bootblacks, I had to call him off, a proceeding that hurt his feelings dreadfully.

Prince Egon, or James West as he was known to a large circle of acquaintances in California, was a most valuable member of the party. The breadth of his botanical interests and knowledge and, in particular, his wide contacts with ornamental horticulture in California and elsewhere, provided him with the proper background for the type of collection that was assigned to him. His linguistic accomplishments were of service on many occasions when one language avenue after another had to be explored before a common one could be found. He continued to travel and collect for me in Peru, Bolivia, and Argentina, long after Florence and I had to return to California early in 1936; and he remained in South America for some time after he ended his connection with the first expedition. Unfortunately he was unable to be with us during the second expedition to the Andes in 1938-1939.

The second expedition was a more ambitious affair than the first. The evidence we had already obtained in South America, together with additional information from many sources, made it clear that in the Andes and nearby there was much more *Nicotiana* collecting of the most important sort still to be done. These vital collecting areas were spread over a great north and south distance and some of them were more inaccessible than any in which we had worked during the expedition of 1935-1936. In many important regions quite distant from one another the best collecting seasons coincided. This meant that one person or one party would have to stay in South America a number of years or plan to commute from the United States to the Andes, if the botanizing I required was to be accomplished. On the other hand, if I could take a large party with me and subdivide it into small, mobile units, then the collecting could go on simultaneously over a large stretch of the Andes, the coasts, and the plains. In this way it should be possible to cover all or most of the important areas in a single year. This second alternative was adopted and proved to be workable, but by no means as simple as it sounds.

One of the units of the second expedition operated exclusively in Peru. It was led by Dr. Harvey E. Stork, Professor of Botany in Carleton College. Harvey was, in fact, the assistant director of the expedition and was prepared to take over in the event of my being for any reason put out of commission. To the work he brought extended collecting experience in the highlands of Costa Rica and therefore knew what to expect in the Andes and how to meet it. He was the ideal combination—a highly trained and enthusiastic botanist, an experienced collector, a skilled photographer; all this, with his keen sense of humor and sprightliness of imagination, made him an excellent companion.

With him in Peru were Ovid Butler ("Bob") Horton and Dr. César Vargas Calderon. Bob had just graduated from the University of California where he had done some work in botany and more in paleontology. Brought up in Wyoming on the dude ranch of his father, Congressman Horton, he knew the mountains, horse wrangling, and the vagaries of pack animals. Physically he was a bit on the short and slight side, while Harvey was the reverse. Thus they complemented each other physically and in every way made a good team. César was the Professor of Botany and Director of the Botanical Museum at the University of Cuzco in the Andes of southeastern Peru. His knowledge of the vegetation of the Andes was extremely useful, and during the periods when he accompanied Harvey and Bob he made important contributions to the success of their work.

Another unit of the expedition was assigned to Chile. First and last it involved five people. At the beginning Dr. Carlton R. Worth and John L. Morrison were the official members of the Chilean party. Later on Rodolfo Wagenknecht joined them and Florence and I made collections during our three months in Chile. Carl, a member of the Department of Mathematics at Rutgers University, was a well-known amateur grower of alpine plants and had studied and collected them in the Rocky Mountains. Unfortunately he was unable to remain in South America late enough in the season to accomplish as much in the Chilean mountains as he had proposed to do. John was well along toward his doctor's degree in botany at the University of California. He had a thorough grounding in his subject and some collecting experience, and developed a remarkable capacity for accepting the punishment that the Andes can inflict. He acquitted himself well on difficult and trying assignments, one of which provided him with the distinction of having been wrecked on Robinson Crusoe's Island. Rodolfo was on leave from his post as Inspector of Roads for the Chilean government. For some years he had been collecting insects in the Andes of Central Chile. He soon developed real ability as a plant collector and his official contacts were put to good use.

The third unit of the expedition collected in certain areas along a winding path which began in Peru, traversed Bolivia and Argentina, reached Magellan Strait, and then turned back into southern Chile. The leader of this unit was Walter J. Eyerdam, of Seattle. He was the unadulterated collector and explorer type with a flair for natural history in general and for shells and plants in particular. Under his name, collections from the South Seas, Alaska, Kamchatka, and elsewhere are to be found in many museums at home and abroad. His activity of mind and body, and his capacity for adjusting himself to new environments and their inhabitants, made him exceedingly valuable. With him, until near the end of the expedition was Alan A. Beetle. At Dartmouth, Harvard, and Wyoming, Alan had done advanced work in botany and proposed to obtain his doctorate at California. His special botanical interest, the sedges, was well served in South America, and he did much other important collecting for the expedition. With Walter and Alan on their Patagonian adventure was a young Argentine, Eduardo Grondona, an advanced student of botany in the University of La Plata.

Flowers and upper leaves of a new treelike relative of the tobacco plant discovered in the Andes of northern Peru—*Nicotiana Setchellii*

Wild and cultivated tobaccos in the University of California Botanical Garden

Flowers of a new hybrid tobacco created in the Botanical Garden

Early in October, 1935, the members of the first expedition assembled in Lima. Mrs. Mexia came from her collecting in Ecuador and the Prince had arrived from California some weeks before Florence and I came into Callao, Lima's harbor. After a week together we separated and did not all meet again until January, in Chile.

Those who had a part in the second expedition were at no time together in one place. Harvey arrived in Berkeley late in June, 1938, a week before Florence and I left for Europe. We spent days together in going over the assembled collecting equipment and discovered the usual last-minute deficiencies. We studied maps and compared them with collecting schedules. We discussed the personnel of the expedition without knowing much about personalities and made tentative decisions concerning the membership of the different collecting units—who would get along best with whom during the months ahead, whose training fitted him for work in one area as contrasted with other areas in which we proposed to collect. Harvey and I did not expect to meet in South America for nearly half a year and so there was a lot to talk over. Finally we had to give up the obviously hopeless attempt to anticipate all the problems that might come up in the interim.

The other members came to headquarters in Berkeley early in July. Then began the final organization and packing of equipment and personal belongings. In addition, some of the expedition members had to be introduced to *Nicotiana* in the Botanical Garden, and all studied other elements of the South American floras so that they would not feel entirely lost among the unfamiliar plants they were to encounter.

On July 27, the six men with Harvey in command sailed from San Francisco aboard the freighter *Capac,* one of a small fleet of freighters at that time belonging to W. R. Grace and Company. Forty days later they left the *Capac* at Callao, Peru, after many stops in Central American ports and in some on the northern coasts of South America. Whenever the ship was to be in port long enough they went ashore to collect plants and to experiment with strange foods and drinks. Aboard they studied Spanish, compared collecting experiences and techniques, and soon had the run of the very informal ship.

In addition to the expedition party that occupied practically all the passenger space on the *Capac* there was an American mining man of large South American experience. He immediately saw to it that the most impressionable members of the party were properly prepared for what they were to encounter in the mountains and jungles. I find in one of the diaries, which all expedition members faithfully kept, the following, which was written on the second day out of San Francisco:

"He told me about some of his terrible experiences among the wild Indians of eastern Peru and Ecuador. He said that a German professor with a good head of hair and a fine large mustache made a trip among the head-shrinking tribes. Nobody knew what happened to him until a few months later his shrunken head was offered for sale in a curio shop in Guayaquil. He also told about the old Quechua Indian who used to work at the Cerro de Pasco mines. Every day when the noon whistle blew he solemnly urinated in his hands, washed his face, smoothed down his hair, and was ready for dinner. Quite a simple procedure to be sure."

Now, I have heard these identical tales more than once in the smoking rooms of West Coast liners when an old timer found the proper audience of tourists. Of course they may be true.

It would be fruitless to attempt to total accurately the number of miles traveled by the twelve members of the two Andean expeditions. Anyway, no total is of much account these days unless it shows nine, or preferably ten, digits. However, if you care to think in terms of the crow flying between San Francisco and New York, I estimate that he would have to make the trip more than fifty times to cover as much distance as we traveled by sea, by land, and by air, on trains, automobiles, trucks, and busses, on horseback and muleback, and on that most dependable form of transportation, shank's mare.

Peru was crisscrossed in all directions—along the arid coastal plain, from coast to Cordillera, in and out of the *montaña* or tropical rain forest—first by the Prince, Mrs. Mexia, Florence, and myself, and later by Harvey, Bob, and César. Lima was general headquarters and Cuzco a secondary one. We met president and peon, Indians and mixed bloods, a few compatriots, more Britishers, Germans, Japanese, and Italians. We were charmingly entertained by cultured Peruvians, received many attentions and much valuable assistance from the government, and were accepted by the Indians of the Andes and the jungle without particular interest or show of feeling. We learned something of the burdensome social and economic problems that face a semitropical country in which the primitive Indian element represents a majority of the population, and where foreign capital has built and controls essential communications and industries; where agricultural labor is exploited by home and foreign interests, and where lack of adequate transportation facilities has hampered extraction from mountains and forests of much of the great wealth that they are known to possess.

For us Peru possessed an increasing fascination. On every hand there were vestiges of pre-Columbian civilizations combined with those of Spanish colonial days, modern life at its Latin-American best rubbing elbows with the primitive, and contrasts waiting around every street corner or beyond the turn of any trail. Then add the immediate physical background of a double rank of some of the world's noblest mountains as well as thousands of square miles of mysterious tropical jungle. Peru is an intriguing conglomeration of elements, each with its own peculiar fascination, the like of which few equivalent areas on the earth's surface can boast.

In Peru, the botanist finds a wide choice of climate and vegetation. First, a coastal desert, containing a remarkable fog-supported winter flora on the tops of hills that rim the sea; next, the Andean complex with foothills both dry and moist, an unusually high snowline, great river gorges, and lofty semi-arid plateaus; and, finally, the vast tropical rain forest, with its wealth of lush vegetation. Chile too, has an arid coast line, eight hundred miles of it in the north. The Andes, which Chile shares with Argentina over a distance of more than two thousand miles, rise to supreme heights, and along their tremendous north-south extension, exhibit wide variations in climates and floras. Interestingly enough, Chile possesses on her southern coast the temperate equivalent of the Peruvian jungle and one of the few extensive temperate rain forests in the world. Be-

tween the arid north and wet south and just below the highest
point on the Andean backbone of the continent lies the heart
of Chile, with its Mediterranean, or if you will, Californian
climate. Chile, like Peru, will always be a magnet drawing plant
hunters toward her from near and far.

We worked along more than half of Chile's twenty-eight
hundred miles of coastline. Most of the rest is the excessively
humid archipelago and narrow Andean coast of the republic's
southern extremity, which held little of importance for us. We
collected in Chile's highlands and lowlands, on the margins of
her deserts, in her wet forests, and in the glorious climate of her
central zone.

Approximately five million people live in Chile. The majority are *mestizos* of Spanish-Indian blood, but Chile has no
social problem comparable to that which Peru's large Indian
population presents. In both Peru and Chile the upper class is
of Spanish descent. In Chile there is a middle class of predominantly foreign ancestry, while to no such extent in Peru
can one speak of a middle class interposed between the Indians
and the descendants of the conquistadors. By contrast with
Peru, a small but significant proportion of the upper class is of
British, Irish, and German origin.

The cordiality and co-operation of private citizens and
officialdom that we had enjoyed in Peru was also offered to us
everywhere in Chile. We set up our headquarters in Valparaiso where Florence and I have spent many happy months. As
a vacation land, Chile offers much, a fact which North American tourists are beginning to discover. If they need sophistica-
tion there is Santiago, Chile's capital, and in particular Viña
del Mar adjacent to Valparaiso, the so-called Monte Carlo of
the west coast. There cannot be many more magnificent areas in
the world than the nearby Andean crest with its culmination in
Mt. Aconcagua, the highest mountain in both Americas. Finally,
Chile offers her "Switzerland," where the dense forests
of the southern Andes begin their sweep toward Cape Horn—
a marvelous land of lakes, rivers, waterfalls, and snow-covered
volcanic peaks.

For the average visitor, Argentina is, of course, Buenos
Aires. We know this great, modern, gay, and beautiful capital.

But we also know something more of Argentina, something of that mighty land that flows eastward from the coastal capital to the Andes, north to the warm moist borders of the semitropics, and south to the cold, blustering Magellanic Provinces. Argentina's progressive atmosphere, the relative stability of her government, and the character of her people, make a strong appeal to most North American travelers because they are reminders of home. But these visitors seldom realize that geographical analogies also can be drawn between Argentina and the United States. We were continually more and more impressed by them.

For example, Argentina's sub- to semi-tropical areas may be likened to Florida, adjacent states, and a part of California; upper Patagonia to our Southwest; the northern portion of her South Atlantic coast to the southern section of our North Atlantic one; her Paraná to our Mississippi, her Andes to our Rockies. To stretch the parallelism to include descendants of ancient floras, Argentina has her Araucarias and we have our Sequoias.

The geographical equivalents just mentioned may have little scientific importance, but they will give you a partial picture, in terms of our own geography, of the types of terrain that the plant hunter explores in Argentina. In addition, these equivalents mean that we can find many fundamental aspects of life that Argentina and the United States possess in common. Why should not they be stressed rather than those distinctions between us in Old World origins and therefore in derived cultures and points of view?

We look back upon our months in the Argentine with great satisfaction. We came to know a fair cross section of the land and its people, and to see and study the vegetation of all the geographical subdivisions already mentioned. As elsewhere in the other South American republics where we worked, high and low alike were kind and helpful. Government officials, particularly in the Department of Agriculture, were most co-operative. In Buenos Aires and elsewhere in Argentina I found colleagues in universities and other institutions, who freely placed at my disposal their technical advice and knowledge of the botany of their areas, as well as the valuable collections of plants in their fine museums.

Argentina has an area greater than Peru and Chile combined, and a population equal to the combined populations of
those two republics. In 1939, Buenos Aires claimed three million inhabitants. Certainly between one-fourth and one-fifth of
the total population of Argentina, with its land surface of over
a million square miles, is concentrated in the *Capital Federal.*
Almost three-fourths of Argentina's people are Argentine-
born and of European descent. The British community is said
to number fifty thousand, and both the Italian and German
communities are also large. Of North Americans, about three
thousand live in Argentina.

Some important collecting was done in Bolivia, but there
was time and opportunity to do only a very little in Paraguay
and Uruguay. Florence and I saw nothing of these three republics except the city of Montevideo. At different times the
Prince and Walter spent a total of two months in various parts
of Bolivia. Other members of the two expeditions crossed Bolivia on the familiar northern coast-to-coast route, from Peru on
the west coast through La Paz to Buenos Aires on the east coast.

Bolivia, like Peru, contains abrupt transitions between exceedingly different climatic zones. As a result, there is a series
of distinct and interesting floras. At the proper season, much of
the six thousand square miles of twelve-thousand-foot plateau
or *puna* shows a transient vegetation, containing many strange
and often beautiful plants adapted in form and structure to
meet the demands of a semi-arid, alpine environment. Then
there are the *Valles,* or highland valleys, the tropical valleys or
Yungas, where the northern mountains are drained by the
Amazon, the fertile Chaco to the south, and, dominating all, the
two majestic Andean ranges, with peaks rising to twenty thousand feet.

These geographical details describing the "where" of two
expeditions to South America have been brief, since the reader
will obtain a detailed introduction to certain of the areas referred to as he follows the route of the plant hunters up and
down the western side of our neighboring continent.

We will soon be off again to South America. On this third
expedition from the University of California we expect to learn
still more of the floras, landscapes, and peoples of Argentina and

to have our first intimate contact with Bolivia, Uruguay, and Brazil. Therefore, it seems best to restrict this book to an account of our plant hunting in Peru and Chile where most of the high Andean collecting was done and where we lived for almost a year. Then, at the close of the forthcoming expedition, I hope to bring together in another book a more comprehensive survey than would be possible now of what the plant hunter sees and finds along the eastern flanks of the Andes, in the pampa of Argentina, in the deserts and mountains of Patagonia, and in the plains and forests of southeastern Brazil.

Now that the "why," "who," and "where" have been answered, we can proceed with our far-flung quest for the South American Nicotianas and for the multitude of plants of ornamental importance that await the plant hunter in the Andes.

Chapter II

MEADOWS ON THE DESERT

FEW OTHER places on this earth are as dry as the deserts of the west coast of South America. From that point several degrees below the Equator, where the rim of our sister continent lies farthest west, to the middle of Chile there stretches a barren waste of sand and exposed rock. It averages fifty miles in width, is washed by the Pacific waters on the west, and bounded by the imperial Andes on the east. In much of this coastal wasteland rainfall is almost completely unknown, for the cool Humboldt Current upwelling along its shores so chills the winds from the southwest that they give up their moisture at sea and become dry as they blow over the warm land. They drive the desert sands to pile them into ever-shifting *médanos* or to carve the basic rock where it juts out to form the foothills of the Cordilleras.

When I tell you that in the midst of this rainless desert, I walked through fields of filmy-leaved flowering plants in water-soaked boots and with clothing wet by the dew from a mantle of delicate vegetation you will shake your head. You will tell me that I make too free with the license accorded every traveler, since the days of Sinbad, who returns from far-off lands. Nevertheless it is true, for there are a limited number of small areas on the deserts of Peru, and Chile also, where dense fogs hang almost continuously over coastal hills and plains during the late winter; with the result that the land is completely shaded from the rays of the sun and the soil becomes moist and even boggy as the saturated air condenses. On these wet spots in the desert a short-lived vegetation springs up, which resembles the woodland wildflowers that flourish in the springtime through our temperate zone forests. These "meadows on the desert" the people of the west coast call *lomas*.

In September the Peruvian lomas vegetation is usually at its height. Since the flora of the lomas had never been adequately studied I wanted collections made in them. I therefore planned the arrival of the six botanists in Lima early in Sep-

tember, even though the best collecting season in other parts of
Peru and Chile begins two months later. Soon after Harvey's
party arrived in the "City of Kings," two of them, Walter and
Alan, began their long journey across Peru, Bolivia, and the Argentine, a journey which was finally to carry them almost as far
south in South America as it is possible to go. Carl and John
were soon to be on their way down the south Peruvian and
north Chilean coast. But just before they left Harvey and Bob
behind to begin the eight months' Peruvian adventure, the four
gringos, or white foreigners, and César saw their first lomas together.

Peru can boast the dean of South American botanists, Dr.
Augusto Weberbauer. For many years he had studied the plants
of coast and Cordillera, of the desert and of the jungle. His wide
knowledge of the Peruvian floras produced dividends in a
famous book dealing with the plant geography of his foster
fatherland. When I first met him he looked to be a little, frail
old man. But how thoroughly he tired me out, then and later,
when we went together for plants into the Andean foothills!

It is a pity that so truly distinguished a scholar should be
forced to supplement his professorship in the University of San
Marcos by teaching in elementary and other schools. Despite
the drain on time and strength produced by a heavy teaching
schedule, he has succeeded in finishing a revision of his book
which includes the results of his and other botanists' work in
Peru during the years that have intervened since he first published it. He was most kind and co-operative during both our
expeditions and went with us on numerous collecting trips
near Lima. During the foggy winter he always takes visting botanists to the Lomas de Atacongo. There on the hills east of the
coastal town of Lurin and an hour or two by train or automobile south of Lima, he exhibits to them one of the vegetationally
richest of all the Peruvian meadows on the desert.

Don Augusto took us to Atacongo in 1935, and in 1938
invited the four California botanists and César to join the
faculty and students of natural science in the University of San
Marcos for a field trip to the same region.

A caravan of automobiles with geologists, botanists, zoolo-
gists, and others aboard, wound out of the city, ran through the

green irrigated fields that surround it, and soon reached the
sandy, barren coastal desert. After some twenty miles along a
good highway they passed the famous ruins of Pachacamac.
Many tourists go there to see the little that remains of what was
one of the most important coastal settlements during the pre-
Columbian era in Peru. They poke among the potsherds and
everywhere find evidence that Pachacamac was a vast necropolis
in Inca or pre-Inca days. In the hotel lobbies of Lima there are
always hanks of hair, teeth, bits of pottery, and fragments of
burial cloths being gloated over by grave robbers who receive
the envious glances of other tour members who did not invest
in the Pachacamac side trip. How many of those grave despoil-
ing compatriots of mine realize that the perfect preservation of
the antiquities they find at Pachacamac is proof that for many,
many hundreds of years the Peruvian coast must have been as
completely arid as it is today?

As the caravan passed Pachacamac, one of the San Marcos
professors referred to the loot of golden ornaments which the
conquistadors were said to have taken from the sandy graves
they opened there. They melted them into bullion for easier
transportation to Spain and thus destroyed museum pieces for
which modern collectors would have paid many times their intrinsic value. Perhaps the great golden plaques that once hung
on the walls of Pachacamac's temples and the other triumphs of
the ancient Peruvian goldsmiths turned into bullion by the
Spaniards, are still circulating through the world in coins and
jewelry. If so, some of it is buried again, this time at Fort Knox,
Kentucky!

Even at a distance the foggy hills near Lurin had a green
sheen, and as the cars drew up in a sheltered valley the lower
hillslopes showed scattered, delicate plants of *Oxalis, Cryptantha, Plantago,* and a *Drymaria* named for Dr. Weberbauer. He
had first collected it in this locality and sent it to Europe for
naming. All the plants were but a few inches high and most of
them in profuse bloom. They had none of the characteristics of
desert plants. The leaves were thin, without heavy cuticle, nor
were they gray in color as are the hairy leaves of many plants
of dry regions. A day's bright sun would have laid them flat.
But at this season there was no day of bright sun. There might

strapping some extra tins of gasoline on the running board. At
two-thirty he checked out at the office of the *guardia civil* and
finally made a start. People in Peru tell a story about a colectivo
that once started on time, but no one who knows colectivos
believes it!

Following a good highway northward from Lima, the colectivo bowled merrily along through the cultivations of the
Rimac Valley, thence out into the sand and over rocky ledges.
At times it skirted the coast to give glimpses of the beach where
white surf separated the red and yellow sands from the blue
waters of the Pacific. Where the coast was abruptly rocky the
highway rose well above the sea, and they looked down upon
vast clouds of guano birds following luckless schools of surface
fish, not hundreds or thousands but millions of birds.

By this time, almost two years after we last rode along it,
the fine automobile road, a segment of the Pan-American Highway, which the colectivo traveled north from Lima, must have
been completed to a point well north of Supe. It mostly follows the coast and this means that it is built on desert sands.
On this highway, Florence and I had an experience, conceived
in imagination and almost ending in reality.

A well-developed, hair-trigger imagination doubtless adds
to the enjoyment of life. Unfortunately, however, you cannot
turn it off at will. This we learned many times on South American roads. Probably long and continuous exposure to critical
situations, made doubly harrowing because you envisage, instantly and crystal clear, their potentially fatal consequences,
will ultimately discourage imagination. This ought to be so
because only rarely are these situations followed by the dire
consequences that you conjure up. But I certainly hate to think
of how much more misery I must endure before my imagination is properly trained!

Through the courtesy and co-operation of La Molina
Agricultural Experiment Station near Lima we were often given
the use of a big station wagon for our collecting trips into the
Andes and along the coasts. An efficient chófer came with the
machine. Including him, that April morning, our party num-
bered seven. First, there was Dr. Weberbauer. He was to guide
us to a special collecting ground in the foothills behind the

coastal town of Huacho, somewhat less than one hundred miles
north of Lima. Florence, Harvey, and I made up the norteamericano contingent. Then there was Miss Agnes Johnson, a
charming little English lady long resident in Peru and a tal-
ented artist, and Dr. Rufino Aspiazu. He was one of the leading
physicians of Lima and an accomplished amateur botanist who
was preparing a book on the plants of the Lima region. It was
to be illustrated by Miss Johnson's excellent drawings of Peruvian plants. We were a very jolly party.

The winter fogs had not yet begun to blanket the coast, and
the wasteland that presses upon the irrigated fields near Lima
shimmered in the heat waves, which rose against the hazy outlines of the steep Andean foothills to the east. After a few miles
across dry plains the highway rose gradually along sandy ocean-
side bluffs. Soon the sea was some hundred or two feet below us
and the road became nothing but a step hollowed out of the
steep side of an immense sand dune, the bottom of which was
the ocean beach. The road was a little better than two cars
wide. On the dune side the sand was constantly sifting and blowing down onto the road surface. On the outside it was just as
constantly falling away down the almost vertical slope to the
water. There was no railing along the edge. To keep the highway in repair, and even passable, a large crew of road men was
always at work. Most of them were sweepers armed with large
homemade brooms. All day long they moved back and forth
on the inner side of the highway, sweeping back the sand which
never ceased to slide down from the dune over head.

We had the inside lane on the way to Huacho and only
when the car swung wide to pass a group of sweepers did we
have a momentary look over the outer edge of the road to the
surf breaking far below against the foot of the dune. This sand-
swept portion of the highway wound for a considerable number
of miles in and out as it followed the contours of the dune.
Sometimes its surface was of normal width and sometimes the
sand had gotten ahead of the sweepers and made the single
passable lane near the outer edge dangerously slippery.

One of our party thoughtlessly remarked that this stretch
of highway must be an unpleasant one to negotiate in the dark.
Forthwith my imagination and, as it later proved, that of all

the rest of the party except the chófer, went to work. I could almost feel the darkness, the back wheels bumping off the pavement, the car's sudden downward lurch, one or two turns in the air—no, no; this won't do, snap out of it, don't be completely an ass! But the seed had been planted and the tag end of imagination kept slyly insinuating a menacing picture long after we left the road around the dune and were again bowling across the level arid plains.

We had a thoroughly good and profitable time in and near Huacho. The prime collecting ground to which Don Augusto was to lead us turned out to be too dry. Still we found much of botanical interest there. I was surprised to see *Nicotiana glutinosa,* a tobacco relative, growing so far north of its center of distribution in the foothills east of Lima. We collected seeds of a *Caesalpinia,* or related genus, which was in full flower and the most conspicuous or at least the most colorful element in the rugged quebradas along the base of the mountains near the coast. It was a compact shrub with light-green leaves, which were almost completely obscured by a mosaic of flattened, bright orange-yellow flowers. It should be an addition to gardens in semiarid parts of California and the southwest unless, as so often happens, too much water and fertilizer will make it go to long, lax stems, many leaves, and few flowers.

We spent the night at a clean and comfortable hotel in Huacho. The next morning Dr. Aspiazu took some of us on an archeological jaunt. He had been born near by, one of eighteen children incidentally. He remembered that in his youth he had located on the family estate one of the innumerable pre-Columbian cemeteries that are found all along the arid coastal plain of Peru. He led us to it but unfortunately we were not to be the first despoilers of the dead. Rather, the graves that he remembered and others also in which we dug had been worked over by more than one set of robbers. Still, we came away laden with skulls, pieces of mummy cloth, and some attractive odds and ends.

With one thing and another, principally an elaborate noon meal as guests of Rufino's brother but also some additional plant collecting, it was well into the afternoon before we loaded ourselves and our miscellaneous spoils into the big station

wagon for the journey back to Lima. The day had been unusually hot and, as we rolled through the desert on the narrow strip
of paved highway, mists began to rise from the cooling sands
and more than a mist rolled in far ahead where the highway approached the sea along the great dune. Conversation had been
lively for the first half hour of the ride. Gradually the combined
influence of a good, abundant, and somewhat vinous dinner,
the rush of cooling air, and the monotony of the landscape induced a comfortable lassitude and even a snore or two; in other
words, a series of delayed siestas was enjoyed.

When I awoke the sun was setting—a red ball sinking fast
into the ocean's horizon, but only dimly seen through the
gathering fogs. The broad, dry plains, a patchwork of vivid
yellows, browns, and reds under yesterday's bright sunlight,
now were gray and misty and exhaled a chilling breath. My return to consciousness was immediately followed, or perhaps preceded, by a premonition of what lay ahead on the breasts of the
great sand dune. I realized that we would begin the miles of
sand-strewn dune step just as the uncertain light of early evening
was being replaced by the treacherous blackness of a foggy night.
In imagination I saw the slow and cautious negotiation of every
foot of those miles. I could almost hear the sound of the breakers, a constant and menacing reminder of what lay directly below the outer lane of the highway along which we must travel.
I remembered other night rides in this same car and with this
same driver. These had been rides along level safe valley roads.
But how dim the headlights had been. Worse than that it suddenly came to me that the station wagon had no headlight dim-
mer, and that this chófer had always slowed down and put
out his lights when a car approached from the opposite direction. I wondered whether he would be willing to disobey the
dimming law on that bad stretch of highway which we were so
rapidly approaching. How many other dangerous and terrifying
contingencies my imagination conjured up as the light began to
fail and the road turned toward the sea, I cannot remember.
The most serious one I had not thought of, but it was not long
in making itself manifest.

The car rounded the first of the broad curves on which the
highway crossed the surface of the precipitous dune and we

"Little Hell" spelled out in *Tillandsia* plants on Peru's coastal desert

Three skulls from an Inca desert cemetery atop a plant press

Yellow-flowered *Caesalpinia tinctoria* in the "meadows on the desert"
Each September the foggy lomas spring into bloom—Loasas and Drymarias

The record of long years of encounter with the stern realities of Andean life
is written deep on the features of this tattered patriarch

With wooden hoe on shoulder this Cuzco Indian lad in ragged breeches and colorful poncho starts for an Andean potato field

could see miles ahead. In a long, broken strand, sometimes two or three together, sometimes singly, the headlights of approaching cars were strung out all along the dune shelf. Yesterday there had been almost no traffic on this part of the highway. Then I remembered that this was Sunday night and we were traversing the only road upon which week-end revelers from Lima could return to their northern homes.

The harrowing uncertainty, insecurity, and final terror of that next hour—for it took us that length of time to cross the relatively few miles of dune—each one of us will always remember. Since the road sweepers had stopped work long before sundown, there had been time for the sand to work its way down and far out into the roadway. In some areas it had crossed it. Driven by a rising wind, the fog swirled about the exposed ridges and rushed up the sandy valleys. Sometimes sand filled the air to decrease visibility almost to the vanishing point. The ineffective headlights cast only a faint glow on the pavement a few yards ahead of the car. At intervals twin spots of light suddenly blazed in our faces out of the murk. They always seemed to rush toward us head on and each time I was certain that our quick turn toward the outermost edge of the road would carry us over the precipice to the breakers, whose muffled roar was always in our ears. But each time by what seemed a miracle the two cars brushed past each other and we were still on the road.

I sat in the front seat next the driver and watched his quiet intentness, his complete absorption in the task in hand. He never faltered and was apparently sustained by a complete faith in his ability to meet the hazards of our position. I had almost lost the power to look ahead and soon gave up the attempt to force my eyes to the side where there was no road and death lay in wait. My attention was fixed on those hands that held the steering wheel. I watched them periodically tighten and then slowly move round as he drove to one or other side to pass an approaching car or avoid the sand where it had formed small drifts on the roadway. I would just begin to draw from his steadfastness a little confidence and then it would drain away when I saw the wheel begin to turn to the right. A dozen times I thought I felt the right wheels leave the pavement. At such moments dumbly, supinely, I waited for the first sickening tilt of the heavy car as the sand gave way and we began our plunge over the cliff.

Gradually the fog blew away and the road became more visible. I knew that we had passed the center of the dune because in the faint light from the clearing sky the dark silhouette of the great mass of sand was gradually lessening in height. The chófer relaxed a trifle and began to improve on the snail's pace that we had so long been maintaining.

Suddenly a car came up behind us very fast. Its insistent horn demanded more room on the left. We slackened speed and cautiously worked over toward the edge. Behind us the horn was still insistent but we could give no more room. Then the angry, perhaps drunken driver, still at the top of his noise, pulled up beside us and began to pass. Just as he cleared our front wheels he viciously swerved his car to the right, across our bows; our chófer wrenched at his wheel to avoid a crash. Instantly we were headed for destruction.

It may have been the sudden change in our situation from relative security to terrible danger, or perhaps the long strain which he had endured had unnerved him; at any rate something made the chófer lose control. At once the front wheels bumped off the pavement and before I could get them back on the road again the rear ones began to skid dangerously. At this, the chófer recovered from his momentary lapse and our combined hands on the steering wheel succeeded in straightening out the car; but not until we had run for fifty feet with front and rear right wheels alternately on and off the road. A dozen times we must have been only inches from the brink of the precipice.

Fortunately we were almost off the dune shelf. In a few moments the lights of Lima glimmered in the distance. On an easy downgrade the car rolled out along the plains. Someone spoke, someone answered, then everyone was talking at once. We began to realize that for an hour not a word had passed our lips. But talking was not enough. Harvey began to sing, "There's a long, long trail," and we all joined in, the chófer humming quietly under his breath. It was our heartfelt hymn of thanksgiving. Another and another song followed and noisily we rode into Lima.

We return now to Harvey, Bob, and the Peruvian passengers in the colectivo. While the smooth road lasted they were in high spirits and conversation was brisk and free. The North Americans concluded that some of it might even be a bit ribald to judge by the roars of laughter that followed stories told in Spanish vernacular too rapid for them to understand. Even the chófer loosened up. At first he had been sullenly uncommunicative, following an argument with one of the women in the front seat. She had refused to pay extra fare for transportation of her two hens which, with legs tied together, she had crowded under the front seat, but which preferred to flop around between the chófer's feet. He had told her that it wasn't the extra weight he minded but that there was a decided nuisance angle involved. The woman, however, refused to argue and each time the chófer showed signs of anger she would take the fowls into her lap and stroke them, as if to smooth the feathers of the whole situation. As the afternoon lengthened the rest of the passengers saw the humor of the situation. After a while the chófer began to thaw and finally joined in the laugh that followed the woman's proposal to give him all the eggs the hens would produce in the course of the trip. A louder laugh went up when she added that considering the age and generally unreliable appearance of his vehicle, this was likely to be no small consideration by the time they arrived at their destination.

The west coast desert of northern Peru is often crossed by larger or smaller streams. They originate in the Andean snows not so far to the eastward and with considerably decreased flow manage to reach the sea. The soils of the lower reaches of these river channels are deep with alluvium and fertile. Desert valleys in Peru, as elsewhere, bloom like the rose when water is made to flow through them in irrigation ditches. Inca and pre-Inca civilizations must have flourished in these fertile valleys, for in and near them are always the ruins of adobe hamlets, villages, and even cities, often guarded by watchtowers and fortresses.

Modern civilization has replaced that of pre-Columbian times in these valleys. Along the larger streams, which continue to flow even at the end of the dry season, there are larger and smaller settlements built upon or beside the ancient ones.

These modern communities have a sameness of landscape—
adobe and galvanized houses, too few of the hardy shade trees
that will flourish in the dry air of the desert, streets sandy and
narrower than is justified by the ample room for a townsite,
somnolent and complacent goats, a surplus of dogs too lazy to
scratch their fleas, and a human population in the melting-pot
era. Being near the sea and therefore in touch with a wider
world the people of the coastal towns are not so impoverished
of ideas as are those who live in the high, isolated, Andean valleys of Peru.

Late in the afternoon green fields came into view. The
chófer drew up on the principal street of a town supported by
these irrigated river-bottom fields. Then he announced thirty
minutes for tea. With a little shifting of the baggage hanging
against the outside of the colectivo they were able to open the
righthand doors and the passengers unpacked themselves to enjoy an unlimbering of numbed joints. From this stopping place
to Supe they had to detour through back lanes and eventually
cross-country over the sand. Going was slow and uncertain and
the lights of Supe were a welcome sight. In nearby Barranca
where they stopped for the night all accommodations were gone
at the Gran Hotel Comercio. The chófer drove on to the hotel
annex. There he found just sufficient room to take care of the
women of the party. The men he delivered at the annex to the
annex. No one was disappointed with the accommodations, because no one expected anything better than dirt floor, four
walls of disintegrating adobe, and improvised bedsteads in the
annex to the annex!

Next morning a good road carried them northward to Paramonga where the river of that name has spread wide plains of
alluvium which are green with checkerboard fields of well-irri-
gated sugar cane. This is one of the agricultural developments
of W. R. Grace and Company, who also operate a refinery there.
As one leaves this fertile valley for the dry hills to the north
there stands on a prominence a picturesque ancient *fortaleza,*
or fortress, visible for miles around. After many centuries it is
still in good condition with sturdy red walls and terraces. The
ancient Chimu, and later Inca, dynasties took advantage of the
favorable geography at the mouth of the Paramonga, just as W.

R. Grace and Company are now doing. One wonders who came before the Chimus, and who will come after W. R. Grace and Company. Let us hope that it will not be Adolf Hitler and Company!

Beyond Paramonga the road weakened, faltered, and finally vanished into fields of soft wind-blown sand. With an air of resignation the chófer extricated himself from behind the wheel and proceeded to let air out of the tires. Then he raced his engine through several spurts like an aviator about to take off and was ready to match his wits against the sand. From that moment he became entirely uncommunicative and refused to pay the slightest attention to questions of anxious passengers. Like a ball carrier running in an open field, it required all his wits to determine which tacklers to avoid and which to charge. Some dunes have a hard crust which bears the weight of an automobile, and others are powdery and lead only to grief. Most of the time he guessed right and the passengers voiced approval, even admiration. Sometimes he guessed wrong, and then the rest of the colectivo team paid for his mistake. The men disembarked to help push. The fat women also disembarked, to make the task of the men lighter.

To extricate the car, the sand in front of the wheels had to be dug away with the hands—no one bothered to ask why the chófer had forgotten to bring a shovel—in the manner of a dog trying to expose a subterranean woodchuck. Thereafter they all fell to and pushed and then trotted after the car until it dared to halt on firmer packed sand. At some of the sand stoppages where they happened to be in hilly country, the task of getting the colectivo under way again was not so laborious. On the sandy hillsides there were patches of a silvery gray desert plant, *Tillandsia straminea*. The chófer and male passengers would collect a large pile of these plants and then feed them to the sand in front of the wheels. It was remarkable how much traction they provided.

This *Tillandsia* is common on all the hills of this rainless region and in fact through most of the length of the Peruvian coast. It is a relative of the Spanish moss and the pineapple, has almost no root system, and holds its place only by virtue of the sand that drifts about its base to anchor it. It takes moisture from the air on occasions when dew forms and this it conserves very efficiently. In the middle of the day when the sun sometimes dispels the fog, the reddish flower shoots droop; but in the morning they are again erect, looking cheerful and vigorous. Sometimes whole fields of these plants have died and partly carbonized, and their black skeletons contrast sharply with the silver-gray stretches of their living relatives. Otherwise, for many miles the desert landscape shows no contrasts. On some level areas, particularly where the sand holds a little clay, belts of *Tillandsia* spread out at right angles to the direction of the prevailing wind and lean toward this wind which brings them moisture. From an elevation and at a distance these belts of silvery gray produce the effect of waves upon the desert.

There being no absorbing root system, *Tillandsia* transplants easily. Travelers have taken advantage of this fact as a means of erecting living memorials to those who have been no match for the desert road, which must have taken a heavy toll in the days of slow travel by horse or burro. Usually in Peru a wooden cross is built by the roadside where a traveler has died. But in the desert there is no wood and so on the hillside the name of the departed is spelled out in Tillandsias. Once, in the past when travel over the coastal sands was less regular than it is today, a luckless colectivo was stalled for two or three days near a considerable hill. By way of diversion the unfortunate passengers recorded in *Tillandsia* the impression their surroundings made upon them, and today one can still clearly read in green characters on the hillside the word INFIERNILLO, which is to say, "Little Hell!"

Aside from *Tillandsia* and some of its close relatives there is little to excite the botanist along this coastal highway of sand. Occasionally you see a few cacti, and now and then a low valley shows some deep-rooted woody plants which succeed in tapping the water table. Plains close to the sea may support a carpet of resistant plants, principally *Distichlis,* which bind the sand and hold it temporarily in place. Otherwise the north Peruvian coastal shelf lacks detail. It is a world of cloudy sky, blue sea to the west, wind-eroded foothills to the east, and behind them a purple mountain wall rising straight up and up into the clouds. Travelers never cease to marvel at the steep slope of the west walls of the Andes. Fifty miles from the ocean stands this great backbone of the continent, a continent which beyond the Andean crest slopes for thousands of miles eastward to the Atlantic. And the descent below sea level from the Pacific shores is equally abrupt, so that near the western mainland of Peru some of the world's greatest deeps occur.

As the Buick chugged through the sands to Chimbote, Harvey, Bob, and César constantly kept as sharp a lookout as they could for evidence of lomas vegetation. Sometimes at a distance a hillside looked to be green but on closer approach proved merely to be covered with greenish shales. These and particolored rock formations northward from Chancai lend a picturesque, somewhat bizarre atmosphere to the landscape, which is reminiscent of the Bad Lands and even of the Grand Canyon of the Colorado or Bryce Canyon. The sands are mostly fine and exhibit a rounded grain under magnification. The rocks protruding from their sandy beds are shales of different colors and conglomerates, with here and there an outcrop of amorphous rock which looks like rhyolite. But there were a few spots genuinely green with lomas vegetation. These they noted down to be visited on the return journey, for they proposed to make it in a hired automobile which would stop upon demand.

On the second night the colectivo discharged its weary human cargo at its destination, Chimbote. The passengers had acquired a considerable physical, if not intellectual, intimacy during the rough desert journey, but they parted silently and with no regret. Each one was anxious to forget not only the hard bottom of the colectivo but also the sharp elbows of his companions in discomfort. Even the jovial lady of the hens was too weary to fire a parting shot at the chófer. But the hens were equal to the occasion. Heads down, they continued to squawk and thrash about as, slung over their mistress's shoulder, they disappeared up a dark Chimbote street. The botanists sought the "new" hotel. It proved to be decidedly modern and quite comfortable, with even an up-to-date bathroom that only lacked hot water.

Chimbote is the principal base for the Peruvian navy. However, the navy wasn't at home while they were there. But they admired the natural harbor which is regarded as the best on the west coast of the continent. It is said that the Japanese have made repeated attempts to negotiate for this harbor as a New World base. The botanists went into the hills behind Chimbote. Only here and there did they see evidence that vegetation had existed even in wet years. Along the Santa River to the north they collected some shrubby plants of the *Baccharis* and *Tessaria* type and various introductions from the Andes and from Chile and Ecuador, as well as some cosmopolitan weeds of the sort found wherever civilization reaches.

For the return trip to Lima they negotiated in Chimbote with those owners of private automobiles who were willing to exchange a desultory taxi business for a long and remunerative desert fare. Finally the owner of an apparently sandworthy 1930 Model A Ford was willing to listen to reason in the matter of charges. He was engaged on the distinct understanding that they were to decide where and how long he should stop along the road.

Even the definitely green lomas which they found on the return journey were quite disappointing and confirmed the Lima reports that this was a very dry season. They botanized the Lomas de Mongon south of Casma, the Lomas de Lachay, and those of Pasomayo, Pativilca, and Doña Maria. In each one there were a few interesting plants to collect. As they moved southward the composition of every lomas was to some extent distinctive. Thus, a series of different species tended to be the common or dominant one in each of the lomas. Always, however, they found evidence of an early dry or relatively fogless season. On the margins of the restricted areas where plants had come to maturity there were far more extensive tracts, which in a normal season would have supported a rich vegetation. But this year these marginal regions showed only seedlings or young plants which in their youth had been dried and burned by the sun—mummies of plant children, stiff and crackling under foot. Goats and cattle, which normally would have been fattening on the vegetation of the lomas, were not there. Little shrines where animals are blessed and shepherds pause to worship constituted the sole evidence that these were the coastal pastures, the only meadows on the desert.

Once in a while they found extensive stretches of vegetation, all in flower. In the Lachay lomas there were areas gay with yellow- and also white-flowered species of *Loasa*. Only at Pasomayo did the fog vegetation carpet the hillsides all the way down to the ocean beach. The yellow *Loasa* was there again forming sheets of color and, at a distance, it was hard to believe that those western slopes of the coastal hills were not covered with our common yellow mustard. On these yellow *Loasa* fields a blue flowered *Solanum* was dotted here and there. Harvey took a remarkable Kodachrome movie shot of one of these steep yellow and blue hillsides. You look across the brilliantly colored flowers down to the surf and out over the blue rollers of the Pacific. In my lecture film on South America this scene is very brief, but audiences always respond audibly to the breath-taking loveliness of this glimpse of what the North Peruvian lomas can be.

As their Ford brought them closer to Lima the moister and even some of the drier hillsides and small plains in the coast range began to show bulbous plants, notably such amaryllids as *Stenomesson* and *Zephyranthes*. Florence and I more than once walked in these truly desert gardens along the road that runs north of Lima, through the light, shifting sands. For miles the wasteland would be pitilessly barren; it was inconceivable that any living thing, animal or vegetable, could long exist there. Then for no reason at all a thousand, ten thousand, slender green stalks were thrust up out of the sand with a tassel of orange or scarlet trumpets hanging from the top of each one. Florence liked to lie prone on the warm desert so that she could look across the foot-high, colored-flower surface that dissolved in the far-off yellow-gray hillsides. When I lay beside her she showed me the translucent, multicolored mirage that floated above this flowery plain.

Absence of normal lomas vegetation, due to an exceptionally dry season, meant that the Peruvian collecting schedule had to be drastically revised. The weeks that were to have been spent in the meadows of the desert on the northern and central coast were assigned to work in the near-Amazonian jungle east of the Andes and in the hinterland of northern Peru. The latter expedition is described in the following chapter and the former in a subsequent one.

Chapter III

THE LOST NICOTIANA

TWELVE YEARS ago in the Botanical Museum in Berlin-Dahlem I came across a folder full of pressed Nicotianas. The label on the outside read "Unnamed Species." Some were not Nicotianas at all, others were, and I was able to name them. Finally there was one plant, a *Nicotiana* right enough, but very different from any member of the genus I had ever seen. A collector's label was attached to this plant. It was written in German and in part read as follows: "Weberbauer, No. 7015, collected on the grass-steppe, at 12,500 feet, between Huama-chuco and Angasmarca, Peru, July 6, 1914." In pencil on the corner of the label, another German botanist had written: "Nicotiana thyrsiflora."

I had never heard of such a name for a *Nicotiana* species; the collector I knew only as the author of a book about the plants of Peru; the place where he had collected it meant absolutely nothing to me. How far beyond my imagination, that day in the German museum, was the sequel to this first acquaintance with *Nicotiana thyrsiflora*. How could I have imagined that I should come to know Weberbauer intimately; that he should try, and try again, and finally fail to get for me the seed of this unknown *Nicotiana;* that we should go twice to Peru in search of it, and that this search was to mean many days of hardship and repeated disappointments before it was successful?

From the moment I first saw it as a dried specimen, I knew that I must have the seed of *Nicotiana thyrsiflora* so that I could grow it, see it as a living plant, study it, and compare it with its relatives already growing in the University's Botanical Garden. I wrote to the collector and after a long time received his reply. Years before on a collecting trip into the high plateaus of northern Peru he had seen only a plant or two of something that he had not even recognized as a *Nicotiana*. He collected it, dried and pressed it, and sent it to Germany to be named; but until I told him that I had run across the plant

in the Berlin museum he had had no news of it. He kindly
offered to try to find someone in the remote region in which it
grew who would attempt to get seed for me. The implication
was, however, that there was not much hope of success—and
so it proved. Eleven years were to go by after I first saw the
dried plant before I saw a living one.

The territory in which this elusive *Nicotiana* was first
found and where twenty years later it was rediscovered, first
by the Prince and then again by Harvey and Bob, is not tourist
country. It lies beyond the north Peruvian coastal city of
Trujillo, founded by Pizarro and named after his birthplace,
and it was the scene of memorable events during the first period
of the conquest of Peru. From the northern desert along the
coast the land rises fast into the high altitudes of the western
range of Peru's Andes. Behind this outermost range are the
higher than ten-thousand-foot plateaus or punas through which
the mighty Marañon has dug a monster gorge, almost at the
beginning of its long journey to join the Amazon and then flow
on to the Atlantic. These high punas are cold and windswept.
They can support only the hardiest of plants. But in the bottoms of the deep steep-walled valleys that intersect them is the
jungle, for this *Nicotiana thyrsiflora* country lies only eight
degrees south of the Equator and that means that all life at
seven thousand feet and below is tropical. Early in December,
1936, the Prince went into this north Peruvian hinterland.
He was to make the first attempt to rediscover *Nicotiana
thyrsiflora*.

In Trujillo the only transportation eastward he could find
was a big open truck loaded with dynamite and headed for the
mines near Parcoy, on the far side of the Marañon. Concerning
the long rough journey, the Prince wrote, "To get an unrestricted view of the countryside, I rode all the way on top of
the dynamite rather than in the cab with the driver. At 3 A.M.
we pulled into our destination, Huamachuco. It was too late
to rouse the staff of the hotel; therefore I slept in the fiendishly
designed cab of the truck."

He had letters of introduction to leading citizens of
Huamachuco, and one of them worked to the extent of eliciting
a promise to find a horse, a mule, and a guide for the *Nicotiana*

thyrsiflora hunt. "But," said his new friend, "it will take time, señor, it will take time. Perhaps the day after tomorrow all will be arranged."

On the third morning the cavalcade was organized—the Prince on a small anemic horse, the plant presses and other baggage on the back of a tiny burro, and Pedro, the Indian guide, on foot. As the trail wound up the hillside out of the city, the general debility of the horse and burro immediately came to light. When at last the top of the first steep ascent was reached they abruptly halted, with heaving sides and drooping heads.

From this first eminence the view was superbly expansive. To the north a sea of green ridges rolled away toward a misty horizon, beneath which lay the Ecuadorian border. To the east, the high ranges behind the Marañon rose abruptly from vast table lands. Far to the south a great white mass, the Cordillera Blanca, hung suspended above a foreground of cloudy ranges, themselves mighty but insignificant by comparison.

That first day they rode and walked slowly toward the twelve-thousand-foot plateau somewhere on which the plant they sought should be waiting for them. For many miles there was no human habitation. At dusk they found a group of miserable huts on the shores of a little, dark glacial lake. It lay in a cup formed by black, rough cliffs so steep and so high that only at noon could the sun illuminate its waters. In the gathering darkness it thoroughly deserved its name, Laguna Negra.

Pedro hailed the huts and from one of them slowly and cautiously appeared three incredibly dirty young women. They were very shy, almost like wild creatures. Clearly they were terrified almost out of their wits by the sudden appearance of perhaps the only strangers they had ever seen. No persuasion on Pedro's part could gain permission for himself and the Prince to occupy one of the huts during the freezing night that was already descending upon them. After some search they found, at a little distance, a shedlike pigsty. It was inhabited by many black pigs and the Prince remarks in his diary, "They were not at all unwelcome as footwarmers, for the night was windy and bitterly cold. Next morning when I tried to perform

my ablutions in the pigsty trough there was a quarter-inch of
ice on its surface."

The next day was a severe strain on all of them. A thirteen-
thousand-foot pass had to be crossed, and the cold wind that
had arisen during the night continued to blow with steadily
increasing violence. They should now have reached the region
where *Nicotiana thyrsiflora* had been collected. But despite a
sharp lookout and many digressions from the trail into promising quebradas, draws, and ravines, nothing resembling the plant
they were hunting was to be seen. Beyond the pass the country
looked very unpromising, only open rolling expanses covered
as far as the eye could reach with nothing but stiff coarse
grasses.

That night they were hospitably received by a friend of
Pedro's who lived with his family in a single large, low, mud
dwelling, built on the slope of a wide depression in the desolate
moor. All the next day they searched without success for
Nicotiana thyrsiflora. In the afternoon the terrain gave more
promise with less grass and more rocky broken hillsides, where
a few strange and charming alpine shrubs and herbs were in
flower. These the Prince collected. They served somewhat to
relieve the discouragement that was beginning to oppress him.
Again that night they found a friendly Indian family and slept
warm, if not altogether in comfort. The evening meal consisted
of boiled *cui,* or guinea pig, served with the small, yellow,
nutritious potatoes of the Andes and a very hot peppery sauce.
The whole was washed down with *chicha,* the homemade corn
beer of the Peruvian highlands.

It is depressing enough to go out into the chicken yard
and slaughter a hen which from long acquaintance treats you
like a friend, but sadder still is it to wring the neck of a bed-
fellow. For the Andean cuis are often bedded down on the dirt
floor of the hut with the members of the family. In one corner
they place a large pile of the stiff but succulent leaves of Puyas
and Pitcairnias, members of the Pineapple family, on which
the guinea pigs are fattened and under which they live and
breed. All night long the little demons squeak and scratch and
rustle among the spiny leaves. Periodically they dash out from
their home in the corner to investigate the hands and faces of

family and guests who are lying on the floor nearby. Their sharp restless claws and unfamiliar odor are added to constant peregrinations over tender spots and sharp attentions of fleas and other undetermined bloodletters—all of which makes sleep hard to capture in the heavy fetid air of native Andean habitations. Only extreme fatigue will bring oblivion.

The next morning the Prince was treated to a typical Indian breakfast. It was eaten under a small arbor which served as combined kitchen and dining room. The family and their guests squatted in the dirt around three half-gourds. One was full of coarse, dry barley meal, another held a thick gruel made of boiled potatoes, and the third a thinner barley soup. Wooden spoons, not enough to go around and therefore shared, were handed about and the meal began. First the spoon was wetted in one warm liquid or the other and then dipped into the dry meal. Or, according to a different technique, a mouthful of meal was taken and then moistened by a spoonful of potato or barley gruel. It is a hearty and sustaining meal, but hygienic considerations sometimes make it hard to swallow.

After three days of fruitless search for *Nicotiana thyrsiflora* and long hard climbs on bad trails, the Prince was thoroughly tired and discouraged. The little horse was fast giving out and could be ridden only for a short time and then only on level ground. The burro began to exhibit every meanness he had inherited from a long line of reprehensible ancestors. Pedro was beginning to be restive and ill-humored. He continually complained of sore feet and insisted upon starting home. Actually, it was the fear of running out of *coca* which afflicted him. His supply of those dried leaves from which he chewed cocaine was low and without them he was lost. Altogether the Prince knew that he could count on only one day more in the high country. In desperation he sought the advice of a quizzically keen, morose old Indian whom they met along the trail and who, after some urging, was willing to use a little Spanish. The Prince repeated over and over again the best and simplest description of *Nicotiana thyrsiflora* that he could devise. But the old Indian only shook his head. Finally, however, he pointed out the direction of a trail which he said would lead them toward the gorge of the Marañon. Along this trail he seemed to think that considerable vegetation was to be found.

The trail which the Indian had designated led them rapidly to still higher ground. Again the view was magnificent. In the foreground, beyond the barren rocky ridges, a partly wooded quebrada sloped down to a curiously formed and isolated hill. Behind it rose range upon range of purple mountains. Gradually they increased in height until they merged into the enormous craggy mass of the Ancash Cordillera. In the farthest distance the glittering apex of what must have been Huascaran towered twenty-two thousand feet into the pale-blue sky.

The country rapidly became wilder and extremely rough and broken. The Prince examined carefully every likely spot where, in the protection of high outcroppings of rock or in the narrow bottoms of steep quebradas, some vegetation managed to maintain itself. As the day wore on they approached the summit of Tres Cruces Pass near the Marañon. It had been agreed that once there the hunt would be abandoned.

Now the trail became almost vertical and terribly rocky. With heads down, man and beast tramped doggedly onward and upward. Automatically, but without much enthusiasm, the Prince at every few steps glanced first to the right and then to the left to note the vegetation. One such glance showed him a group of low shrubs and growing up through them what looked to be a giant yellow-flowered foxglove. He was so tired, so convinced that the hunt had completely failed, that at first this extraordinary plant, so different from anything he had seen on the punas, failed to interest him. Then suddenly he stopped and looked again, and instantly he knew that he had found *Nicotiana thyrsiflora!*

It stood seven feet high, a tall wand, leafless for the upper half of its length, and below covered with long, narrow, wavy-margined, somewhat twisted leaves. The top of the stem was enlarged for two feet into a mass of small yellow flowers tightly fitted together. He had come across nothing like this during the previous three days. Such a large and distinctive plant would have been seen literally for miles across the almost level plateaus he had been traversing. So at least he had the satisfaction of knowing that he had not overlooked the object of his plant hunting. In addition he realized that the living plant was quite different from the mental picture of it that I had drawn from the dried, pressed specimen in the Berlin museum.

However true it may be that the charm of anticipation often exceeds the joy of realization in most human affairs, this relationship is always reversed in plant hunting. For a dyed-in-the-wool collector there is nothing so solidly satisfying as the termination of a successful quest. All the strain and weariness, all the aggravations small and large, all the defeats and disappointments, are instantly forgotten. His eyes gleam, he gloats, he begins to whistle, he may even indulge in a bit of affectionate profanity. If some snakebite remedy is handy he is likely to take a drink—or even two. The Prince never told me just what happened when he found his plant, except that he promptly gave Pedro a *sol* by way of *gratificación.* Probably his satisfaction was tinged with a shade of disappointment because this one plant of *Nicotiana thyrsiflora,* the only one in sight, did not bear any ripe seed. He knew that it was the seed that I wanted.

By the time that he and Pedro had looked about for additional plants the afternoon had gone and the evening winds began to blow very cold across the moors. All day the trail had passed only a deserted and tumble-down hut or two. Pedro had never been so far from home and had no knowledge of human habitations in the neighborhood. Hungry and cold they lay down and in such shelter from the icy wind as bunches of tall grass provided they tried to sleep. With the first light, the hunt for seeding plants of *Nicotiana thyrsiflora* was continued, with absolutely no success. Indeed, they found only one other specimen. It was a poor thing, not in flower and with only a few empty seed capsules left over from the previous year's blooming.

I am certain that if the Prince had been alone or free to remain near Tres Cruces, nothing would have kept him from continuing the search. But Pedro had broken down completely. Long-continued and unaccustomed exertion, lack of food, the severe exposure of the previous night, and especially many hours without coca, had left him in such a weakened condition that without help and encouragement he could never have reached Huamachuco. There was nothing to do but strike

What the well-dressed women and children of Ayaviri, Peru, will wear is what they have always worn; oil cans are treasured possessions

An embossed silver staff designates this Peruvian Indian as an honorary
alcalde who aids the authorities in policing his district

Native Peruvian highlanders have a more or less strong mongoloid cast of countenance and their faces are careworn and even sullen

Two highland maidens rest in a niche of an ancient Inca wall near Cuzco;
not often is a family's black sheep so tenderly cherished

across country at the best pace Pedro and the animals could maintain in the hope of reaching civilization before nightfall. They made it, but it was a bad day for all of them.

In Huamachuco the condition of Pedro as well as that of the horse and mule excited so much public comment that it was hopeless to get other animals or another guide. Who could be expected to go out again with this *gringo loco* to climb about in impossible places hunting for nothing more exciting than weeds? And so, with great reluctance and keenly disappointed at his failure to fulfill the most important part of his assignment, the Prince returned to Lima.

I did what I could in my letters (for Florence and I had long since returned to California) to cheer him up. I proposed another trip to the *Nicotiana thyrsiflora* country at a better season, but he was inconsolable and worried himself into a decline. I tried to persuade him to forget plant hunting for a month or more and in particular urged him to stay out of the high country for a while. But he must have known that hard work was his only salvation. At any rate, his next letter came from the Andes of southeastern Peru and it was full of nothing but enthusiasm for the collecting he was carrying on there.

The psychological hazard of plant hunting over considerable periods of time in remote and dangerous regions and at high altitudes, where one's only contact is with primitive peoples, can often become more acute than the physical one. A fine physique and some enthusiasm for the work is not enough. It is difficult to tell in advance whether one possesses the necessary combination of steadfastness of purpose and adaptability of mind and temper that will enable him to carry on under adverse conditions for months on end. Almost complete intellectual isolation, added to a continuous physical strain, ultimately comes to make heavy demands on the disposition.

One of the special objectives of the second Andean Expedition was a further search for *Nicotiana thyrsiflora*, which would be successful only if seed was obtained. Harvey and I had talked over this problem in detail and it had finally been left to him to determine when and how the north Peruvian country, in which *Nicotiana thyrsiflora* was now known to be growing, should be visited. After their collecting trip through the meadows on the desert the dry season even in the Andes continued to persist. Until the rains came, there was obviously to be a collecting interlude in central Peru, and Harvey decided to use it for the *Nicotiana thyrsiflora* hunt. With a handful of official and unofficial letters of introduction from Lima to prominent people in the north and with plenty of plant presses and driers, Bob and he left Lima in November.

They traveled by Faucett plane to Trujillo. In less than two hours from Lima they had passed Chimbote, and recalled that some weeks before in their sand-fighting colectivo it had taken them two full days to get there. No wonder air travel is so popular on the west coast. Across its deserts and over its high mountains the airplane not only reduces the time of your journey by hundreds of per cent, but even more important it reduces to a minimum the discomforts and dangers of overland travel through exceedingly inhospitable country. Of course, there are sometimes plenty of bumps in air pockets, more than one hair-raising side slip, and for a few moments at a time extreme altitudes that seem to make the heart go "dot and carry one." But when these disquieting things happen, you just look down and visualize what a traveler would have to endure on the hot sands or across the lofty passes that you see below.

The flight north from Lima over the coast was an extremely interesting one for Harvey and Bob. They recognized many landmarks that they had passed during their colectivo journey. Often they flew low enough to identify the elements of the scanty vegetation and obtained a new and valuable picture of its distribution on the coastal desert and in the nearby hills. The green carpets of *Distichlis thalassica,* the common beach grass, were more extensive than they had realized. There were many gray-green hillsides which they knew meant a heavy growth of *Tillandsia.* From the air the river valleys were brilliantly green and the contrast between them and the yellow-brown desert was intense and startling. Above the riverside cultivations they could watch the series of steps by which the heavy vegetation gradually diminished, ultimately to leave only barren, cactus-covered hillsides.

Some of the lomas in which they had collected lay under

their air route. A light-green tint on hilltops indicated the position of these lomas but the green was fading fast. They were impressed again with the small total area on the north Peruvian coastal hills that is subject to the amount of fog necessary to support lomas vegetation. From the air even more than on its surface, the coastal strip leaves the impression of infinite aridity and almost continuous desolation.

On the morning following their arrival in Trujillo they arranged for transportation to Santiago de Chuco. This would bring them well up into the mountains and also into the *Nicotiana thyrsiflora* country. When the hour for departure arrived they discovered that, like the Prince on a previous occasion, they were to enjoy a truck ride. Like the Prince again, their truck was loaded with dynamite. Perhaps it was some of the supply for Peruvian mines that had come with them from San Francisco on the *Capac*.

For the first few hours, the wide and moderately good gravel road ran through hot, boulder-strewn desert, which was decorated only with the now familiar columnar cacti. Then they began to climb up a valley wall and the road became a shelf clinging to precipitous rock cliffs. With even this first small increase in altitude, trees and shrubs, but no herbs, began to appear. Low Algarroba trees (*Prosopis*) were common and in places grew in grovelike aggregations. Among them they saw *palo santo* and *Bombax* which themselves made small groves in places. *Acacia* and *Capparis* were among the more scattered elements of the vegetation. Higher still and now well into the mountains the road entered the "rainy-green" shrubland. It grew more and more dense and finally merged into a region of evergreen shrubs and perennial herbs with which the valleys in particular were entirely filled.

Near one of the villages in which they stopped a yellow-green flowered herb attracted their attention. It proved to be the first tobacco relative they had come across on their trip into northern Peru. It was *Nicotiana paniculata* and its discovery there was the first evidence that this species grew so far north and in country well behind its characteristic coastal area of distribution. In the middle of the afternoon the shrubland was left behind and the road flattened out onto the cold, drizzly, monotonous puna.

At the American-owned mining camp of Shorey, the road forked. On the left it turned northward to Huamachuco, to the right toward Santiago de Chuco, their destination, and, according to agreement in Trujillo, the destination of the truck also. But in the offhand manner of Peruvian mountain transportation the original understanding had no validity. The truck was going to turn left to Huamachuco, and Harvey and Bob could get off and wait for another truck to come along that might take them to Santiago de Chuco, or they could stay aboard, or they could go to blazes, just as they pleased! They disembarked. Their baggage was tumbled by the roadside and the truck rumbled away. On such occasions, Harvey could always be relied upon to repeat a refrain he had learned in France in 1918, "We might as well be here as where we are!"

Actually they had fallen into the lap of luxury. The Shorey camp was idle and under the care of a mining engineer, Don Ricardo Schuster, to whom Harvey had a letter of introduction. He was a German who had married a French woman from the Pyrenees. For many years he had been engaged in mining in northern Peru. The warm Schuster home with its warmer welcome provided a striking contrast to the cold, foggy, desolate out-of-doors at this twelve-thousand-foot elevation. While the afternoon light held, the botanists went out onto the puna and collected a few species of grasses, a gentian, and several composites that eked out an existence by keeping close to the soil. A few llamas and chickens represented the only animal life. At six o'clock an elaborate tea was waiting for them. At nine came a wonderful chicken dinner. With stories and reminiscences the cheerful party lingered over the dinner table until after eleven.

Don Ricardo told them that possibly a truck would be coming through for Santiago de Chuco that night. But when midnight arrived without its making an appearance, beds were prepared in a spare room and the *botánicos* turned in. The room was very cold. They put on all the sweaters and the wool socks in the duffel bags and were dozing off when Don Ricardo came in to announce the arrival of the truck. Half-awake they pulled themselves and their belongings together. Then came prolonged farewells by the family, all of whom had dressed and come out to see them off. Finally they climbed into the large covered truck among freight and other passengers.

The heavily loaded truck got slowly under way. As it left the mining settlement there was a terrific crash and it came to a dead halt. To the passengers inside it sounded like an exploding bomb. However, nothing had really happened except that the road passed under a viaduct designed for hauling ore and the roof of the truck was an inch too high to clear it! After much maneuvering they managed to start on again. From that point the truck followed precarious shelf roads where they prayed that the driver was keeping thoroughly awake; but at three in the morning he brought them safe and sound to the hotel in Santiago de Chuco. All was dark within and the door heavily barred. Polite knocking brought no results. Finally a loud battering which all but bashed in the door attracted attention. A sleepy lout pulled their baggage into the hotel patio and then led the way with a candle to a room, elegant because it had a wooden instead of a dirt floor.

The morning sun showed an extensive city of low buildings with red tile roofs, eucalyptus trees forming a fringe, and a colorful but very dry mountain landscape. It was a large town, with a population of ten thousand. In fact it was decidedly too large. There is little justification for such a population center since the country round about is not fertile for agriculture and any mining that was ever carried on would require only a relatively few laborers. The people are extremely poor. How they live is a mystery. Mountain streams carry water down the middle of the dirty streets in open sewer ditches; but in the dry season or when the rains are late, water is flushed through these ditches only at intervals. In them cooking utensils and clothing are washed and into them the city's refuse is dumped. At some street corners are small wells in which the filthy water accumulates and to them come a constant procession of water carriers who fill utensils of various kinds.

Santiago de Chuco certainly was no place in which to linger. The nearby vegetation was poor and dry and collecting was not promising. Local information suggested that the Cachicadan area five hours further on was much better. But this meant horses to ride and a mule to carry the collecting equipment, and in Santiago de Chuco almost all such animals had long since been driven off to higher mountain valleys where there was enough grazing to keep them alive until the rains came. Harvey and Bob therefore appealed to the city authorities who actually had a brilliant suggestion to offer. In Cachicadan, they said, there was a Señora Francisca Haggenmüller, *una famosa botánica,* who would know what to do. Also near Cachicadan the grazing was good and undoubtedly the *bestias* there were more *valientes.* Finally there was a telephone line to Cachicadan and a messenger could be sent to find the señora botánica and bring her to the telephone.

In the Andes the maintenance of a telephone line is a problem because stealing wire of every sort is a recognized outdoor sport. Only the authority of the government can cope with this situation and therefore its lines are the only ones that connect all the larger communities. In Santiago de Chuco an elderly lady was in charge of the mysteries of the telephone, the operation of which attracted a number of loafers who crowded the door of the dirt-floored office when Harvey went in. With unexpected efficiency on the part of the operator the desired connection was completed in about two hours. Señora Haggenmüller proved anxious to co-operate and promised to send horses and mules the next day if possible and on the day after that for certain.

True to the "for certain" promise a *mozo* arrived with two saddle horses and a white pack mule. They loaded up immediately and were off. The airline distance to Cachicadan was not great but the road was extremely circuitous. It threaded in and out, zigzagged down into a steep gorge and then climbed out again, always presenting superb mountain views against white clouds in an intensely blue sky. As they slowly approached Cachicadan more vegetation appeared. A yellow-flowered *Stenolobium,* a member of the family to which the trumpet vine belongs, was the dominant shrub, and both red and blue Salvias mingled their spots of color with the yellow tufts of Calceolarias.

Cachicadan is a small place surrounded by magnificent

mountains. The houses are scattered on a slope and at a distance
the village is lost in a grove of eucalyptus trees. Señora Haggenmüller and her daughter Irma were anxious to entertain
Harvey and Bob but finally agreed that in the nearby pension
they would also be comfortable. It turned out to be a most
agreeably situated little place, near natural springs of boiling
water that bubbled up in various formations. The algae in these
hot waters had the same color range—sulphur-yellow, pink,
red, and blue—that is so admired at Mammoth Hot Springs in
Yellowstone National Park. There was a bathhouse and a pool
some seven feet square, through which the hot water flowed
continuously. Here was one place in the Andes where bathing
was popular despite the fact that it was always difficult to get
the water cool enough. The temperature of the pool was regu-
lated by going upstream and diverting either the hot or cold
water into other channels until the amount entering the pool
was just right. This was not an easy task especially when per-
formed at night by flashlight.

The numerous hot springs in the neighborhood have a
decided influence on the population who are one and all quite
cleanly, a condition not often met with in Andean towns or
in a good many other out-of-the-way places, some of them in
the United States. Occasionally tourists come from Lima for a
holiday in this "Yellowstone of the Andes." The "Mammoth
Hotel," however, is represented by a little pension with three
guest rooms.

While her husband was employed in mining operations in
various parts of Peru, Señora Haggenmüller led a busy life.
Her first duty was the maintenance and management of several
small farms located in various areas on the mountainsides. She
rode among the surrounding neighborhoods as a sort of agricultural adviser, efficiency expert, homeopathic physician, and
Good Samaritan in general and in particular. She maintained
excellent gardens in which many introduced as well as native
plants were in bloom when Harvey and Bob were there. There
were gentians, valerians, and mints which she used in her medi-
cines. The red *floripondio* (*Datura sanguinea*) as well as two
varieties of the white species (*Datura arborea*), one scented
much more strongly than the other, were flowering. Most attrac-

tive were several kinds of passionflower which she had introduced from the mountains. Two plants of cultivated tobacco
were in bloom. She took a great interest in foreign plants and
remarked that for a long time she had wanted to experiment
with various species of *Eucalyptus* and some of the conifers in
addition to the cypress which she had been growing. A month
later a collection of the seeds she desired was on its way to her
from California.

She had great faith in the healing properties of various
herbs. On a nearby mountain there were so many of her medicinal plants that she had named it Cerro Botica (Apothecary
Mountain) , and this name was used by the natives. She referred
to plants in terms of what they were good for rather than by
name, although she also had native Quechua designations for
most of them. She frequently encountered the use of an abor-
tifacient herb among the mountain women endeavoring to
exercise population control. Unfortunately its use is dangerous
and frequently results in a violent contraction of all the muscles
of the body, often with fatal consequences. But if she is called
in time, an antidotal herb tea of hers will pull the patient
through. She seemed reluctant to identify the plants she used
and apparently considers them to be a professional secret. She
was known for miles around and was highly respected and even
revered by the native families, many of whom she has helped
in sickness and in health. Everyone called her La Gringa and
her daughter Gringa Irma, since they were the only foreigners
anywhere in the neighborhood.

The most extraordinary plant in the señora's garden was
Nicotiana thyrsiflora and the very thing, of course, that Harvey
and Bob were looking for. It appeared that years ago, following
my original request for seed, she had found a colony of this
little-known species of *Nicotiana*. She collected seeds and sent
them to Lima. They arrived moldy and lifeless and so had not
been forwarded to me; but some of the seed she had saved to
grow in her garden. The señora agreed to lead them to the
plants she had found. In other words, the search for *Nicotiana
thyrsiflora* was practically at an end almost before it had begun.

At daybreak next morning two horses were waiting at the
pension for Harvey and Bob. With the señora mounted on a

fine white mare they were soon off to see *Nicotiana thyrsiflora*
on its native heath. She led the way, a splendid figure dressed
in corduroy, erect and square-shouldered, sitting solidly in her
old German side saddle. It was hard to believe her laughing
claim to sixty-five years. What a contrast she made to the slouch-
ing barefoot Indians who scrambled out of the way of the
horses. Running behind, now and then taking a shortcut across
zigzags in the trail, was her faithful peon. She had taught him
her plant lore, and often entrusted him with collecting the
potent roots and leaves when her pharmaceutical supply needed
replenishing.

Starting from an elevation of nine thousand feet the route
led up quebradas and across ridges to higher altitudes. Now
and then they passed tiny mountainslope fields of maize, *habas*
(beans), *papas* (potatoes), and *ocas* (*Oxalis tuberosa*). From
earliest times ocas have been cultivated in the Andes. The
tubers are not large and tend to be more watery than potatoes,
but they are quite nutritious and sustaining. But any love for
ocas depends upon acquiring a taste for their rather peculiar
flavor. Sometimes in the middle of a plantation there would be
a pile of boulders supporting a crude wooden cross. Thus the
Church left its mark, even on these remote mountainsides.
Without the cross the crop might not succeed.

Occasionally they passed a shy Indian shepherdess watching her sheep, one or two or several, never a large flock. Invet-
erate spinners are the *serranas* (mountain women) throughout
Peru. While they tend their sheep, they continually twirl a
wooden spindle to fashion a remarkably fine thread from the
mass of wool carried in the shawl over their shoulders. The
education of the little girls consists in learning at the mother's
side the few household arts that will meet the simple requirements of daily existence in the cold, cheerless puna country.
Spinning is one of the most important of these arts. Often a
little tot of not more than five stands at her mother's knee
spinning thread with a smaller spindle—not so smooth, perhaps, as her mother's but strong and serviceable. These little
folk of the steppe do not look like children; rather, they are
miniature grownups. Their garments are cut and fashioned
like those of their parents. They act like adults. Seldom do

you see them at play in groups, and laughter is almost as unusual with them as it is with their elders. Sometimes one wonders whether they have any more voice than the llamas pastured
on the mountainsides.

In protected valleys above Cachicadan there were growths
of shrubs and small trees. The most familiar in appearance was
the Peruvian alder, *Alnus jorullensis,* which supplied most of
the fuel used in the village. From the introduced Eucalyptus
some wood was obtained when older trees died or branches
were shed. A small tree, attractive because of its reddish, papery
bark, and its unsymmetrical habit of growth, was the *qqueuña*
(Polylepis incana). Buddleias also occurred, white on twig
and underside of leaf. A low St.-John's-wort, *Hypericum larici-*
folium, with needlelike leaves, was everywhere under foot in
the grassy steppe.

The señora then led them gradually upward, still higher
into the mountains. Finally she turned her horse into a sheltered valley. She called it "Inca Corral" because all about were
the ancient ruins of neatly constructed stone corrals. In the
shelter of these Inca walls, they found *Nicotiana thyrsiflora,* not
one plant, but many plants. Some were small and misshapen,
probably because in their youth the goats and sheep that frequented the ruined corrals had trampled them. Others were
in their prime, large, vigorous, and much branched. One was
almost ten feet high. The inflorescences were sometimes over
four feet long, packed with hundreds of flowers. There was
abundance of ripe seed. With great satisfaction in the knowledge that the *Nicotiana thyrsiflora* hunt had at last been
brought to an entirely successful conclusion, Harvey and Bob
leisurely collected the seed, put abundant specimens into the
presses, and took many still and moving pictures of the plants
in their native environment.

They would now have been glad to return to Cachicadan.
They needed time for care of specimens, repair of equipment,
and writing up notes and diaries before starting out next day
toward other collecting areas. The señora, however, had not
the slightest idea of going home. It was not even time for
luncheon and there was a great deal she proposed to show the
visiting botánicos. Now that the *Nicotiana thyrsiflora* business

was over, she was impatient to be off. Her enthusiasm was so
infectious that Harvey and Bob began actually to look forward
to the long day in the saddle, which she obviously proposed.
The opportunity to see one of the least known parts of Peru
under the guidance of such a remarkably well-informed person
as the señora was worth a sacrifice.

She took them eastward into the still higher country,
through lofty mountain passes, and along the margins of deep
ravines. They toiled slowly up into a saddle between two precipitous peaks. On their steep slopes hung Inca or pre-Inca
terraces, buildings, and fortresses, only partially in ruins. Into
the face of smooth cliffs, recesses had been hollowed out by the
pre-Columbian inhabitants of this high, exposed, and forbidding mountain retreat. These recesses extended some three feet
into the solid granite, and were two to three feet square. Did
the ancient peoples use them as places of storage for products
of their agriculture, or were they rock tombs? Nearby, a vertical
depression had been cut into a wall of rock. It was so situated
as to command a wide and unobstructed view over the countryside. Large enough to shelter a small man from the rain and
the strong cold wind, was this a stone sentry box from which
the approach of an enemy could be seen? Or, in those long-
forgotten days did an overseer stand in this niche to direct and
keep to their tasks the agricultural laborers who were culti-
vating the soil in the narrow terraces below his feet?

In Peru, the innumerable and usually well-preserved evidences of ancient civilizations constantly give rise to speculations
concerning the particular significance of certain of these remaining evidences of highly developed and utilitarian cultures.
One of the questions that always occurs to even the most casual
observer is why so many of the ancient peoples of Peru and
adjacent regions lived exclusively in the high mountain ranges,
where life must have been far more difficult than in the lowlands. More than this, why did they so often select as sites for
their settlements the steep walls of river gorges or narrow
saddles between lofty ridges? On them, or over them, they had
to build with infinite toil terraced fields of imported soil on
which their meager alpine crops could be grown. Perhaps it
was to gain protection from enemies, or freedom from the pesti-

lences of the river-bottom jungles and the coastal plains. Such explanations are obvious, but not entirely satisfying.

The señora showed Harvey and Bob some of the least known and most difficult to interpret of all the antiquities in Peru. But first they made a brief halt for luncheon among the caves and ruined terraces on the high saddle between the peaks. Then on she went, still further across the apparently trackless ridges and quebradas, always climbing. Soon they left the rocky defiles and rode across lofty punas. At once, strange massive monuments began to appear, monolithic monuments each of which must have weighed several tons. Near them were many rectangular basins carefully carved out of the basic rock surface of the moors, some of them seven feet square and three feet deep. Each had once been covered with a great slab of granite, fashioned exactly to fit its basin. Often the cover stones had been raised and thrown to one side. In one case the cover had merely been propped up along one edge. All the basins were empty.

According to the señora, only one archaeologist, a German, had, up to that time, made a brief study of these moorland relics. He had concluded that the race that left behind these evidences of its presence and accomplishments was very different from that which culminated in the Inca civilization, destroyed by Pizarro. He thought of them, not as sun worshipers like the Incas, but as moon worshipers. Harvey's diary should be quoted at this point:

"I think the German was off the track. How could any race which undertook to live on those cruelly cold alpine plateaus have failed to worship the sun? We certainly welcomed every one of its infrequent rays. Or were these ancient puna dwellers superromantics, ever living in a dreamy, moonlight-and-roses reverie! Roses, certainly not, in this bleak climate, but possibly the Lobelias and gentians which were blooming in recesses of the ruined monuments. They spoke to me of days long past when they had been cherished and protected by a simple people who lived close, all too close to nature. Perhaps they used them in their medicine, as the señora today brews from them some of her herb teas. One she called *corpus hui macho*, efficacious in male diseases of the blood and kidneys, the other *corpus hui hembra,* effective in similar diseases of women. The latter species was *Gentiana stricticaulis.*"

Bob and I coveted all the antiquities we saw in Peru. His was simply a strong acquisitive instinct where strange and attractive objects were concerned. Mine was acquired from a father who taught ancient history. As a very small boy how well I remember tiptoeing through that long quiet museum, past the mummy cases, to my father's office. Irrespective, however, of the origin of our covetousness, the methods we took to satisfy it were equally reprehensible in many cases! I am willing to confess that Bob's technique was more refined and effective than mine, but that was only because he stayed longer in Peru, and therefore had had more practice!

On this occasion Bob stood it as long as he could, and then he asked the señora whether anybody had found *huacos* (grave pottery), other art objects, or any treasure among the ruins of the "moon worshipers." His diary contains her answer and his comments upon it:

"She was very reticent and quite discouraging. Apparently some huacos and other things had been found, but no treasure. She claimed that the labor involved wasn't worth the reward— I wonder! She herself has made some pretty big hauls, a part of which she exhibits. The natives will not touch an ancient grave. If they do, ill fortune will be their lot for the rest of their days. In this belief the señora certainly does not discourage them. Only her faithful peon, José, who spent the day like a hunting dog, sniffing here and there for this herb or that one, is free to excavate and retrieve antiquities for her. 'But,' I asked her, 'does he not share the fear of his fellows that the spirits will be offended?' 'Oh, yes,' she said, 'certainly, but I know an herb, it's a secret of mine, and from this herb I make him a broth which relieves him from any visitations by the spirits of those whose tombs he has defiled.' Who said anything about a monopoly in restraint of trade? The numerous figurines and vessels which the señora had found are carved from solid granitic rock. Some are very intricately worked and seem to indicate a highly developed artistic feeling and technique on the part of the 'moon worshipers.'"

The botanists were tiring fast. But on the homeward journey, which was almost as difficult as the outgoing one, they were able to give more attention to the general character of the country they had been traversing. There was an intangible something in the aspect of those remote alpine moors, rocky mountainsides and pinnacled peaks, of which they began to become conscious—something infinitely elemental and primitive, something with a spiritual quality. It brought detachment from the ordinary concerns of life. In part this may have been the influence of a continual series of magnificent, unrestricted mountain panoramas.

On one side of the trail and then on the other side superb landscapes were always before their eyes. As they topped a lofty ridge and looked to the south the panorama held them speechless. It was almost the same scene at which the Prince had marveled three years before, except that they saw it just as the setting sun turned all the foreground into shadow—the white head of Huascaran, seventy miles away it must have been, and on its left the Piel de Gato, or Cat's Skin, black mountainsides splotched with white snowfields, and on its right the snowy crests of the Cordillera Blanca. That night in Cachicadan, Bob wrote in his diary:

"Nowhere in the United States is there anything to compare with the limitless sweep of lofty mountain ranges and deep broad valleys that one keeps continually seeing at these high elevations. It is hard to realize that so much of Peru lies above twelve thousand feet. I know that such mere trifles as the Grand Tetons, the Sierra Nevada, or the Grand Canyon can never again give me as great a feeling of awe and insignificance as they used to. I wanted to stay for hours to drink in that indescribably magnificent view and to attempt to grasp its meaning."

Mountain views were an old story to the señora and she finally tore them away from this one. With no abatement in vigor and enthusiasm she pushed on. On the steepest, roughest parts of the trail the tired horses had to be led or dragged along, and the two North Americans were panting for breath much of the time. But not the señora. She talked continuously about the vegetation, the ruins, and the geology of this countryside which she thought of as her very own. They rode into Cachi-

cadan long after dark. She said: "You men no doubt are somewhat tired and wish to rest, and so I shall not detain you. I still
have much work to do." What a rebuke to a retirement plan
for sixty-five-year-olders!

I had suggested to Harvey that if their *Nicotiana thyrsiflora*
hunt was successful I wanted them to spend additional time
in northern Peru to determine something about the geographical range of this practically unknown species. To this end he
and Bob decided to make for the city of Hualgayoc, one hundred and twenty-five miles north of Cachicadan and less than
half that distance from the Ecuadorian border. In that area
the terrain would correspond to the one in which they knew
that *Nicotiana thyrsiflora* grew. By going almost as far north
as they could and still remain in Peru, an upper limit of distribution for this tobacco relative might be established. If they
didn't find it then they could work south from Hualgayoc until
it appeared. This proposed sojourn in Peru's farthest north
was destined to provide them with some rather unusual experiences.

To get to the north from Cachicadan they returned by
truck to the coast at Trujillo, went up the coast to Pacasmayo
—an attractive town near the sea—and thence inland to the
dry, dusty, not so attractive town of Chepén. It must, however,
he said in Chepén's favor that its streets displayed a considerable number of Jacaranda trees which went a long way toward
lifting its curse of ugliness. Jacarandas are extensively planted
in the cities of temperate South America. Their masses of blue
flowers are universally admired by tourists. Harvey once asked
Agnes Johnson, the English artist whom we have already met,
just how she would describe the blue of Jacaranda flowers. Her
reply was: "Jacaranda blue!"

Not the same day of course, but actually on the *mañana,*
the truck in which they had taken passage from Chepén to
Hualgayoc started eastward. At the beginning it took them up
the valley of the Jequetepeque (pronounced Heck-e-te-péck-e)
over a road like the one along which they had traveled from
Trujillo to Santiago de Chuco. The first night out was spent at
San Miguel. In the afternoon of the next day the road left the
dry shrub land and came into the high puna they were begin-

ning to know so well. The air was hazy and the sun glowed red through the smoke from distant grass fires. In the dry season herdsmen burn the grass that grows on the steppe, so that when the rains come their llamas and sheep can have better grazing on fresh tender grasses.

A long stop was made for generator repairs on the chilly puna near a village of grass huts, which had been constructed by a gang of laborers doing pick-and-shovel work on the road. The rest of the trip to Hualgayoc was punctuated with frequent stops, for in spite of all the chófer's tinkering the generator refused to show any charge. It seemed obvious that the field or the armature or both were burned out, but nobody could tell the chófer anything. He maintained that air of aloofness characteristic of chauffeurs at home and abroad. Nevertheless, he was quite happy to have a gallery of passengers who, with respect and with awe, watched him take the generator apart and then put it together again. To his audience of country people an engine was a bit of man-made magic, which would respond only to the will of a superior magician.

After long deliberation the chófer apparently decided that the bushing was too loose and that the journal had too much play. He found an old tin can, cut out a shim, and shaped it around the journal. It really fitted pretty tight and his audience thereupon expressed great admiration and offered congratulations. The fact that, when the engine was started, the ammeter registered nothing was generously overlooked. It was doubtful whether the chófer really expected anything much from his repair job. Probably it was the audience that he had primarily in mind.

As the truck coasted downhill from the puna into its narrow streets the late afternoon sun shone redder still through the smoke and cast an eerie light over the grass thatch roofs of the ancient city of Hualgayoc. More than two hundred years had written their record in the cobbled streets and on the ancient dwellings. As the city accumulated antiquity it also accumulated dirt. On the thatch which was Hualgayoc's most conspicuous and characteristic architectural feature, successive crops of weeds and grasses had come and gone. They had left behind a quantity of humus, which in the dry season sifted

Llamas are the Peruvian Indian's best friends—source of wool, burden bearers, companions on lonely trails, and, finally, a meat supply

Near Cuzco an Indian housewife dressed in the height of highland fashion spins her llama wool on a visit to this lofty Andean town

Harvey finds that the flower stalk of the lost *Nicotiana* of the northern
Peruvian Andes measures almost five feet in length

"La Gringa" and José at Inca Corral—*N. thyrsiflora* in the background

César and Bob collecting *Nicotiana glutinosa* in northern coastal Peru

down as a brown powder into the streets. But with the coming of the rains there would be a sudden transformation and Hualgayoc's roofs would all be green.

The streets were unbelievably narrow. They had been laid down in a period of Peru's history when there were only two kinds of people, peasants on foot and noblemen on horseback. Therefore the streets needed only to be wide enough for horsemen, foot passengers going to the wall or under the hoofs of the horses as the case might be. There are other cities in Peru that preserve an atmosphere of the Middle Ages, but none can surpass Hualgayoc in the impression of antiquity that it makes upon the foreign visitor. Every vista along its streets carries unreality, but with the authenticity of a Hollywood unreality. An artist with easel or camera might prowl about for days and find always new and appealing compositions, as light and shade play over this quaint old "City of Thatch" with its flanking mountain walls.

So far Harvey and Bob had seen nothing of *Nicotiana thyrsiflora* along the road. Since the generatorless truck was going on twelve miles beyond Hualgayoc to the town of Bambamarca they decided to stay aboard in order to see still more of the countryside. The chófer had done something so that his engine would start, but that was about all. A few miles along the road he decided that more repairs were required. This time he hauled out the generator and fan assembly, gazed at it with passionate resentment, and then with profane comments, threw it into the back of the truck. He thereupon became doubly an optimist. First, he hoped to keep the engine cool without its fan by coasting all the way to Bambamarca. Second, he hoped to get there in daylight since now he had no headlights. Hualgayoc lies at an elevation of twelve thousand feet and Bambamarca is about three thousand feet lower; but coasting is perilous on a narrow mountain road in Peru where it is often necessary to come to a dead stop in order to make a hairpin turn. In addition, it was not all downhill and there were places where the road had to climb over small ridges.

Coasting out of Hualgayoc, Harvey and Bob saw a plant or two that looked like *Nicotiana,* in the open shrubland where goats and sheep were browsing. As the truck reached some old

Italian mines, the chófer halted to cool the motor and take the
generator to the mine shop on the chance that it could be
repaired. Meanwhile, botanizing on the mountainsides was in
order. They found two more clumps of the same *Nicotiana* that
they had just seen. The plants were badly damaged by grazing
animals but what was left of their leaves looked like those of
Nicotiana thyrsiflora. The chófer returned, shook his fist at the
generator, threw it back again into the truck, and the party
was off once more. From then on they often saw the Nicotianas,
but all of them low and bushy and none of them with the vigor
or foxglove-like inflorescences so characteristic of the plants at
Cachicadan. It was getting dark and the other passengers became
fearful of negotiating in the coming darkness any more of the
difficult road than was absolutely necessary. They could not be
blamed, because it had become another of those narrow shelves
hollowed or built out from steep cliff sides. The sheer drop on
the outside of the road was anywhere from five hundred to a
thousand feet. Obviously, the chófer could not stop for plant
collecting.

The truck crept slowly toward the lights of Bambamarca,
far below. Bob impersonated a headlight by hanging out one
side of the truck and flashing his spotlight. Sometimes, where
the road was particularly narrow or otherwise especially treacherous, a passenger or two climbed down and walked ahead to
pick out the best ruts for the truck to follow. It was a fine
clear evening. The distant hills were illuminated by the grass
fires. On the whole, they considered it quite an experience,
enjoyable in a way and also not so enjoyable.

Next morning in Bambamarca they hired horses and rode
back along the road to examine and collect the Nicotianas seen
the previous evening. The day was clear and bright. The haze
from the burning grass had been dissipated during the night.
Dry hills supported dusty shrubs, a few in flower. It was a
Lantana-Rubus-Eupatorium type of vegetation, which looked
weedy now but gave promise of a botanically interesting countryside when the rains set in. The formations were mostly limestone—some chalky, some dolomite; and the boulders were
wind- and sand-etched. Now and then groups of them simulated
tombs and at a distance spots on the mountainsides suggested

burying grounds. Sometimes whole mountainsides showed regular furrows, as though white clay had been turned up by a plow, where the layers of limestone were tilted on edge and irregularly weathered. The lower hills were superbly colored—red hills, vermilion hills, chalk-white hills. To the south they saw a few extraordinary rock pinnacles formed by differential weathering and colored white and scarlet like some of those in Zion and Bryce National Parks. Now and then on the hillsides there were pure stands of the cosmopolitan bracken fern, but it was quite dry and weatherbeaten and stood only knee high.

The Nicotianas proved to be *Nicotiana thyrsiflora*—there was absolutely no doubt about it; but only one out of hundreds was equivalent to those they had seen near Cachicadan. The rest were large shrubby growths without a prominent main stem. This was due largely to injury by sheep and goats and llamas. The branches and stems were quite brittle and probably were annually broken off in quantity. They were constantly exposed to hot drying winds, by contrast with those the señora had found for them that appeared to seek protection from wind.

They had now established a northern station for this *Nicotiana*. How much farther north, perhaps well into Ecuador, it can be found I do not know. If anybody wants to know he can go and find out for himself! I personally do not propose to go into the north Peruvian "back of beyond" and certainly I am not willing, a third time, to ask someone else to go there for me.

I have a feeling that when, in the Botanical Garden in Berkeley, Harvey and Bob come across a beautiful amaryllid whose orange petals are striped and patterned, they will remember a race between two horses and a truck on that morning when they were collecting near Bambamarca. As soon as the *Nicotiana* had been taken care of with the necessary seed collections and specimens and photographs, they turned to some general plant collecting. It is peculiar how an absorbing hunt for some one particular plant will almost completely blind the collector to the nearby presence of other, perhaps equally interesting or attractive, species. Thus, they had entirely overlooked a fine, orange-flowered *Stenomesson* on the ride out from Bambamarca. But on the return journey, they saw it in quantity blooming along the edges of the road cuts above their heads. Promptly dismounting they dug two sacks full of the bulbs. The tying of these sacks to the backs of the saddles was just completed when they heard a truck coming around the turn of the road behind them. The horses had been hired from an outlying *hacienda* and even the sound of a truck made them nervous. There was not enough room for the truck to pass even if the horses had been willing to let it approach them. For a number of miles there would be no chance either to climb the cliff on one side or to descend the steep declivity on the other side. Going downhill the truck had picked up considerable speed and the truck driver gave no indication of being willing to slow down. In other words, there was nothing to do but keep well ahead of the truck and the horses agreed entirely with this proposition. They immediately went into a gallop and ran away from the rumbling menace behind them. Flopping plant presses, camera cases, and sacks of bulbs only added to the consternation of the horses and their riders. It became a mad race. The horses were so terrified that anything might have happened. Just as Bob and Harvey were about to be unhorsed, a level stretch of brushland appeared beside the road. They pulled the horses out into it and the race was over.

This was their first and last gallop in the highlands. Usually one has to exercise all his ingenuity to get much in the way of motion out of the underfed, lazy, Andean four-footed type of transportation.

As they approached the town it began to look as if "all roads lead to Bambamarca." Along every mountain trail the Indians, dressed in fiesta costume, were converging on the town. The women carried children in the shawls on their backs and bundles in their arms; the men carried packages and jugs. It seemed impossible that so many people could come from the neighboring mountains, which always appeared to be sparsely populated. But they kept on coming and coming until nightfall and then on late into the night. The next morning still more drifted in. Upon inquiry it appeared that this was *the* Sunday when an especially grand fiesta occurred at the nearby Hacienda de Chala.

The Bambamarca market that Sunday was one of the

greatest of the year. Not only the plaza but all the streets of
the town were crowded. The women wore multicolored, full
woolen skirts, shawls, and silly little white straw hats. The men
were draped in cinnamon brown ponchos with huge white hats
above. Almost all of them were full-blooded Indians.

Hundreds of women squatted on the ground in the plaza
with their wares spread out before them. Whether they sold
anything or not seemed to make no difference. The main business was gossip with friends and neighbors. Only a relatively
few different kinds of commodities were on sale but most of
them were displayed in quantity. There were piles of potatoes,
some dark red, some light red, some yellow, but all of them
small in size. There were mounds of white mealy pellets, representing what was left of potatoes that had been frozen in the
high mountains and then washed and dried. These dessicated
potatoes produce what is called *chuño,* a staple article of diet
in the high puna country and elsewhere in the Andes. For
fifty centavos (ten cents, U. S.), you could buy a bundle of
rye straw sufficient to make yourself a new hat. Little heaps of
powdered aniline dyes attracted the mountain women who had
spun enough yarn to weave a new skirt and who were hoping
to make the neighbor ladies jealous with the brilliance of its
rainbow hues. For the men's ponchos the somber brown dye
extracted from the native walnut, *Juglans peruviana,* was good
enough.

There were piles of dried corn, the ears always small, but
brightly colored. There were little bundles of green alfalfa and
of green barley straw for those buyers high enough in the social
stratification to ride on their own ponies or donkeys. Pigs, goats,
sheep, and chickens on the hoof were for sale. One woman's sole
stock in trade consisted of six heads of teasel, the thistlelike
heads of *Dipsacus fullonum* used in carding wool. This plant,
a native of Europe, has been carried over the world wherever
wool is produced. The teasel market appeared to be on the
bearish side. In the morning she had six heads, at noon she still
had six. Profits in general must have been meager.

In the larger stores of North American cities, tired shoppers
may refresh themselves at the soft drink counter or in the lunch
room. In that respect the Bambamarca market was up-to-date.

For five centavos you could buy a pick-up in the form of a ladleful of *caldo,* a soup with ingredients you knew better than to investigate. For another five centavos there were plate dinners with choice of boiled potato, rice, hunk of *charqui* (jerked meat), leg of cui or guinea pig, or even a morsel of chicken. The men always found it necessary to wash everything down with another five centavos worth of *chicha.* For the foreigner, the safest bet was a small ear of corn on the cob, called *choclo,* which also cost five centavos.

The gringos were much interested in this remarkable concourse of mountain people, and in their wares. The Indians were equally interested and stared silently but raptly at the two oddly dressed, pale-skinned foreigners who were so restless and who kept continually pointing their mysterious cameras at somebody or something. Children cried when they saw them and ran away. Dogs barked at them, a gang of older and bolder children followed them about. Some of the men knowingly explained to one another that the people of Bambamarca were being highly honored; undoubtedly their faces would soon be shown in the cinema palaces of the world. A policeman offered his assistance in making the grand spectacle appear in its best light. For him this market was the most important event of the year. He considered it well worthy of being pictured to all foreigners not fortunate enough to visit the Bambamarca *feria* on this, its grand fiesta day.

In the afternoon the crowds gradually drifted out of town, over a bridge and up a hill along the trail that led to Chala, center of the celebration. Grogshops along the way did a riotous business, even though most of the celebrants carried their own jugs of chicha. A Peruvian Indian's idea of whoopee is to acquire a fried guinea pig, a gallon of chicha, and then foregather with his neighbors similarly provisioned. When between twelve hundred and fifteen hundred are thus congregated, that makes a rattling good fiesta. Chicha provides the Indian with a feeling of balmy contentment. All's well with that world with which on ordinary days he must contend. His face muscles relax into a smile. He may go so far as to laugh boisterously, slap his neighbor on the back, and even embrace him. Although ordinarily uncommunicative and often sullen, chicha makes the

Peruvian highlander positively loquacious. The jabbering of hundreds of them in their strange guttural Quechua tongue reminds one of the din produced by colonies of parakeets and macaws in the Amazonian forests. There was dancing every-where—most of it go-as-you-please or at least not conforming to any set pattern. Some couples, however, danced the graceful handkerchief dance called *la marinera*.

Only a few fights marred the generally peaceful proceed-ings. They were precipitated by some gay young blades who were not content with chicha, but had to fortify it with *aguardi-ente,* the fermented juice of the sugar cane. Distilling was a technique unknown to the Indians until the white man came to Peru, bringing with him the benefits of civilization in the form of Christianity and the copper still. His native chicha contained only about 6 per cent of alcohol. It did not do him any good, but on the other hand it did not do him very much harm, and it enabled him to relax and take an optimistic view of life for a little while. But with the still he can step up alcohol content. Then he wants to fight his neighbor instead of embracing him. Aguardiente is bad medicine for the Peruvian Indian. One of its addicts at the market tried several times, unsuccessfully, to mount his horse amid a crowd of shouting, jeering spectators. When he realized that he was too drunk to do it, he tried to inflate his ego by brutally beating the horse and calling it names in Quechua. They sounded pretty bad, even to a foreign ear which did not understand them.

Almost the only sober members of the crowd that swept back to Bambamarca after the fiesta were the infants who jounced about in the shawls on their mothers' backs. Some of the revelers found the steeper parts of the trail hard going. One tipsy woman kept slipping and falling. Her real difficulty was that she wore shoes. They were quite rare among her sisters, but except for unshod extremities, the women were really over-dressed. Apparently they wore all the clothing they possessed to the fiesta—a matter of display. The best and brightest skirt was on the outside. On the way to the fiesta and going home it was gathered up and bound about the waist to guard against tears and mud. Most of the women did not cross the bridge when they returned to Bambamarca after the fiesta; rather, they went down through the stream and seemed to get the greatest satisfaction in soaking their feet. They should have soaked their heads as well!

A roadside shrine in a niche of the rocky ledge that edged the road was a center of attention. Some couples were dancing the marinera before it. Many passers-by paused to watch. Some lit candles and placed them before the image, which was soon surrounded with a blaze of flickering yellow light. From a rock crevice, high above the road, issued a trickle of water; beside it, on the smooth rock, was a crudely executed painting of the Virgin. Many climbed laboriously up the slippery path to drink and to reverence the painting.

Next day, while the town was holding its head and beginning to sober up, Harvey and Bob left Bambamarca and headed north to Chota. They were outfitted with two saddle horses, two pack horses, and a general nuisance who called himself their guide. The country between the two towns, indeed the whole expanse of mountains and valleys roundabout, was almost completely barren. For centuries it had been grazed and cultivated. No doubt, in the remote past even more intensive cultivation had been practiced. Many of the hillsides were red and yellow where erosion had carried off the surface soil and exposed the rocky substratum. Again there were square miles of limestone outcrop weathered to a fairly even level, with giant furrows and ridges. Cemetery-like areas showing prominences of limestone like tombstones appeared again here. At a distance the gray rock masses could sometimes be mistaken for flocks of sheep pasturing on the mountainsides.

They passed rows of scattered stones that indicated the course of ancient fences, as did also lines of barberry and a species of *Mutisia,* a member of the Sunflower family. Barberry is common throughout the Peruvian Andes, and some of the more spiny species are used in hedges. A shrubby *Mutisia* with long thorns is often built into barricades against grazing animals. The most successful plant along the trail was *Iochroma grandiflora,* long ago introduced into horticulture and much esteemed in frostless climates, particularly for its masses of tubular, rich, purple-blue flowers. It stood out, a vigorous, dark-green shrub, among the thickets of *Baccharis* and brambles in rocky quebradas, along old stone walls and even in heavily grazed pastures. About the hovels of shepherds and covered with white bloom, was a small elderberry, *Sambucus peruviana.*

In fence rows and along streams near Chota, the most common tree was a cherry, *Prunus capuli.* Its fruit had a large pit and little flesh, and was sold in the markets throughout the Peruvian Andes. A species of *Duchesnea,* which they found on dry hillsides, bore fruits like our wild strawberries, but its petals were yellow rather than white. Twining in hedgerows was a *Passiflora* or passionflower. Its blooms were gorgeous, with large scarlet petals and dark-purple corona fringe. The Indians called this striking flower *ccoto-ccoto,* in the belief that if you pick it you will become goiterous. A fine pink-flowered *Passiflora,* which they saw first in Cachicadan and was there called *pfuro-pfuro,* which in Quechua means "feather," also grew about Chota, and its common name was the same as that of the red-flowered species. Goiter is, and has for centuries been, all too common in the Andean valleys remote from the sea.

The most important resident in Chota was a foreigner, German-born. He ran the mill, managed the local electric light plant, and served as *profesor* of the English language in the *colegio.* Before World War I, he owned a hat factory in England which later was confiscated, during the period of his internment. He married an English woman, and after the war they went to Germany, but found it difficult to make a fresh start. He had often read of Peru, and persuaded himself that it must be a land flowing with milk and honey. So one day he said to his wife, "Let's go to Peru." So they did, and almost starved during the first year when they attempted to establish themselves in a coastal town. Later on they struck out for the mountains. There they came into touch with a German missionary priest, long resident in Peru. The recent expatriate spoke English without a flaw, and the padre finally found a place for him in the colegio at Chota. But this position did not pay a living wage. He therefore proceeded to develop the electric light plant and later built a flour mill along the Rio Chota. With these three irons in the fire he maintained a good home, and looked forward to educating his three daughters abroad. When Harvey and Bob were in Chota he was not very proud of his electric light, for during a prolonged dry season there was hardly enough water to keep his plant in operation. Often the filaments in the tiny bulbs showed only a faint glow.

They had barely arrived in Chota before it was discovered that bubonic plague had broken out. One victim had died three weeks before, a second one on the following week, and a third had just succumbed, all in one family. The botánicos decided that a stay in Chota was undesirable, but the hotel proprietor, with an eye to prolonging the visit of such well-paying guests, scoffed at the report that *bubonica* was actually in town. He insisted that it was silly to dignify a bit of influenza by such a name. But the cat popped out of the bag when without warning the district health officer arrived from Cajamarca and put up at the hotel. At once he ordered the Indians and townsfolk to kill all their guinea pigs because, together with rats, they were known to spread plague. So everyone feasted on guinea pig. The rats, more difficult to deal with, remained at large. The stricken family was moved out of town to a hovel on the riverbank, and all their bedding was burned.

In larger centers of population in Peru, an outbreak of bubonic is usually caught in time to prevent a serious epidemic. But when it appears in isolated communities far off in the Andes there is a different problem. A death, irrespective of the cause, is made the occasion for a gathering of the clan from near and far, together with as many neighbors and friends as are permitted to share the liquid refreshment provided for the wake. When the celebration is finally at an end and the often thoroughly infected celebrants go home they may carry the plague to a dozen or more small mountain communities. In a short time a large area is involved, and the health authorities find it difficult to cope with the situation.

Harvey and Bob were headed for Sócota, via Tacabamba, with their horses, mules, and so-called guide. They left Chota on a trail along the river. The hillsides were covered with a shrub vegetation, most of which would have been in flower had this not happened to be one of the rare seasons when the rains were very late in arriving. Among a few species in condition to be collected was a *Bejaria*. It looked much like Azalea and the plants were brilliant with bright-pink flowers. *Emboth-*

rium grandiflorum showed some of its pastel-pink flower clusters, but not the gorgeous ones we were to see later in the Andes
of southern Peru. *Puru-puru, Erythrina* trees, were common.
The hard, scarlet beans they bear are prized by the Indians who
string them to make attractive necklaces.

The flavor of life throughout that remote portion of northern Peru in which they now found themselves can be sensed in
the account of their experiences which Harvey gives in his diary.
The preface concerns their ride from Tacabamba to Sócota:

"The trail was extremely mountainous, particularly the
last part. For a whole hour we wound around and up a mountain and down on the other side to accomplish only a mile or
two of horizontal distance. We climbed into switchbacks, turn
upon turn, until the horses were almost dizzy, only to find that
we must descend into the next valley along another hundred
or more zigzags. Finally, after an unusually long, steep climb,
we suddenly looked in breathless amazement over the brink of
the biggest hole I've ever seen in this world. It was an immensely
vast valley enclosed by tremendous mountains. The Grand Canyon of the Colorado would be lost in it. In the middle reposed
a mountain of no mean size, as if it had been dumped there.
To the north there was enough level ground to accommodate
a small village, San Antonio. On the south side nestled Sócota,
our destination, beside the river of the same name. On a steep,
direct highway one could have coasted down in a car in ten
minutes. This was one o'clock. At six o'clock we arrived, after
zigzagging all around the mountainsides.

"As we began to descend into the tropics, new wayside
shrubs and weedy growths appeared. It was evident that in the
rainy season there would be much to collect here. But at that
time the roads would be terribly treacherous. Finally arriving
in the valley of the river, we came upon a sugar and aguardiente
hacienda. Our guide and Bob at once began chewing sugar cane
to quench their thirst, but soon discarded this delicacy in favor
of unripe oranges. A *muchacho* offered to pick some oranges
from a tree that he knew bore ripe ones. He brought three
dozen and when asked how much he wanted for them, replied
hesitatingly, 'Dos reales' (two cents, U. S.). We were, perhaps,
the first foreigners to spoil the little boy by giving him more

money than he dared ask. Over parts of our route limestone had prevailed. On the last descent fossil-bearing rocks were much in evidence, with various species of seashells embedded in them.

"Arriving in Sócota we sought the home of the local *cura,* the German missionary priest who had befriended his compatriot in Chota. He gave us a hearty welcome and promptly cleared out the rubbish from a spare room. Here we set up our plant driers and arranged our bedrolls. The kindly padre invited us to eat with him in the refectory. He had been in Peru since the outbreak of the first World War; indeed, he was en route when war was declared in 1914. Professionally he is a somewhat discouraged, disillusioned man. The people love him as a father, but it is, perhaps, too much to expect them to respond to his efforts in their behalf. He imported seeds, planted fruit trees, showed the Indians how to improve their agriculture, how to build their thatched roofs so that they would not leak, but he could teach them almost nothing. True, they planted the fruit trees, but took no care of them, and finally the goats ate them. As for new methods of tilling the soil, why should they change? Their fathers had gotten along all right, hadn't they? When he overnights in their homes in the rainy season, they move his cot around until they find the place of honor—the spot where the leaky roof drips the least. Yes, when it is dry again they will repair the thatch—of a certainty they will make it a most excellent roof. When it's dry again all is forgotten. For twenty years he has tried to teach them that in the rainy season they must cut the grass, dry it, and store the hay over against the days when there will be no rain and their animals will have no feed. Each dry season they faithfully promise that when the rains come they will put up much hay. The rainy season comes and with it the lush grasses. Then all ambition to put up any hay departs from them. Why worry? The animals have enough to eat, haven't they?

"For a few years a person can meet all this with patience and forgiveness, then the futility of it all is overwhelming. Just now the Indians are discouraged by the long duration of the drought. The horses are half-starved and can do no work. The cows give no milk. There are no eggs. It was almost impossible to find any fodder for our horses and pack animals, and there was no grain. True, one could buy maize, at a price. But maize is human food and never fed to animals. Anyone seen feeding an ear of corn to a horse would be set down as insane. It would be as though, at home, you saw someone feeding bread to a horse. No, corn is for making choclo when in the milk stage, hominy and parched corn when dry. When germinated, dried, ground, and fermented, it produces the beloved chicha.

"Times, the cura complained, were no longer good. Once the people contributed well to the church, not always in money, but sheep, cows, and horses. He could sell these animals and use the money for the church. It was not uncommon to receive a fat cow for a marriage.

"Having established ourselves in Sócota, we decided to collect up a small river which flows nearby into the main stream. We asked the padre if we could find a muchacho who would carry our plant press. He agreed to speak to the director of schools about it. After a little while he returned to say that he had located the director in a poker game and that, rather than recommend a boy, the director himself would accompany us, but not just yet. We should please wait until after lunch. Ultimately, word came from the director that the *alcalde* or mayor, as well as the recorder of the town, would like to go along. All we had asked for was a muchacho to carry a plant press; now it appeared that we were to have an official entourage. This meant that after all we would carry the plant press ourselves; those august officials could certainly not be expected to carry anything. Menial tasks of any sort were not for them. However, when three members of the gentry and the flower of officialdom showed up, they brought with them a mozo to do the carrying. Before starting, the director made a further request. Another friend of his would like to shut up shop and come with us if the *exploradores* had no objection. Of course we consented and were soon joined by a shifty-looking character who had come from Spain some years ago to this remote spot.

"After the going got a little hard, up the river, the mayor produced two sticks of dynamite from his pocket, and said that he thought he would like to stop a while to fish. The Spaniard stopped with him. We continued botanizing upstream. The school director and the recorder proved to be good sports on a long climb with hard going through brushland. Cassias, Solanums, Crotons, yellow-flowered Jussiaeas, and the rank *Ambrosia peruviana,* were among the plants we collected. This last is a vile weed in many parts of Peru. It even gets into the cultivations of the east coast of South America. In practically all respects it is the counterpart of our ragweed of bad repute among hayfever sufferers, except that it grows several times larger and in favorable situations may be as tall as a horse. On dry hills throughout this region, *Dodonaea viscosa,* a member of the Sapindaceae or Soapberry family, is very common. It has a wide distribution throughout the Peruvian mountains, and is used for making mattresses. The leaves, as the specific name indicates, are viscid. When growing on dry hillsides they are not moistly viscid, but just viscid enough so that, if the twigs and leaves are gathered and made into a bed, the whole mass sticks together and can be picked up and handled as a mattress.

"We had expected to hear the dynamiting of fish by the alcalde and the Spaniard, but the afternoon wore on and nothing happened. On our return that night, the padre asked me whether the alcalde had taken any liquor with him. I said that all we had seen was dynamite, but that he might have had something else in his pocket. The padre felt sure that there must have been some alcohol along because the alcalde had fallen in the river and the Spaniard had brought him home soaking wet. He was now in bed, preparing to come down with pneumonia.

"As we sat before the cabin that night, frogs were attempting a few uncertain croaks in the quebrada below. An old man passing by said to us, 'They are announcing the coming of rain.' The frogs were not wrong. In the night we were awakened by the patter of rain on the roof, thatched with sugar cane. Ordinarily it might have been conducive to sleep, but the thought of the slippery clay roads which we must travel for four or five days to get back to civilization took some of the poetry out of the situation, as did also the ominous drippings that were beginning here and there about the cabin. I fared better than Bob did, for one of his boots was exactly under a drip. and in the morning he poured a pint of water out of it."

We must now leave Harvey and Bob. After a somewhat uncomfortable but uneventful journey, they reached the coast and then returned to Lima. Soon thereafter they began their long and arduous collecting trips in the middle and southern Andes of Peru and beyond them into the montaña, that vast, eastward expanse of Amazonian jungle. In succeeding chapters we shall often come across them and their experiences.

Chapter IV

COAST TO CORDILLERA

H ISTORICALLY speaking, Lima, City of Kings, was the gateway to South America for the European. At least it was the front door by which the first entrances were effected. Glancing casually at a map of the Western world, you would hardly point to Peru as the first approach to South America from Europe. Yet it was there that the conquistadors first came, to found a permanent capital. From Lima, expeditions, overland and coastwise, ramified into the rest of the continent. The Church sent its missionaries there. Thence, these missionaries carried on, over the mountains and across the jungle into what, today, we call Bolivia and Argentina.

Altogether, Florence and I made Lima our headquarters for over three months. We have a great affection for this colorful, friendly, and increasingly progressive city. Someone has said that, geographically and otherwise, Lima has little excuse for existence; that it is unproductive and lives parasitically upon the wealth created in other parts of Peru which, therefore, are unable to enjoy equivalent prosperity. So long as human beings prefer to herd together and create large centers of population, some products of this disposition will always grow up in places where they may not belong. If anything is radically wrong with Lima it has been wrong for a number of hundreds of years and, hopefully, will continue, if it must, to merit the economists' displeasure for some considerable time to come. In a Latin-American sense it is a capital to be proud of, and, provided that modern improvements are not permitted to encroach too actively upon the many authentic remnants of Spanish colonial architecture and atmosphere, it will continue to preserve one of the few American counterparts of that appealing historical mélange that was characteristic of some smaller European capitals.

Lima is a city of vivid contrasts. In newer suburbs one sees elegant homes whose architecture has a modernistic, functional feeling. In older suburbs there still remain adobe huts with

Pizzaro in bronze before the cathedral in the Plaza de Armas, Lima

Guard mount before the palace of the president, Plaza de Armas, Lima

Highly decorative Chimu pottery in the Museum of Anthropology, Lima
Birds, mammals, and plants often inspired ancient Peruvian potters

The author in the cactus-ridden foothills of the Peruvian Andes

A cactus (*Espostoa lanata*) landscape, west slopes of the Andes

From afar, cushion cacti (*Opuntia lagopus*) simulate patches of snow

Three Turk's-cap cacti (*Cactus Townsendii*), Santa Eulalia Valley, Peru

straw-thatch roofs. One of the commercial gardens owns extensive glasshouses in which orchids are grown on agar in thousands upon thousands of sterile flasks, the last word in orchid culture. In a field just beyond, one sees oxen drawing crude plows. In the matter of transportation, passengers may travel in big autobusses built in Mannheim, Germany, and originally ordered by the city of Madrid. When Madrid was not able to take delivery because it was being used as a proving ground for modern war's machines of destruction, they came to the peaceful city of Lima. But once beyond the business district these fast, ultramodern busses dispute the right of way with primitive burro and llama transportation.

In Lima many nationalities and races have met and mingled. Wilhelm Müller, in his *Das Schöne Süd-America,* says that this city has special significance because of its varied racial mixtures and that in perhaps no other city in South America does one encounter so many hybrid types—creoles, mestizos, mulattos, quadroons, quintroons, chinos, zambos, cholos, and chino-cholos.

During most of our sojourn in Lima we lived in the Hotel Maury, well known to discriminating visitors because of its excellent café. We also liked its large, airy suites of rooms. For many weeks we occupied one of them, its principal attraction being a long balcony or gallery overhanging a busy, and characteristically narrow, thoroughfare. On our gallery we dried plants, and the dwellers in the improvised penthouses across the way must still be wondering why the *norteamericanos* were forever laying out gray blotting papers where they would catch the maximum of hot Lima sunlight, and then picking them all up again. When quantities of wet plants began to come in by air from Harvey and Bob, the sun did not dry the felt driers fast enough. Then we obtained an electric stove and hung the plant presses over the heat, doubtless to the still further mystification of our vis-à-vis.

For Florence, this balcony, with its ever-changing panorama of Lima's busy life, was a great joy. From it she could look up the street to the Plaza de Armas and in the opposite direction past a traffic-filled corner, down another street of shops. She frequently called my attention to all sorts of interesting and amusing things that were going on below. We often watched the fine automobiles of Lima society draw up to the curb next swanky shops and from them descend charmingly dressed señoras or señoritas, always with the smallest feet imaginable. It is reported that a Peruvian gentleman about to visit the United States was commissioned by his lady friends to buy North American shoes. When he attempted to fulfill these commissions and mentioned the sizes or showed the outline of a foot, he was promptly directed to the children's shoe department.

The things we saw at night from our gallery were the most entertaining. On one occasion we were awakened by noisy talk and snatches of song. We looked down to see a street deserted except for an intoxicated youth. Now, in the Latin America we know, it is rare to see an adult so drunk that he will make an unfavorable exhibition of himself in public. Therefore I was suspicious that this was a case of youthful "arm waving" or that the noisy person was a foreigner, possibly a compatriot of ours. Although his identity was never revealed, my first suspicion was confirmed by the character and effect of the technique which a policeman applied. He appeared from nowhere, walked for a few steps behind the noisemaker, and then applied a vigorous kick to the right spot. The victim stopped, looked around, sized up the situation, and walked off a bit unsteadily but very quietly. Apparently shock is one of the remedies for "arm waving."

It was this same policeman who was in view on a subsequent night when the heat drove us from our beds to the gallery for a breath of air. We pulled chairs close to the long line of open windows and, with elbows on the sill, rested heads on arms and looked down to the dark street. It was very late. Everything was peaceful and quiet; delicate, refreshing drafts of cool, sweet air were drawn past us from the Plaza de Armas. Half awake and half asleep, we gradually became aware of an unfamiliar, elusive, intermittent sound. It was as though someone was periodically drawing a large wood-rasp lightly across a resonant timber. The sound seemed to come from around a nearby corner and to be slowly drawing nearer. We looked at each other inquiringly and then turned our heads toward the corner. After a moment or two a small block of kindling wood slid out into the intersection of the two smoothly surfaced streets, and behind it appeared our policeman. He was walking his beat very slowly and, like a small boy employing similar means to add interest to running an errand, was kicking this bit of wood ahead of him. Sometimes he kicked for distance, sometimes for accuracy, and sometimes he merely tried to regulate his stride so that the kick would become an integral part of it. As it skittered over the street, the little billet made a pleasant noise—not loud enough to disturb sleeping citizens but sufficient to echo faintly up and down the empty street. We followed it until our eyelids began to droop. Returned to bed I watched Florence fall asleep with a recurring smile at each diminishing echo of the policeman's little game.

When we sailed from Valparaiso for Peru, our friend the General brought to the stateroom a large, brown, Chilean tarantula, ensconced in a round, wooden, cheesebox. I remembered that Florence had admired a preserved specimen she had seen in the General's insect collection and his presentation to her of this live spider was one of his practical jokes, to the perpetration of which he is constitutionally addicted. Florence, however, chose to look upon his parting gift as a challenge to her courage and to the quality of her scientific curiosity. In other words, by appearing to take it for granted that this was a bona fide *recuerdo,* and one that she was supposed to guard and cherish, she gave the General no satisfaction. I saw her take the donor aside and heard her gravely inquire concerning the food and other requirements of the fearsome-looking, many-legged, hairy beast, which when extended covered a good-sized soup plate. I was amused to watch the General's expression. Obviously he was not sure whether Florence was serious or whether his leg was being pulled. Recognizing the symptoms, however, I was quite certain that Florence, in her own mind, had already decided to introduce this delightful little stranger into our cabin; and so it proved. The name "Edwyn," after the donor, was promptly bestowed upon the tarantula, with "Edwinia" held in reserve should subsequent evidence necessitate its substitution. I am thankful to say that the alternative designation was not required.

For the next four months we traveled with Edwyn, not he with us. His daily requirement of two or more live flies or moths kept us constantly on the alert. Since on ships, trains, and in hotels objection to Edwyn's presence might be anticipated, we could not reveal his identity by enlisting the aid of the crew, the brakemen, or the porters, in catching his food. Therefore we went about armed with a small net and a ventilated bottle and, by dint of making ourselves unpleasantly conspicuous in public places, managed to keep Edwyn well fed.

The Plaza de Armas was our principal hunting ground in Lima. Early in the morning, before the city loafers had occupied the benches in the plaza, we swept the edges of grass plots with our net and rushed about wildly when a particularly promising insect buzzed past. I sometimes thought that I could detect a puzzled expression on the bronze face of Pizarro as he looked down upon our activities from his high pedestal on the steps of the cathedral. Early rising citizens were equally in doubt about us, but probably thought that, like most gringos, we were a little mad; in this case, harmlessly so.

During the homeward voyage on the *Santa Maria* from Peru to New York City, we sat at Captain Tom Williams's table and Florence hinted so often and so broadly at the possibility that his ship was carrying a many-legged stowaway that she was finally forced to exhibit Edwyn to the captain. He entered into the spirit of the situation and, thereafter, the natural history of tarantulas and the efforts we made to feed ours aboard ship provided the principal topic of conversation at table, and nearby diners must have wondered about the cause of our hilarity. After two long voyages with Captain Williams we came to know him somewhat intimately. He was much beloved by crew, as well as passengers. His death in the harbor of Valparaiso, some weeks after we said good-bye to him in New York, was a great shock to us.

On Florence's lap, in a glass-topped, tin candy box, Edwyn rode, from New York to Berkeley. Except for the rubbing off of some of his auburn hair, he appeared to be little the worse for his long automobile journey. At home in Berkeley he lived happily for more than a year in a large, glass-sided box, filled with sand and vegetation and covered with wire netting. He and

Florence became devoted friends. At the sound of her voice he rose up on a number of his hind legs and waved a welcome with his feelers. The next summer we were away from home for two months, and, despite the meticulous, if somewhat unwilling, attentions of our son, poor Edwyn died. A broken heart was doubtless responsible, because a tarantula, like Long John's parrot, "lives forever, mostly." I should, perhaps, have said that Edwyn was a nonpoisonous species, technically known as *Mygale rosea.*

Returning again, after this faunistic interlude, to the Plaza de Armas, we found it, in 1939, not the same place we knew in 1935. In preparation for the 1938 Pan-American Congress, which met in Lima, someone had tried to modernize it. The fine, old palms were gone and in their place stood small shade trees that did not appear to be very happy. A certain spaciousness which we remembered seemed to have been lost, but perhaps nothing but the palms had actually disappeared. Despite the effects of horticultural experimentation the Plaza de Armas will always remain an appealing place. We came to know it well, not only in the early mornings but also at other times of day and night.

The most direct route from the Hotel Maury to the Central Post Office took us through the plaza, and a day rarely passed that we did not have letters to be registered, as well as air-mailed. Except when the noonday sun confined us to the gallery under which two sides of the plaza could be traversed, we walked along the two opposite sides, which were much more attractive. Whenever there happened to be a camera along, I made Florence wait while I climbed the low, broad steps of the two-towered cathedral and vainly attempted to get just the shot I wanted of mailed Pizarro on his war horse, together with the right amount of sky and a part of one of the two towers, as a background. I liked to step for a moment into the cool interior and watch the far-off, high, silver, candle-studded altar take form as my eyes gradually became accustomed to the semi-darkness of the great church. We sometimes stopped to admire the tremendous, round-topped, ancient wooden doors, many inches thick and decorated with interesting wrought-iron knobs, and to wonder whether they might have belonged to the more magnificent cathedral, built during the early years of the vice-regal regime and later thrown down by one of Peru's most destructive earthquakes. Often as it was that we went inside, we never examined the famous glass casket in which tourists are convinced that they see the mummified remains of Captain General Don Francisco Pizarro. We always said that if the chapel in which he reposed were once free from the whispering curious, we would go in. But it never was and, besides, some of the ancient paintings and the splendid silver altar were much more attractive. Some people claim that the precious metal which covers this altar represents a part of the treasure with which Atahualpa's followers thought that they were buying the Inca's freedom.

Beyond the cathedral we walked beside the ornate but architecturally interesting Palace of the Archbishop, with its beautiful and intricately carved black wooden balconies that always give such satisfyingly "contrasty" photographs. The cathedral and palace fill one whole side of the plaza. On the fourth side is the low, spreading Presidential Palace, with its big, cobbled forecourt behind a decorative, but thoroughly businesslike, high stone and iron fence.

The strolling citizenry and country visitors to the capital always paused to gaze through the bars and past the soldiers standing by the gates, at the coming and going of government officials and the occasional automobile that was passed by the guard and rolled up to the presidential steps. Late one afternoon in October, 1935, Ambassador Dearing, Mrs. Mexia, Florence, and I mounted those same steps. Through the United States Embassy, I had presented to President General Benavides of Peru a colorful document containing greetings to him from the State of California. In return, the president had granted us an interview. Therefore, at the proper hour, a big, shiny, black automobile, exhibiting the insignia of our country, and containing Mr. Dearing, pulled up before the Hotel Maury. From that day forth our stock went up considerably, so far as the hotel staff was concerned.

Arrived at the palace we walked up the steps and then from the brilliant light of the plaza into the gloom of the presidential corridors. At the same instant there was a low-voiced command

and, with the rattle of accoutrements, a file of soldiers on each side of us presented arms and then grounded them with a crash. On the first step up to the palace I had become a bit nervous, and the sudden and unexpected attentions of the soldiery made me jump in an embarrassingly undignified fashion. The ambassador, with his accustomed tact and thoughtfulness, took my arm and thereby quieted me immediately. Where the military left off, the presidential secretary was waiting to lead us into a charmingly decorated anteroom. In a moment President Benavides appeared, greeted the ambassador warmly, and gave each of us a cordial handshake.

He was short and heavy set, with a fine head and rather prominent eyes. His dignity was that of a military man—easy and natural but very real. We were with him for half an hour. He talked with Mrs. Mexia in Spanish, with me through Mr. Dearing as interpreter, and with Florence in French. His perfect command of that language was gained during the years of his long exile that he spent in France. Florence told him that she was going to write down in her diary everything that he said to her. He laughingly asked her whether she really kept a diary and she promptly produced a minute volume in which she said that the first pages had been reserved for recording our audience with His Excellency. This amused him very much and, with a bow, he expressed his appreciation. With Mr. Dearing's assistance I endeavored to thank the president for all the courtesies and co-operation of his government and referred to my hope of being able to reciprocate by sending seeds of North American and other tobacco varieties, for testing in the Peruvian tobacco-growing areas. Altogether it was a most interesting occasion and by no means the perfunctory sort of affair that I had anticipated.

With Dr. Giesecke of the embassy staff, I had already paid my respects to the heads of a number of the ministries and made requests for credentials that would introduce members of the expedition to local dignitaries in the districts of Peru in which we expected to collect. Dr. Giesecke, the friend and adviser of most North Americans who have had work to do in Peru, knew the proper persons to be approached and the sorts of official documents we needed. In the weeks that followed we often found that the government had been following the itinerary that I had provided and was sending ahead of us instructions for our care and entertainment in the various *Departmentos* we visited. Dr. Giesecke suggested that it was desirable to give interviews to the Lima newspapers, which, he said, were widely read in the back country. This proved to be excellent advice. More than once, in some very out-of-the-way place, people would tell us that they knew all about what we were doing and had recognized us, because they had seen our pictures and interviews in the Lima newspapers. Sometimes this recognition was a little embarrassing, but in most cases it was helpful, especially in eliminating suspicion of our activities in areas where foreigners were rarely seen.

In Peru, as elsewhere in South America, we considered ourselves fortunate to meet, and later to know rather intimately, many Latin-American families. They were most hospitable. We did as much as hotel dwellers could to reciprocate. They entertained us in their cafés, their clubs, and their homes, put their automobiles at our disposal, and, when we departed, overwhelmed us with gifts. Their continued interest has been evidenced not only by a desire to keep in touch through correspondence, but also by sending their traveling friends to us and by showing thoughtful attentions to our friends who have visited South America. Where they have botanical inclinations, their co-operation has been sustained and, since our return to California, we have received much valuable plant material from them.

Nowhere in Peru, Argentina, and Chile, did we obtain any strong impression that the United States or its citizens were looked upon with distrust or dislike. The first questions that must be answered by a North American traveler, lately returned from South America, are: "How did the people down there treat you?" and "Did you notice a lot of antagonism toward the United States?" Most of the friends we made were in university work or in technical branches of government service, and such people are likely to be rather well-informed and tolerant, as well as polite. With them we met nothing but friendliness, an anxiety to co-operate, and a willingness to get to the bottom of the intellectual and temperamental distinctions between us, and to seek for common ground. Of course, the people of the two Americas still have a long way to go if intellectual and economic understanding and co-operation are to be achieved. The current formulas and mechanisms that we are devising to accomplish this end are, avowedly, nothing more than straws cast into the maelstrom of world events, in the hope that they will soon accumulate somewhere to build a temporary bridge over which interchange of ideas may effectively be carried on. In our experience the desire that understanding and intellectual co-operation may come is thoroughly mutual.

It should be noted, however, that some of the North Americans we saw in action in South America could hardly be called ambassadors of good will. I do not refer to touring compatriots who, in hotels throughout the world, make loud complaint— how those raucous voices ring out—about conditions of life and travel, and who, thereby, do little more than exhibit their own ignorance and provinciality. Every nation breeds such people. We were, however, thoroughly disgusted with resident North Americans who insisted upon insulting the citizens of the countries in which they were living. The fact that our fellow citizens had usually consumed too much alcohol before indulging in actual discourtesy did not excuse them; indeed, their overindulgence only added to the resentment of those who suffered at their hands.

A local newspaper has been carrying, almost daily, the reactions of one of its staff to South America. With a party sent out under Washington auspices, he traveled, by air, an immense number of miles in a remarkably short time. Already repercussions of some of his published statements are coming to me from friends in South America. Of more significance, however, is the way in which his articles play directly into the hands of the totalitarian propagandists. With an inconceivable naïveté, and doubtless the highest motives, he belabors the official organization, and heaps ridicule upon the character and effects of our so-called "goodwill" efforts in the Latin-American world. He refers to the commissions we send to South America as interested primarily in free champagne, and reports that the financial assistance which the United States offers the Latin-American republics is looked upon with loathing by the recipients. This morning I was amused to note that this latter piece of information was accompanied on the front page of his newspaper by extended reference to the large, additional loans which an official of a South American country was in Washington to negotiate.

Those who know South America are not satisfied with some of the ways and means by which we are attempting to increase hemispheric solidarity. However, this does not mean that, with all our fumbling, we are not laying important foundations for better understanding. Of this I have abundant evidence. Why, therefore, did not our traveling reporter make it his business to seek out the individuals and the organizations who acknowledge their indebtedness to North American education, technical advice, and financial co-operation, so that he could offer constructive alternatives to those "good-will" mechanisms he abuses? But the harm is done, and I have no doubt that his destructive criticism is being reprinted by the Nazi- and Fascist-flavored portions of the South American press to exhibit openly, or by insinuation, what will be called the disruption of public opinion in this country and the self-confessed failure of our attempts to increase cultural and economic co-operation between the American republics.

To me the archaeological collections in Lima were singularly attractive. Through the kindness of Dr. Tello and Dr. Valcarcel, Peru's well-known archaeologists, I enjoyed a number of personally conducted tours through the Archaeological and Anthropological Museums, and the collections in the University of San Marcos. In addition I saw some of the places, in the neighborhood of Lima, where excavation was under way and where other research was being carried on.

Long before the possibility of visiting Peru had occurred to me I saw an illustration (in, I think, a German report on Peruvian antiquities), of a piece of Inca pottery, that I never forgot. It showed a huaco, almost spherical in shape, on the surface of which was depicted an Inca noble sitting in the middle of a raft that was being propelled by swimmers. The feeling for form and composition, the perfection in the proportions of the figures, and particularly the unconventional and still entirely natural manner in which the swimmers flowed over the rounded surfaces of the huaco, prepared me for the even more remarkable evidences of pre-Columbian ceramic art to be seen in the Lima collections. The quality of the Chimu pottery portraiture is extraordinary, but I spent most of my time in front of the cases that contained the smooth, beautifully colored huacos that come from Nazca on the south Peruvian coast. I have one that is decorated with a broad band of reddish brown flamingos on a white background, and another, more complicated and less sophisticated, that shows faces of monsters, geometrical designs, and, at the bottom, a ring of jolly little mice.

I was, however, particularly concerned with the representations of plants and plant products to be found among the Inca ceramics and the evidence they gave of the extent to which the ancient peoples of the Andes had employed and improved their native food plants. There were huacos in the form of potatoes, corn, yuca, peanuts, squashes, pumpkins, melons, and papayas. Others represented pre-Columbian food plants that either are not now consumed in Peru or have not been extensively cultivated elsewhere. In addition there were representations of a number of plants that were difficult to identify and may no longer exist in the Peruvian and Ecuadorian Andes. The collections of wonderfully well-preserved plant products, found with the mummies in the coastal burying grounds, were also important. There is a good deal of research in Peruvian ethnobotany still to be done.

The botanical collections in Lima are not so large or so well cared for as they should be, in terms of the diversity and scientific and commercial value of the Peruvian floras. A beginning has, however, been made to remedy the latter defect by proper housing of the valuable Raimondi collections in the new Natural History Museum, a part of which has been constructed. When its building program is completed this should be one of the important museums in South America. We received many courtesies from Dr. Carlos Morales Macedo, the director, and were given the freedom of the room in which Raimondi's plants are assembled.

Antonio Raimondi arrived in Peru from Italy in 1850. Almost at once he began a series of journeys and explorations

that continued without interruption for twenty years and, ultimately, provided him with a more comprehensive view of the
geology, geography, and botany of all parts of Peru than any
other single investigator has since obtained. He is, perhaps, best
known for his map of Peru and for his geological studies. His
botanical contributions include a collection of over twenty
thousand dried plant specimens.

The unwearied activities and sustained enthusiasm of the
early naturalists in South America put the modern plant hunter
somewhat to shame. We were wafted by train, automobile, or
airplane over hundreds of miles of the difficult country that our
predecessors spent weeks or months in traversing, on horseback
or on foot. Only in the most remote areas did we have to adjust
ourselves to the primitive conditions of life that Raimondi encountered almost as soon as he left the few centers of coastal
civilization. There were occasions upon which he spent between
two and three years at a time away from his Lima headquarters,
when he was engaged upon intensive studies of the natural history of some particular area in Peru. The present-day plant
hunter would hesitate to engage himself to carry out an equivalent program under the conditions of life and travel that Raimondi had to endure.

We much enjoyed, and decidedly profited by, our pleasant
contacts with the nearby La Molina Agricultural College and
Experiment Station. It was a government institution, and adequately housed and equipped. Surrounding a group of buildings, there were fields on which experiments with a variety of
crop plants were in progress. I intentionally use the past tense
in referring to La Molina's buildings because, unfortunately,
the recent Peruvian earthquake did serious damage there. In a
fine lecture hall I spoke to the students and staff on a number of
occasions. It is hard to realize that, almost in an instant, this
building was partially reduced to ruins. The record of achievement which La Molina can boast, the enthusiasm of Director
Victor Marie and his colleagues, and the intelligent interest in
agriculture which the Peruvian Government has long displayed
will, I am confident, mean the rebuilding of this experiment
station and the continuation of its teaching and research activities.

Through the director's kindness we used La Molina station-wagons on many of our collecting trips along the coast and in the foothills of the Andes. Among the station staff we received special courtesies from Doctors Boza and Garcia, and appreciated an opportunity to do something for them when they came to the United States to study problems of cotton production.

There was a small botanical garden at La Molina. I was attracted by a beautiful species of *Passiflora,* the passionflower, which was growing vigorously, but not too vigorously as some passionflowers do, on a high wire fence behind the garden. Its flowers were large, flat discs, colored a remarkable pastel shade of bluish lavender, the margin of which was narrowly incised to form a deep fringe. Whether it was a wild or cultivated species I could not determine, and I unfortunately neglected to take specimens for later identification. Some of the pink- and red-flowered Passifloras from higher altitudes in Peru are attractive and grow well in Berkeley, and I hope that this, more desirable, blue one will prove to be hardy in southern California at least.

Until recent years most tourists up and down the west coast of South America saw only coastal Peru and, in particular, Lima and its immediate environs. Nowadays more and more visitors make the journey eastward into the Andes on that amazing railway that runs from Lima almost straight up to the highest altitude which a standard gauge train has yet been called upon to negotiate. In one hundred miles the passenger is transported from approximately sea level to an altitude of over fifteen thousand feet; and the highest point on the line is almost sixteen thousand feet. Members of the two expeditions many times made this increasingly popular journey from deserts to snowfields and return; sometimes on the railway and sometimes by automobile. The going up was always breath-taking, literally and also in terms of the magnificent scenery which borders the track or the highway at altitudes above ten thousand feet. The coming down was always a bit tame, but flavored with anticipation of the fleshpots that await the half-starved, Andean sojourner in Pizarro's ancient capital. However, initial enjoyment of them is often decreased by the onset of a cold that

prefers to settle in the head and ears. This affliction is, apparently, produced by the rapid descent from high altitudes to sea
level and exchange of the cold, dry air of the Andes for the
warm, humid atmosphere of the seacoast. If you meet a friend
on a Lima corner and he cups an ear at you, it is good evidence
that he is just down from the highlands.

The Rio Rimac flows through Lima on the last of its journey from Cordilleran sources to the Pacific. Along its first,
broad, and then narrower valley the highway and the railway
run side by side up into the high altitudes. For twenty miles
inland and until you have ascended about three thousand feet,
unirrigated areas in the valley bottom and the slopes of Andean
foothills are almost as arid as the coast itself. Such terrain
abounds in desert and rock plants. At somewhat higher altitudes there are spring and summer rains, and, except in the
long dry season, the mountainsides are green, sometimes all the
way down to the floor of the valley. The trip to the town of
Matucana (elevation 7,400 feet) and return carried us through
both desert and hillside vegetation, and could be accomplished
by automobile in one day—a long and strenuous fifteen hours.

The first time we went to Matucana, the Prince was in the
party. Cacti were his long suit and he was overwhelmed by the
number and variety of those that infested the Andean foothills.
He was, for the first time, surveying a cactus enthusiast's paradise, and among enthusiasts, like the Prince, none is so engulfed by his addiction as the cactus enthusiast. There were tall
and slender, large and powerful cacti; barrel-shaped ones, both
little and big; green ones and gray ones; smooth ones and woolly
ones. Best of all, many of the various kinds were in flower and
some in fruit.

The collecting of cacti takes time and some apparatus—
heavy gloves, metal tongs, and, particularly, cartons or similar
containers in which to transport the prickly prizes. Since we
had none of these things on the reconnaissance by automobile
to Matucana, the Prince was only tantalized. I was, therefore,
prepared for his suggestion that the two of us go back again to
the cactus country. He proposed that we take a train, stop here
and there at stations near which cactus collecting looked good,
go on by the next train, and ultimately end at Matucana for the

night. Concerning what would happen after that the Prince was rather vague. I told him that the scheme sounded good, but that I would not become a party to it. I felt confident that the best collecting would appear at the loneliest and dirtiest station on the line and that his collecting enthusiasm would lead us so far away that only nightfall would bring us back, too late to catch a train to Matucana or anywhere else. At that time I had not attempted to spend the night in an isolated Peruvian railway station and, if possible, I did not intend to do so. After dark, inebriated citizens and cur dogs are invariably drawn toward country railway stations. This always involves an unnatural increase in the flea population and I could foresee a hasty retreat to neighboring mountainsides, there to recline among cacti on a rocky slope. Finally, I knew the hazard for a tall, heavy man when the climbing pace is set by a companion who is built close to the ground. No, decidedly; the Prince should conduct the proposed excursion by himself, and so it was arranged.

Just before his departure for California some well-wisher had presented him with the longest and yellowest of leather wallets. In this useful but rather inconvenient object, the Prince took measurable pride and it accompanied him everywhere. When dressed for the street he wore it in an inside breast pocket, with the result that a large, yellow corner projected up between the lapels of his coat. Whenever I walked with him on the streets of Lima, it seemed to me that the eyes of certain of the more hardened characters we encountered had a way of brightening, as they fell upon the protruding corner of the yellow wallet. I therefore suggested that if he kept anything valuable in it he had best use a hip pocket, where coattails would conceal it from admiring eyes and acquisitive fingers. This turned out to be poor advice.

Two mornings after our automobile trip the Prince took the earliest train which left Lima for the Andean foothills—and their cacti. Anticipating a lot of climbing on hot hillsides he wore only a thin shirt, khaki shorts, stout leggings, tennis shoes, and the yellow wallet. This last was inserted, according to my advice, in a hip pocket of the shorts and exhibited to the public at least four inches of its length. In one hand he carried a large, flat, knocked-down carton, and in the other his plant press and digging tool.

Early in the morning the station platform was deserted, except for a handful of country people hurrying, along with him, toward the waiting train. Late the following afternoon, when he returned to Lima laden with spoils, the platform was crowded with passengers and station riffraff. The carton, now expanded, was full of cacti and constituted a transportation problem. It was bulky and heavy and, in addition, he had a large press full of drying plants. The Prince theoretically solved the problem by tying the press on top of the carton and carrying the combination on his stomach, his arms encircling the carton. By this arrangement he was just able to peep over the top of his load, and under this considerable handicap he began to steer his way toward an exit through the crowd.

As he explained it to us afterward, the weight of his load, which seemed to increase at every step, pulled him down in front. Bending continually further and further forward he realized that the yellow wallet must be sticking straighter and straighter up in the air, to offer a more and more unmistakable invitation to the pickpockets who were reputed to frequent this railway station. Hardly had this picture presented itself to his mind, when he felt the invitation being accepted and, the next instant, saw the yellow wallet disappearing down the platform in the hands of an active young hoodlum. Wedged into the crowd, and decidedly bulky in front, the Prince took a moment or two to extricate himself and start in pursuit. His first thought was to drop the carton and press, but if he did so it seemed probable that they, too, would disappear. So, clinging to his burden, he made what speed he could along the platform, yelling "Stop thief" as often as his supply of breath would permit. For a time the race was even, but soon the pickpocket outdistanced the Prince; though not until pursuer and pursued had traveled almost the length of the freight yard and acquired a swarm of noisy urchins who had appeared from nowhere as the chase progressed.

Florence can always see the funny side, and usually the silver lining, of the dark cloud. That evening, when the Prince was soberly recounting his sad experience to us, the picture he

Collecting bulbs near Lima—Palma, Dr. Weberbauer, Mrs. Mexia, the Prince

Peruvian arrieros roping plant presses on a blindfolded pack horse

One of the expedition's pack trains on steep grades in the Peruvian Andes

Young Indian girl hoeing Andean corn with a primitive wooden tool

unconsciously drew of a small man in shorts, clutching a bundle half as big as himself and galloping for dear life along a crowded station platform, was too much for her sense of humor. After a startled moment we also caught the picture and joined our laughter with hers. Actually, the yellow wallet itself proved to be more valuable than anything that it contained.

The Prince was a most accomplished plant collector, and where cacti were involved he had few equals. This first foray among the Peruvian ones demonstrated the extent to which his knowledge of cacti made it possible for him to collect only those species which were new or little known and to pass by the more familiar ones. To be as discriminating as this, in unknown territory, where new environmental factors create unexpected variation in the more familiar species is a real test of collecting capacity. The carton that he had clung to during the chase in the railway station contained small living specimens of a large number of different cactus species. To have found such a varied assortment he must have covered a lot of territory, in less than a full collecting day. I did not inquire how or where he spent the night or provided himself with food. He had probably forgotten such unimportant details. In succeeding months we discovered that, when the collecting was rich, nothing else mattered to him, food and sleep least of all. He could do a punishing day's collecting and then stay up most of the night to write notes on the plants he had taken. Next morning he would be as lively as a cricket and full of enthusiasm for the next day's work. For weeks on end he could maintain this punishing schedule, and never seem to tire.

The day after the Prince had dug them from the rocky foothills of the Andes the cacti went to California by air express. All soil was carefully brushed off their roots; they were individually wrapped in newspapers and packed in a light carton. Like all the plant material we sent home from South America, except seeds and dried and pressed plant specimens, this shipment of cacti carried our United States Department of Agriculture importation permit number and was addressed to the Bureau of Plant Quarantine in San Francisco. When it arrived the cacti were unpacked, carefully examined for injurious insects and other pests, and, if necessary, fumigated, before being sent on to the Botantical Garden in Berkeley. We received fine co-operation from the Plant Quarantine Service. They gave special attention to perishable material and in other ways assisted the rapid clearing of our importations. On our part we tried to send back only healthy, clean plants, and I think that our record in this regard was at least average.

Rapid air transportation of human and other freight is making large contributions to the success of the high-geared existence we seem to have devised for ourselves. It certainly meets some of the pressing problems of the plant hunter who works in far-off lands. One of these problems is the transferring of seeds, bulbs, roots, or cuttings, in the shortest possible time from their native habitats to the distant foreign soil in which you want them to grow. Of course, if you have plenty of time and conditions in general are right and convenient, then you can collect the seed or bulbs at just the correct season, ripen them thoroughly, dry them for the proper length of time, and, finally, ship them home by parcel post. Even if they are a month or more in transit most of them will survive the journey and, on arrival, be in condition to grow successfully. In South America, however, we usually moved pretty fast from one collecting area to another. This meant that we had to collect the plants and their seeds, or other propagative parts, in the condition in which they happened to be at the moment. Sometimes they were thoroughly ripe or mature, and sometimes they were not. Sometimes there were woody plants we wanted to grow in California but not even half-ripe seeds could be found. This meant the taking of cuttings and getting them home to be rooted within two weeks, or less if possible. We rarely had time to dry or ripen the seeds and bulbs artificially. We therefore blessed the airplane that made it possible to get plants and plant parts to California in almost their original condition.

While the westernmost side valleys of the Rio Rimac are easily accessible from the paved highway that leads to the top of the Andean roof of the Peruvian world, during most of the year they yield only meager collections to the plant hunter. In the months of March and April, however, the returning rains awaken leaf and flower so that even cactus-dotted, desert slopes break into bloom. One of the valleys we found to be particu-

larly attractive was that of the tributary, Rio Santa Eulalia.
There was a narrow, deep-green area in the cultivated and irrigated portion of the valley floor where eucalyptus, willow, pop-
lar, alder, and "pepper trees" grew thriftily. About habitations
and along fence rows there were shrubs and herbs. The contrast
between the attractive green and blossoming bottom lands and
the two- to three-thousand-foot, stony mountainsides was sharp,
and the line of transition abrupt.

We spent many hours, on a number of different days, working over those steep, rocky slopes in the Santa Eulalia Valley.
Each time we stopped, the car was turned off the road at the
same point and parked beside an Inca wall, which ran along
the bottom of the hillside and formed the support for a wide
terrace. On it a monstrous species of columnar cactus grew
abundantly, along with many of its lesser relatives. This exceedingly stout, cereus-like cactus was colored dark, blue-green
between the prominent ridges that paralleled its squat, bulky
body, and its spines were long and strong and needle sharp.
From three to a dozen of the four- to six-foot columns grew together. Many of them were a foot in diameter. Their unusual
girth and dark color made an impression of size and power that
I never felt among the more slender but far taller Cerii, so common on coastal ranges and Andean foothills in Peru and Chile.
All about were the more delicate, gray-spined wands of the *lana
vegetal* cactus, with its brown, woolly cortex breaking through
the prickly surface in long stripes. Below these taller relatives
there were plants of semi-cylindrical, greenish brown *Cactus
townsendii,* with round bonnets of reddish hairs and soft spines
perched atop. Nestled in each of these hairy tufts, bloomed a
dozen or more little, brilliantly pink, urn-shaped flowers, and
sometimes scarlet, pear-shaped seedpods had succeeded the flowers. When the digging tool was driven into the hard soil below
these engaging barrel cacti, they came out with a tassel of roots
attached. Grasped by this soft tassel the sphere could be lifted
off the ground and transferred to the collecting carton without
danger of skin puncturing by *townsendii's* short but numerous
spines. There were other, still lowlier, cacti, and especially one
that looked like a series of short strings of small fat, gray-green,
hairy sausages, all radiating from a common center. When I at-

tempted to dig it up most of the sausage strings promptly fell to pieces. Every sausage that arrived in good condition at the Botanical Garden in Berkeley took root, and when they have grown sufficiently to show the rather remarkable character of the mature plant, and especially when they flower, we can tell whether or not this Santa Eulalia cactus is a new species.

Above this cactus belt the mountainsides proved hard to climb. There were too many big boulders and the smaller ones were too loosely packed for easy going. Now and then small depressions and flatter areas held accumulations of soil. In and about them grew a thin, herbaceous vegetation, but a rather varied one. Almost every one of these miniature flower gardens included a plant or two of the brilliant *Onoseris,* which decorates, vividly, many a hillside in the valley of Rio Rimac. A low, spreading composite, it bears large, bright discs, colored pinkish magenta around the margin and dark-yellow in the center, and grows happily and flowers profusely in an almost dry soil. I remember it as a most friendly, cheerful plant, and one that certainly deserves a trial in gardens.

Sometimes one of the big cacti extended its altitudinal range far up the mountainside and then, clustering around its base, a few delicate plants that could not endure full exposure enjoyed its shade and gained some protection from the drying winds. Once I found a golden-backed fern tucked so tightly between the bases of spiny stems that I could not collect it. Some one of millions of microscopic fern spores, blown across that dry mountainside from a moister valley, must have fallen down through the cactus spines, to find a spot of moisture between the roots of the blue-green columns where it germinated and grew into a mature fern plant.

On the last afternoon that Florence and I spent in the Santa Eulalia Valley something new had been added to the barren mountainside. The gay flowers of *Onoseris* had passed their prime, and we busied ourselves collecting the seed they were maturing and that of a number of other less attractive plants. We climbed higher through the rocks and soon the breeze, which, near the close of day, blows gently up the valleys of the Andean foothills, stirred the drying vegetation and brought a tinge of coolness to the atmosphere. With it came a

spicy fragrance that was reminiscent of an old-fashioned garden
full of *Dianthus*. Although we knew that it could not be growing there we searched the rocky surfaces for something that
might look like a garden pink. The pleasant odor came and
went and was hard to follow toward its source. Finally, on the
far side of the ridge, we found scattered groups of a composite
from whose yellow flowers the *Dianthus*-like fragrance was exhaled. It was not a very attractive plant, a little like a straggling,
bushy *Coreopsis*, but we took the few seeds that had ripened,
in the hope that from this species some fragrance might be bred
into its more ornamental but odorless relatives that we grow in
gardens.

Near the stark but now fragrant mountainside two or three
low, reed-thatched huts had been built beside a diminutive, but
rapid-flowing, stream of doubtful-looking water. Its course had
become a strip of green lushness, six feet wide and colorful with
more or less familiar herbs. Heliotrope had first pre-empted
such stores of moisture as the little brook could give to the
parched soil through which it meandered, and the odor of sachet
from the dense, dark-purple flower spikes floated everywhere
above the narrow meadow. Through the trailing heliotrope,
Salvias threw up slender stalks set with deep-blue flowers; four-
o'clocks, in quantity, grew strong but bloomed scantily; and a
scarlet-flowered mint curled in and out, and up and around,
its less recumbent neighbors. Along the margin of the green
streambank some of the species that endured the bleak aridity
of the nearby mountainside had moved down, and were re-
sponding to the influence of a moister soil by becoming something far greater in bulk and, therefore, almost unfamiliar.
Fourcroya occidentalis, first collected nearby and sent back for
naming to Europe many years ago, had grown prodigiously and
could well have been mistaken for a species distinct from its sisters of the wastelands.

We walked upstream along another Inca terrace, and then
collected down toward the streamside habitations. As we approached them two faces, side by side, were framed in a window
of one of the huts; or, perhaps, it was not a window but only
a part of the wall where building material or energy had been
lacking while construction was under way. The faces were cof-

fee-colored, smiling ones, with eyes watching us intently. Florence walked toward them and added her smile to theirs. Greetings were exchanged and she at once became one of the family and disappeared through the low door under the thatch. After a little she called me. Since it appeared that standing room in the tiny hut must be at a premium, I stuck my head through the opening that served as a window and surveyed the situation inside. Florence and her hosts were bending over a framework of saplings that was raised a few inches from the uneven, dirt floor. This was the only piece of furniture in the room. When I wanted to know what was going on they stood aside, and I saw a small pink object, squirming on the rough cowhide that covered the framework. Someone has said that an extremely young baby looks like a dissipated alderman—protruding belly, flabby cheeks, pouchy, popping eyes, chubbily purple—and this mite of Peruvian mestizo flesh and blood confirmed the analogy.

The mother brought her tiny son to the door for my inspection. He grimaced violently in the bright light reflected from the hot gray mountainside, and then began to bubble, puke, and drip as he sat in the cup of his mother's hands. The combined age of his parents could not have been much more than thirty years, and this was the first of the annual increments they would contribute to Peru's population. Over the years the little thatched hut would expand and the bit of cultivated land before the door would increase; there would be additions to the simple furniture and to the array of smoke-blackened pots lying beside the cooking place. Life, however, would continue to be simple and peaceful, and free from the benefits of education and those doubtful blessings which, for the near primitive, follow in its train. That young, Andean foothill family and its material environment possessed the superpastoral atmosphere which the ease of existence in the semitropics so often bestows. When Florence finally succeeded in tearing herself away from the baby, and after I had transferred a small gratuity to its father, we continued our collecting down the road.

There, on the stony banks, the four-o'clocks had gone on the rampage and dominated the otherwise increasingly sparse vegetation. The only unusual plant we found was a single specimen of a shrubby *Abutilon* that grew in the ruins of an ancient

terrace. Its flowers were noteworthy, because the petals were reflexed and thus simulated a giant-flowered cyclamen. Lower
down the valley a species of *Clematis* was common. It trailed
across rocky slopes and, in moister places, accumulated in
masses, and fountained up with hanging sprays of delicate,
green branches that were covered with hairy fruit balls. On
driest valley walls bromeliads grew in quantity. Their spiky
leaves and tall, slender flowering stalks relieved the monotony
of the foothill landscape, but at the same time intensified its
desert aspect.

Considerable contributions to knowledge of the vegetation
of the Lima area can still be made, although for two hundred
years botanists have headquartered in the City of Kings. They
did not, however, spend much time in the surrounding countryside, but looked forward only to pushing eastward, up the valley
of the Rimac, to gain the Andean heights. Therefore, during
various seasons of the year, we made many one- and two-day
collecting trips out of Lima, and worked the floor and walls of
the Rimac Valley up to fourteen thousand feet. At the beginning I was particularly concerned about two Peruvian tobacco
relatives which Linnaeus himself had named. He called one of
them *Nicotiana paniculata* and the other *Nicotiana glutinosa,*
and his dried specimens of both of them had originally been collected near Lima. Apparently the early plant hunters sent seed,
as well as dried, pressed specimens, to Europe, because these
two Nicotianas have been grown in botanical gardens for a hundred years at least. Peculiarly enough, however, my search in
European museums for later collections of *N. paniculata* and
N. glutinosa in the original locality had been largely unsuccessful. In other words, there was little evidence that today these
species were elements of the vegetation in the neighborhood of
Lima. The fact that we found them in great abundance in the
lower Rimac valley confirmed my impression that botanists
have paid relatively little attention to the Lima region.

Florence had the distinction of spotting the first *Nicotiana*
that we saw in South America. This was in October, 1935, a
day or two after our arrival in Peru and while we were getting
our first glimpse of the vegetation of the Andean foothills,
under Dr. Weberbauer's guidance. It took three automobiles

to accommodate the large party, which included Mrs. Mexia and her assistant, Palma, the Prince, Dr. Aspiazu, and Miss Johnson. After we had passed through Lima's suburbs the road toward the mountains was bordered by fields filled with the brown stalks of last year's cotton, and in them the only hint of green followed the banks of small irrigation ditches, now almost dry. I was profiting by the first of many conversations with Dr. Weberbauer about the plants of Peru, which he knows better than anyone else, and was paying little attention to the countryside. Suddenly Florence, in the front seat, leaned back, pointed to the roadside, and said, "Aren't those Nicotianas?" Immersed in my attempt to follow Don Augusto's picturesque, hybrid English-German, I gave a hasty glance toward something green beside the automobile, shook my head, and turned again to our conversation. The next moment I was violently pounding the chauffeur's back and was half out of the machine. In my preoccupation it had required that brief moment for the significance of those green things to register itself upon my consciousness.

Florence had been one hundred per cent correct, and her identification was the more remarkable because these plants of *Nicotiana paniculata,* which grew in quantities in the roadside ditches and out into the cotton fields, were five times the size of those we had worked with in the Botanical Garden in California, and had, therefore, acquired a decidedly unfamiliar appearance. It was not a very attractive plant. Spikes of small, tubular, yellow-green flowers were borne on tall stems, thickly set with large, stalked, heart-shaped leaves. Flowers, stems, and leaves were thickly set with glandular hairs, whose sticky exudate had gathered a coating of dust and dirt that covered the entire plant surface. Furthermore, it stank abominably. All in all it looked like a noisome weed, and thus the farmer doubtless designated it.

To us, however, it was a happy augury of success for the Andean plant hunting. Within the first few hours of its beginning this hunting had turned up one of the plants I most wanted to find. The whole party gathered around, while I put the pieces of the plant in the press. I was, secretly you understand, very proud of Florence, who, making no claim to being classified even as a near botanist, had put a number of professional plant hunters distinctly and definitely in the shade. She acted as though it was a huge joke and twitted us unmercifully, but I knew that she was only trying hard to camouflage the emotional reaction that, for both of us, followed the finding of this grimy weed. It represented concrete evidence that all the things which we had hoped to accomplish in the Andes might actually be accomplished, and that the many months of preparation for this South American adventure, and the investments in our proposals by family and friends and research institutions, were going to pay dividends.

Later on we collected *Nicotiana paniculata* many times in the Andean foothills of central and southern Peru. Except where the soil was rich and moist, it corresponded in appearance to the plant Linnaeus named. In very dry locations, however, it was diminutive and differed from Linnaeus's plant in general appearance as much as did the giant variant that Florence identified. At higher altitudes in the Rimac Valley, this first of our Peruvian Nicotianas disappeared, to be replaced by *Nicotiana glutinosa*, the other species that had originally been described as growing near Lima but had been hitherto overlooked. Like *N. paniculata*, it grew rank where soil conditions were optimum and was reduced to pigmy stature on dry, thin soil. Too often, undiscriminating botanists have described such variants of well-known species, and particularly the diminutive ones, as new species. One of the greatest sources of satisfaction in my Andean plant hunting was the opportunity to see large numbers of plants of many *Nicotiana* species growing in their natural habitats and exhibiting the extremes of their responses in form and structure to differences in environmental conditions. Without such information it is difficult to evaluate the evidence presented by the dried, pressed specimens that others have collected, and upon which stay-at-home botanists, concerned with a particular plant group, are forced to depend.

Along with the higher-altitude *Nicotiana*, we found many charming plants in flower beside the rushing waters of the Rimac and up the deep quebradas in which its tributaries flow. A vetch-leaved *Mutisia* sprawled over low bushes, and once, on the bank of the river, made a variegated pyramid of red and

green, where it had taken over the skeleton of a massive columnar cactus killed by flood waters. The bright flowers of many
composites, among them *Heliopsis buphthalmoides,* were conspicuous. This species shows a curious distribution, since it is
known from nowhere else except Costa Rica, upon the other
side of the Equator. A striking and curious shrub or small tree
was a species of *Colignonia.* Its inflorescences were inconspicuous, but below them were modified leaves that simulated a
flower and thus reminded us of poinsettia, except that Colignonia's so-called flowers were white instead of red. The Calceolarias, a number of different species, were abundant and sometimes colonized the shadier sides of the steep quebradas, turning them into fields of gold. Along with these Peruvian plants
was the yellow mustard, a foreigner that is rapidly taking possession of favorable climatic zones in the Peruvian Andes. In
places it has already become so well established that the non-
botanical observer classifies it with the native vegetation. Sometimes Fuchsias appeared in favored niches on the ever more
precipitous slopes of the Andes' lower shoulders. There was one
species we found upon which I shall never look without a
qualm. We not only found it but succeeded in bringing it home
alive. However, the intial steps in that achievement might well
have started one of us home dead.

They occurred while we were collecting between ten and
thirteen thousand feet, along that fine piece of highway engineering that makes it possible for an automobile to go east from
Lima, almost as straight up into the Andes as does the Central
Peruvian Railway. We had left the capital very early in the
morning and had driven far up this highway, before we undertook serious collecting. As the altitude increased the highway
and the railroad began to follow more closely the steep and
winding course of the Rimac. Above the mountain valley, in
which lies the sleepy little town of San Mateo, the river ran
tumultuously in a deep and ugly gorge. Just overhead the snowy
peaks rose to more than fifteen thousand feet, but were unseen
because the high cliffs that wall-in the river pile up too steeply.
From the melting snows above, small torrents flowed noisily
down every depression on the cliffs. Along these rivulets, and in

the moist, hanging meadows they create, we found many valuable plants.

Our program consisted in dropping off a collector and driving on, up the highway, to a spot where there was room enough
to park the car, either against the cliffs or on the edge looking
down a hundred feet or more to the roaring river. From each
parking place a second collector started to work forward along
the highway. When the one who had been left behind had collected up to the car, it started on and, depending upon collecting conditions, either passed the second collector or picked him
up and left the first one behind again. Florence stayed with the
car, to arrange and pack the plants that we periodically dumped
into her lap.

There were a few things worth collecting beside the highway, but mostly we had to climb for them. They grew in crevices, on narrow ledges, or over rocky outcrops, far above our
heads, and you had to find a rock slide or a little ravine in which
to work your way up the steep cliff walls. When you came to a
ledge you collected along on either side, as far as it was possible
to go. Then you struggled up again and out along another
ledge. The going up was only a hard scramble, slightly damag-
ing to toes and knees, but the coming down was not so good.
It was like descending the steepest and roughest flight of steps.
With one arm, and often both arms, full of plants you had to
lean as far back as possible and, at each step, drive your heels
into the gravel and loose rock. When there were only big boulders you bent almost double to maintain equilibrium, as you
jumped down from one rock surface to the next. I never properly learned this latter technique and had a disagreeable habit
of making a three-point landing. My complaints about the resulting soreness were unfeelingly received by my companions.
They seemed to think that my sufferings were inevitable, and
referred to my having become too heavy by the stern. However,
I noticed with satisfaction that, after a few days of cliff collecting, I was not the only member of the party who suddenly
assumed a very dignified posture when we lowered ourselves
into our chairs at table.

I happened to be the one left behind when the automobile
reached the most amazing section of the highway we saw that

day. Both it and the railway line go through some of their worst
contortions at this point—corkscrew turns for the former,
switchbacks for the latter. The gorge of the Rimac is very narrow, continually winds in and out between outjutting cliffs,
and rises so rapidly that the gradient is close to 4 per cent along
the track, and worse in the sharpest turns of the highways. On
both walls of the deep ravine, parallel ledges, sometimes cut out
of the living rock, carry the road and the railway. Bridges have
a habit of disappearing into tunnels, and tunnels turn into
bridges. The whole thing becomes positively fantastic when
you see the river drop out of sight into a tunnel, so that the railroad may gain altitude more easily by occupying what was,
originally, the river bed.

This part of the gorge is called Infiernillo and constitutes
an entirely different, but just as real, "Little Hell" as the stretch
of coastal desert highway similarly designated and described in
an earlier chapter. In the Andean one, everything is at right
angles to everything else, but mostly straight up and down, and
overwhelmingly rough, barren, and desolate. The flood of the
Rimac fills Infiernillo with deafening noise. A continuous,
menacing rumble rises from the boulders that are being ground
together in the deep bed of the river. It provides a deep-
throated undertone for the high-pitched roar of the white, racing, surface water. Echoing back and forth from one high rock
wall to the opposite one the din is prodigious and acquires an
eerie quality, as powerful, but variable, downward drafts of air
suddenly increase and then decrease the intensity of the sound.

Collecting slowly up the highway through Infiernillo I
tried to project myself back four hundred years to the days
when Pizarro's mailed horsemen were riding up the narrow
footpaths that the Incas had built through the Andes. There
must have been more than one passage like Infiernillo, or worse,
that only the compelling lust for gold could have induced them
to attempt. Some of these ancient trails are still being used, and
if, in Pizarro's time, they were as hair-raising as their remnants
are today, the nervous systems of the conquistadors must have
been shattered long before they captured the mountain capital
of the Inca Empire. As elsewhere in mountainous terrain,
trails in the Peruvian highlands follow the sides of river valleys.

Every now and then a vertical cliff shoulders its way out to the river's edge, and then the trail is carried around it on wooden platforms, built against the rock wall. Too often these narrow shelves are in need of repair, and the traveler picks his way over them gingerly, and in prayerful mood. Much of the flooring is loose under foot; sometimes part of it is entirely wanting. These gaps, some wide enough to demand a jump, frame unpleasant vistas of fast-flowing rivers, rough with great boulders, or of steep mountainsides, strewn with sharp rocks far, far below. On these rickety sidewalks I lost all shame and hugged the rock walls or touched them furtively with my hand, in the hope of gaining a sense of security that I knew would be false. At the time the danger to life and limb seemed very real, and in retrospect it appears even more so; but I suppose that John Muir was right when he said that "Few places in the world are more dangerous than home."

Standing on the highway bridge in Little Hell, I let my eye range over the cliff sides for evidence of interesting vegetation. I had a good view up and down the gorge from the lower edge of the bridge, but only one spot looked promising. There, a hundred feet above the far end of the bridge and two hundred yards down stream, I saw a large V-shaped crevice, the broader, lower end of which was covered with a green tangle. It appeared to consist of only one kind of plant, with bright green leaves, and a few dots of color that meant flowers. Since the broad end of the crevice ended in an almost perpendicular cliff, one hundred and fifty feet above the river, I saw no chance of climbing directly up to get a closer look at the plant. There was, however, a ledge on the cliff wall just above the crevice that ran uninterruptedly from the point I wanted to reach almost to the edge of a broad shelf of rock, not far above my head.

By climbing the shaky handrail of the bridge and balancing on it, I gained enough height to shove my elbows over the rock shelf and, finally, to drag myself up onto it. Then it was easy to crawl over to the narrow ledge. Once there the going was not difficult except that, now and then, there was a particularly rough or narrow spot. It was beginning to be somewhat late in the afternoon, and the flow of the river was increasing.

Just below me, as I climbed along the ledge, an immense boulder had fallen half across the river's bed. The Rimac struck it with smashing blows and spouted high against its shoulder. This never-ceasing conflict filled the bottom of the gorge with spray that rose to the level of my ledge as a gentle, refreshing mist.

Slowly approaching the crevice I saw that the plant I sought was a fine *Fuchsia*. It grew thick and lush, and completely covered the lower end of the V-shaped crack. I cannot understand why the rampant luxuriance of its growth did not immediately sound a warning note somewhere in my consciousness. Probably I was too intent upon reaching my objective, which was now so close at hand, or perhaps fatigue had dulled the edge of caution that must be kept keen when one is collecting in rough and unfamiliar territory. At any rate, without hesitation I lowered myself into the narrow, upper end of the crevice and, holding on to its edge, began to slide down toward the *Fuchsia*. When I reached it I let go the rocky edge, and clambered out across the deeply matted tangle of dead and living stems and branches. There were a number of flowering shoots, and I reached out my hand to take one of them. I kept reaching out and reaching out, farther and farther, and suddenly it dawned upon me, first, that the flowers were actually moving away from my hand, and second, that the whole mass of vegetation on which I was standing was beginning to slide over the lower end of the crevice.

Immediately I began to stamp my feet down through the latticelike plant surface in an effort to settle them in the rock or gravel beneath. Instead, however, of finding a more or less firm bottom, I splashed into thin, muddy rubble in which my feet began to sink. Some instinct, stirred perhaps by the sound that the rocky mud was making as it began to splash over the precipice, warned me not to flounder but to throw myself, full length, on the surface of the brush, and to crawl across it to the safety of the edge of the crevice. This I finally accomplished, and then pulled myself over the edge, and over onto the steep cliff side. Already more than half the heavy, straggling *Fuchsia* had slipped to the margin of the precipice, and the brittle stems were beginning to crack and splinter and drop large sections of the plant down into the river, far below.

Now I could see what had happened. The broad lower end of the crevice was a very shallow basin, in which water had collected from slow but continuous rock seepage. Probably this seepage began at the upper end of the crevice and followed along its solid rock bottom. Certainly there had been no hint of water at the upper end, when I had first entered the big crack and began to walk over the top of its deep accumulation of loose gravel. Of course, the *Fuchsia* thoroughly appreciated the excess moisture and responded by growing so vigorously that it had completely covered the lower end of the crevice. In the loose, wet soil, the roots could not anchor the plant firmly, and probably, in a few more years, its increasing weight and bulk would have toppled it over the edge. In other words, disaster was certain to follow additional weight, and this I had supplied.

After a little I recovered my breath, and, what was more important, my nerve, and again went down into the crevice to get what I could from that part of the *Fuchsia* that had not already gone over the edge, been torn to pieces, and carried away by the river. Part of the time I held on with one hand to the rocks that stuck out from the crevice wall and, reaching out, dragged toward me some of the larger stems that bore flowering shoots. The flowers were four-inch-long tubes of glistening, dark maroon that ended in a frill of short, greenish white, triangular lobes and were borne in loose sprays of eight to twelve flowers each. The leaves were light green, almost circular, with fretted edges, and very large for a *Fuchsia*. None of the stems I could reach showed even half-mature fruits; indeed, it was probably too early in the season to expect anything but buds and flowers. Since there was no seed, the only possibility of reproducing this fine species at home was by cuttings, and so I broke off a dozen pieces of stem of various ages and tied them into a little bundle. In addition, I took a few flowering shoots to go into my plant press that had been hidden near the bridge.

Before starting back I buttoned the bundle of cuttings and the flowers into my shirt, because I suspected that I would need both hands free during the descent along the ledge. This turned out to be the case. The recent near disaster in the crevice must have overstimulated my imagination, for the ledge looked much narrower than it had on the way up. Once I become worried and overcautious in rock climbing, my judgment is so impaired that crawling on hands and knees sometimes seems to be the only safe thing to do. I didn't get quite to that stage, however.

Our collecting in, and above, and below Infiernillo was very profitable that day, and we returned to Lima heavily laden with plants. Early the next morning I wrapped the cuttings of the crevice *Fuchsia* in oiled paper and packed them in a reduced shoe box. By air express they reached San Francisco in eight days, and on the following day were placed in the rooting bed in the Botanical Garden. Without such rapid transportation there would have been practically no chance of getting these cuttings home, alive and well.

This was not the only occasion when air express saved the day. As already suggested, we used it with great success to carry unripe bulbs, tubers, and roots, which, if they had been sent by parcel post would have rotted during the long journey by water from Peru, Chile, or Argentina to California. In South America itself, we often used air transportation to send plants to headquarters for drying and pressing. This scheme made it unnecessary for the collectors laboriously to carry their accumulating collections along with them, as they went from one locality to another, or to stop work for a sufficient number of days to complete the drying of the accumulation of plant specimens. Where collections were being made in wet or tropical areas, this system was almost necessary. For example, when Harvey and Bob worked east of the coast of northern Peru in the year of the big rains, the atmosphere in that area was so nearly saturated that, even if they had had time or opportunity to use the drying lantern, their plants would have been decayed by molds. As a result, they collected and traveled fast, and, as often as they touched civilization, sent, by the coastwise air service, bundles of pressed, but still very wet, plants to us in Lima. We went to work on them at once and, by frequent changes of bone-dry, heated felts, pulled most of them through without too much molding.

In the Rimac Valley the coastal desert ends at an altitude

Snowstorm on Peru's Andean crest, photographed at 15,000 feet
A scarecrow and cactus-topped wall protect this Andean farmstead

Canary creeper (*Tropaeolum peregrinum*), common in the Peruvian Andes

Rose-colored bracts of Dalechampias brighten borders of Inca trails

of about eight hundred feet. Above, some rain may fall, but apart from cacti no appreciable amount of native vegetation is to be seen until the valley floor has risen another three thousand feet. There, the increasing vegetation includes certain sizable shrubs that attract the attention even of the casual observer. They are given a wide berth by the natives, and should be admired at a distance by everyone except the botanist who may find himself required to give them his close attention. We knew them as species of *Jatropha,* a genus belonging to the Euphorbiaceae, or Spurge family. There are a number of Jatrophas in Peru. We collected one of them in the Lachay Lomas. It wound its thick, smooth, gray stems over the sand and rocks, in an unpleasantly reptilian fashion. In the lower part of the Mantaro canyon two erect species were common. They are provided with vicious thorns, and horses as well as men have learned to recognize them and to keep their distance. Not all the Peruvian species are spiny, but, since they are euphorbs, their juices as well as their spines must be held under suspicion of causing skin irritations, sometimes serious ones.

In the valley of the Rimac, and elsewhere, species of Jatropha are referred to in the vernacular as *huanarpo,* and, more specifically, as *huanarpo macho* and *huanarpo hembra.* Apparently, the former designation refers to a red-flowered, and the latter to a white-flowered, unarmed species. Today, and perhaps for many centuries, huanarpo has been alleged to possess aphrodisiac properties, and the words macho and hembra, or their genders, serve to indicate the sex for which each is appropriate. More than once, in widely separated areas, we were asked by smirking natives whether we had found "our huanarpo." On one occasion, in an Andean market town, a peon, upon learning that we were plant collectors, said with a wink that he knew where he could find some huanarpo, and this brought guffaws of laughter from a crowd of hangers-on. A merchant in Chincheros was positive that a mere prick from a thorn induced the wildest impulses. In addition, he could himself vouch for the fact that when you inhale the smoke from burning brush in which stems of huanarpo are included a highly disturbing reaction is instantly obtained. He also said that when groups of young people are picnicking it is considered a vulgar joke to bring in huanarpo and toss it on the camp-fire.

In the popular mind huanarpo has much to do with the *verruga* disease. This malady, one of the medical curiosities of the world, first attracted attention in the seventies of the last century, when a highly fatal epidemic appeared among the workmen who were constructing the present railway from Lima up into the Andes. The original terminus of the railway was Oroya. During the several years of railway building there was, among the road crews, a total of seven thousand deaths from all causes, and the majority were due to what was then called "Oroya fever."

Today, the disease is recognized as having two clinical aspects. One, called *verruga peruana,* or simply verruga (Spanish for wart) , the more common form, is relatively benign and characterized by an eruption of nodules, which vary in size from pin points to hazel nuts. They usually cover the extremities and the face, but any part of the body may be affected. Heavy with blood and easily ruptured the nodules give the patient a loathsome appearance. After several weeks or months they heal spontaneously. The other form is a severe anemia, often accompanied by high fever, that does not respond to treatments useful in other anemias and, therefore, is usually fatal. If the patient survives the anemia he has still to endure the eruptions.

The epidemic along the new railway was suspected of being medically related to an eruptive disease long known to be prevalent in middle altitudes in the Rimac Valley and elsewhere in the Andean foothills. In 1885, Daniel A. Carrión, a medical student, inoculated himself from the nodule on a patient afflicted with this eruptive disease, and died with symptoms of the anemia that had killed so many of the railway men. In other words, he established the two-fold character of the disease. Technically, it should be called "Carrión's disease," but in popular parlance both forms are referred to collectively as verruga. Ultimately Carrión was recognized as a national hero, and the anniversary of his death is now marked by appropriate ceremonies.

Beginning in 1926 the work of Noguchi and his associates

furnished bacteriological proof of the unity of the disease, by the cultivation of what is probably a bacterium (*Bartonella bacilliformis*) , from both the eruptive and the more fatal form. We came to know a good deal about the research now in progress on certain still obscure and important aspects of verruga, because the Peruvian contingent of the second expedition made Dr. Marshall Hertig's home their Lima headquarters. Originally loaned to the Instituto Nacional de Higiene y Salud Pública by the Harvard Medical School, Dr. Hertig has spent a number of years in Peru and has added much to knowledge of the transmission of a disease that, in the case of the ignorant native and the unwary foreigner alike, is the scourge of the Andean foothills. I watched him at work in his laboratory, and he told me about the discoveries that patient, laborious, and sometimes dangerous work has revealed; and also about some of the other things that appear certain, but which, with the caution and conservatism of the research man, he is not ready to announce.

It is now clear that verruga can be contracted only in a relatively restricted altitudinal zone (2,500 to 9,500 feet) , in the north central portion of Peru (6° to 13° S.) , and also that it can be contracted only during the night. This suggests insect transmission, and Dr. Hertig, in his Lima laboratory, has succeeded in transmitting verruga to Rhesus monkeys by permitting them to be bitten by a certain species of minute, bloodsucking, nocturnal sand fly, which he captures in the foothill zone where the natives contract the disease.

The insect (*Phlebotomus verrucarum*) , one of the Diptera, which to my eyes looked like an exceedingly small edition of the common mosquito, will pass without difficulty through windowscreening or netting, and, with the primitive housing of the mountain people, protection against his (or rather her) bite is practically impossible. She attacks man ruthlessly, and where she is most abundant a foothill family may suffer a nightly average per person of from twenty to fifty bites the year round. In individual cases Dr. Hertig has counted as many as two hundred bites received in a single night. No wonder that the railroad workers who camped out along the advancing roadbed suffered such heavy infection.

The Institute of Hygiene and Public Health is a handsome, modern, well-planned, and well-equipped building in a Lima suburb. Fortunately, the last earthquake did relatively little damage to it. In a laboratory, partly filled with a big tent made of heavy cloth, Dr. Hertig was investigating the development of the organism that causes verruga and the mechanism of sand-fly infection and transmission. In glass dishes he was raising colonies of the bloodthirsty, winged midgets and feeding them on decaying organic material. I couldn't help wondering whether a few might not have escaped and be loose about the room. I must have, involuntarily, passed my hand across my face or, unconsciously, done some scratching, because Dr. Hertig took me into the tent and explained that all experiments involving the possibility of escape of *Phlebotomus* from their glass-walled homes were carried on under its cover, and that the interior was thoroughly sprayed and otherwise disinfected at the end of each experiment. I was, however, just as glad not to linger, either in the tent or in the laboratory in which it hung. That day in the Instituto, I felt more keenly than ever before a sense of personal indebtedness to investigators like Dr. Hertig. How rarely we appreciate what they are doing for us; especially the bacteriologists, who stand on the firing line and, without bustle or display, fight humanity's battles with obscure and vicious diseases.

Following the demonstration in 1928 by Noguchi, Shanon, and colleagues that the causal organism, *Bartonella bacilliformis,* was present in wild sand flies from the verruga country, a series of problems presented themselves. Dr. Hertig has discovered that the tip of the sand fly's proboscis contains a remarkable infection with minute organisms, and he has twice succeeded in isolating *B. bacilliformis* from infected proboscises. If this means that it is regularly on hand when the little bloodsucker starts operations on human victims, then we have an effective mechanism of transmission. However, the most extraordinary thing about these proboscis infections is the fact that they occur in both males and females, although only the latter sex is bloodsucking. In other words, proboscises are infected not as the result of a blood meal obtained at the expense of some animal, including man, but from another source, as yet unknown. At this point huanarpo, the *Jatropha,* which, as we have seen, is part of the vegetation of the verruga belt, comes back into the picture.

For many years it was insisted by both the laity and the doctors in Peru that verruga was contracted from the drinking water of the Andean foothills. Today, this theory is still widely held by many nonmedicos. The notion that the disease is plant borne has been urged with equal vigor. Since the eruptive form of verruga is best known, any plant to the juices of which people may be allergic is automatically given prominence as a source of the disease. A number of different species growing in the Rimac Valley were pointed out as dangerous, and on one occasion the chauffeur of a collecting party protested violently the moment Harvey started to put specimens of *Lobelia decurrens* in press. When he later discovered that this press was going to ride in his car there was a tremendous outburst and one that we had difficulty in quieting. During the remainder of the day he got out of the car and rested at a safe distance whenever we made a stop. His perturbation was a product of the fact that contact with this *Lobelia* gives certain people a skin eruption, resembling the one produced by poison oak or poison ivy, but less severe, and, of course, in no wise corresponding to the disgusting, pustulate form of verruga.

At the moment certain scientific circles in Lima are firmly convinced that huanarpo macho, the red-flowered *Jatropha,* is the reservoir of verruga and that from its tissues the sand fly acquires the bacterialike, causal agent of the disease. This theory is, I think, based in part upon the report of some untrained man with a microscope who mistook a harmless species of flagellates that frequents the milky juice of huanarpo macho for the apparently dangerous *Bartonella bacilliformis.* However, the relationship between *Phlebotomus* and huanarpo has been so urged that all *Jatropha* plants were ordered cut down before laborers were sent into the Santa Eulalia Valley to construct an aqueduct and tunnel for the hydroelectric plant there. Despite the popularity of this theory that plants are implicated in the sequence of events that results in man's affliction with verruga, the coldly scientific evidence in its favor is somewhere near zero.

Although we knew that *Phlebotomus,* with its infected proboscises, flies only after sunset, and even though we had no fear of infection from any of the plants we collected, there was one spot in the Rimac Valley that, even in daylight, we avoided if possible. It was the so-called Verruga Canyon, a gorge at right angles to the main valley, over which the railway runs on a six-hundred-foot-long, three-hundred-foot-high steel bridge. The present bridge is the third at this site. The first one, built in the seventies, was washed out, and the second, considered inadequate, was replaced in 1937-1938. The bad reputation of the canyon under this bridge depends upon the near certainty of contracting verruga there, the severity of the infection, and the fact that so many deaths occurred at this point during the construction of the first two bridges, when nonimmune Peruvian laborers and foreign engineers in considerable numbers were employed for many months at a time in bridge construction. When the present bridge was being built there were almost no cases of verruga, because most of the workmen were taken by train, late each afternoon, to spend the night in Chosica, a town just below the lower limit of *Phlebotomus* distribution. However, among police and soldiers doing guard duty few escaped, and the fatal cases have been one or two for every twenty-five men exposed.

Beyond Infiernillo, the traveler by highway or by rail enters the Andean fastnesses. The limit of shrub vegetation occurs at about twelve thousand feet. Above that altitude wood is at a premium and the huts of the alpine shepherds are built of turfs. These blocks of sod, cut from the high, barren plateaus, serve also for fuel. Sometimes it is hard to decide where the banked-up layers of fuel end and the hut itself begins. The sod contains a high proportion of organic material, so that when once alight it makes a fair substitute for firewood; except that the amount of acrid smoke it emits is out of all proportion to the amount of heat that it evolves. The hardy mountain people, who barely succeed in keeping body and soul together in the bleak punas of the central Peruvian Andes, make nothing of a little smoke; it does not even constitute a minor aggravation. For effective cooking or baking, however, something hotter than a sod fire is necessary, and they use the resinous *tola* heath,

Lepidophyllum quadrangulare, which burns readily, even when green, and produces a hot fire. Bundles of this plant accumulate in great heaps near railway stations at elevations below the upper limit of shrub vegetation, waiting to be shipped up into the shrubless, puna country.

The vegetation of the highland plateaus is limited in number of species. Thousands of square miles are covered with the coarse tufts of *Stipa ichu,* which derives its specific designation from the ancient Inca name for this alpine grass. The tufts, which grow at rather close intervals, are often as much as two feet in height and about a foot in diameter. When actively growing and green, and also when dry and hard, herds of llamas and alpacas graze the ichu. A careful hunt among the hard grass tufts disclosed low-growing herbs, mostly perennial ones, in some variety. A number of species of dwarf composites, a few gentians, valerians, madders, and even lupines and Violas hide in the ichu and, in its protection, carry through successfully their brief, alpine life cycle.

On the broad plains beyond the first Andean crest, glacial lakes occur, and in them grow a few water plants, which are, perhaps, responsible for the large frog population, and thus, for the trade in frog's legs that goes on between passengers and natives at railway stations in that part of the highlands. On the alpine meadows we sometimes saw an abundance of the cosmopolitan mushroom, *Agaricus campestris,* but had no evidence that it was eaten by the mountaineers. Various waterfowl visit these alpine lakes, and colonies of white herons make a charming picture as they methodically fish the margins of the blue expanses.

The puna people devote themselves principally to grazing, but also grow a few meager crops. Most important is the potato, cultivation of which continues up to fourteen thousand feet. Usually the tubers of these high-altitude varieties do not correspond to our potatoes either in bulk, color, or taste. Decidedly on the small side, and often strongly colored, many of them have an agreeable, nutty flavor. Along with potatoes, ocas (*Oxalis tuberosa*) are commonly grown and do well even at extreme altitudes. In less exposed areas on the puna certain varieties of beans are grown with some success.

Members of both expeditions, more than once in some instances, collected on the puna and along the margins of the snow fields, on both sides of the highway that crosses the center of the Peruvian Andes and traverses the valleys and altiplano south toward Cuzco and east toward the jungle. On a number of occasions the mountain city of Huancayo was collecting headquarters. It is a provincial capital and, of late years, rather frequently visited by tourists who have a day or two to get some view of the Andes and their peoples. Its principal attraction is the Sunday market, which is one of the most important and colorful of all Andean markets. It is said to attract the largest number of different clans of highland Indians, who bring their distinctive wares for sale to the tourist. There, he can buy the finest of white alpaca rugs or blankets. The one we brought home was selected from hundreds that a local expert kindly agreed to examine as they came into the Huancayo market. Each week we expected our purchase to be sent down to Lima; each week the buyer claimed that he was not satisfied with the quality of the skins offered to him. Finally it arrived and proved to be worth waiting for, because all the different fleeces that made up the five- by seven-foot product were perfectly matched in texture and uniformly white.

The market is held on Huancayo's broad main thoroughfare, said to be a segment of one of the major Inca highways. On a good Sunday, with fifteen thousand people milling up and down, the boast that this is the largest outdoor market in the world sounds conservative. The quantities of vegetables, fruits, cereals, and livestock on display give it the atmosphere of an old-time county fair at home. Because this is the garden spot of the Andes, where agriculture and its products are of a better quality than elsewhere, the appearance and character of the commodities on sale are superlative by contrast with other Andean markets. Thus, for example, the tanner has the finest hides to deliver to the artist in leather, who fashions a variety of ornate sandals, saddlebags, and smaller articles. A saddle, that mark of aristocracy in the highlands, becomes in his hands a work of art, ornamented with colored leathers and chased silver. One tourist from our Western cow country had acquired a superbridle that pleased him so immensely that he didn't see how he could wait to get back to the States to display it to his fellow dudes.

The abundant supplies of sheep, llama, and alpaca wool make for a most gorgeous display of ponchos, blankets, and other woven goods. Would that the crude effects produced from German aniline dyes had never come to the Andes to replace the soft pastel shades obtained from juices of madder, barberry, walnut, and the other long-forgotten vegetable resources of the ancient dye artists. The vendor of dyes piles his varicolored powders in neat little cones on his table. He uses a crude, home-made balance to weigh out five centavos or ten centavos worth. The serranos find it hard to pass up such an enticing array of intense shades. They linger beside the table and select, not what will harmonize, but rather what will be most arresting.

Near the dye merchant is the apothecary's table. There you may examine an incredibly varied collection of dried leaves, roots, fruits, seeds, fungi, as well as dried lizards, toads, snakes, animal entrails, insects, and, in largest quantity, a series of objects of unfamiliar, and probably best undisclosed, origin. All the drugs have Quechua names, and the vendor is prepared, at the slightest encouragement, to reel off a list of those diseases and misfortunes that each of his wares will cure or ameliorate.

Tourists usually buy elaborately carved gourds, one of the specialties of the Huancayo Indians. Gay, little plaster figurines, which look almost as though they had been imported from Italy, also have an attraction for the visitor, but by the time they reach Lima heads and legs often require the glue pot. For the discriminating foreigner the products of the silversmiths should have the greatest appeal. His purse will be considerably lighter when he leaves these descendants of an ancient and relatively honest guild, but his recuerdos of Huancayo will be a good investment, of which he will never tire.

The tiendas and more ambitious stores that line the highway project their stocks of goods out over the sidewalk and onto the pavement. Nevertheless, they find it hard to compete with the appealing atmosphere of the truly out-of-door markets. Therefore some of the more ambitious shopkeepers operate loudspeakers, through which announcements are made in the Quechua tongue of alluring bargains on sale within. Between

these announcements a program of victrola music roars out, and
knots of serranos gather around with awe and wonder on their
faces.

Lying at an altitude of almost eleven thousand feet, in a
somewhat protected location in the valley of the Rio Mantaro,
Huancayo is a sunny, temperate oasis within the battlements of
the Andes. In the center of a rich farming country its population has a somewhat opulent appearance; something that is rare
in the highlands of Peru. Round about are groves of eucalyptus
trees. The hillsides show the effects of two centuries of over-
grazing and overcropping in eroded areas that are beginning to
claim much of the formerly extensive stretches of cultivated
land. The Huancayo region is old, geologically speaking. It
differs from most Andean terrain in having remained stable,
with no uplift of the land blocks for long periods of time, and
so the hills are rounded and the valleys filled in. Its horizons
are undulating and soft, rather than saw-toothed and grim.

One of the most successful forays from Huancayo into the
snowy passes was made by Harvey, at a season when the alpine
vegetation was at the height of its flowering. He needed temporary collecting headquarters nearer the mountains and had
letters of introduction to Don Lopez Alizega, who owned the
Hacienda Acopalca and several thousand head of sheep. There,
on the margin of the steep mountainsides, Harvey was hospitably received and his work facilitated. Once out of the valley
over which the hacienda sprawled the altitude increased rapidly
and the snow was not far above. Along the edge of the extensive
snow fields, and on the banks of cold rivulets that issued from
them, he found the most extreme of alpine types of vegetation.
Mostly the soil was heavy with moisture, but the herbs that
he collected did not respond to maximum supplies of water,
as do the plants of lower altitudes, by growing lush and rank;
rather, they hugged the ground and aggregated themselves into
low mounds or thick carpets, taking care not to expose more
surface than was necessary to the chill and rarefied air and to the
intense insolation of the high altitudes. The genera, which at
lower altitudes elongated their axes to form sizable herbs,
shrubs, or small trees, were, nearer the snow line, represented
by rosette plants in which the axis had been completely tele-

scoped. On the nearby, rocky, arid ridges, in full exposure, were alpine cacti and particularly *Opuntia floccosa,* which formed white cushionlike masses. At a distance they simulated piles of wool, which could have been sheared from the many sheep cropping the low vegetation on the cold, wet mountainsides. Harvey's bag from the squashy meadows, their drier margins, and the stony ridges contained a greater variety of plants than he had anticipated. Among others there were dwarf members of the geranium family, three-inch-high yellow gentians and two or three really minute ones, some of the same valerians and Violas that had been collected in the ichu-carpeted punas, and a species of *Werneria* whose yellow dandelion-like flowers were, as he said, "kept down so close to the soil line that one could imagine that they were trying to escape the lawn mower."

Above him, as he worked from one collecting ground to another, the zigzags of a dim trail across the face of the rocky cliffs led up into a lofty pass and, still higher, into small alpine valleys. An inconsiderable traffic wandered up and down this trail. Once he saw an enterprising local merchant urging on a string of burros, whose panniers dripped with the melt of ice chunks cut from the glaciers, miles behind the pass. In Huancayo he would obtain ten cents a load from what was left in the panniers after the burning alpine sun and the furnaces within its transportation had taken their toll. Such is the competition of those who sell American- or German-made electric refrigerators in the Peruvian Andes.

In April, 1939, two weeks before the last of us left Peru, I had a report from California that the natural-color motion pictures taken here and there in the highlands to show something of the landscape of the highest altitudes were not up to expectation. Therefore I asked Harvey and Bob to arm themselves with tripod and cameras and make one, final, excursion up into the land of snow and ice. Lima was delightfully warm and dry and sunny on the morning that we saw them off at the railway station. In a few hours their train had gophered through tunnels, climbed the steep walls of the Andean barrier like a mountain sheep, and finally deposited them at Ticlio station, near the top of the pass, to face a roaring, alpine blizzard. They had made arrangements to stay in a mining camp at

Maracocho, ten miles away. In the forbidding climate of the plains and valleys just beneath the highest peaks the Indian shepherds, inured to hardship, do not maintain habitations fit to protect the wayfarer against the days and nights of the highland winter. Indeed, in any season, the naturalist in the higher altitudes of Peru would fare badly, were it not for the mining camps and their hospitality.

At Maracocho a warm welcome awaited them. They were taken in charge by one of the North American mining engineers, and spent an unforgettable evening before his fireplace, in which discarded mine timbers burned with a roar that competed effectively with the muffled whine of the blizzard. Finally, decency demanded that "good nights" should be said. They bundled up and, once out of doors, had difficulty in steering a safe course toward the dormitory. In it they had anticipated a night sleepless with the penetrating cold. Imagine, therefore, their surprise upon discovering that the turn of a switch brought into action an electric stove geared to defy the arctic climate.

What was left of the alpine afternoon, following their arrival at the mining camp, had been too cloudy and snowy for pictures. The early morning of the next day, however, was almost clear and the light good. Shafts of bright sunshine flooded the white peaks and vertical mountain walls, to give unexpectedly fine studies in light and shade; but not for long. Soon the bitter winds were astir, bringing a drizzle of rain that was almost at the freezing point, that fogged lenses and found its way under turned-up coat collars. Imperceptibly the rain became sleet and the sleet became snow, and soon they were again facing an Andean blizzard. The white flakes began to pile in drifts, to flow down the long valleys, and to turn the lower slopes from brown to dirty gray with the light coating of new-fallen snow. Nevertheless, the motion pictures taken under these unfavorable and unpleasant conditions turned out well. They give a striking picture of the stark crudity of Andean snowline landscapes, and reproduce the onset of an alpine storm as it darkens the sky and creates increased contrasts between the background and the white peaks that spring up out of snow fields and glaciers.

Next day the rapid train ride down from the land of snow

and ice gave Harvey and Bob their last, and most impressive, view of the zonation of vegetation that characterizes the brief journey from snow fields to deserts in central Peru. A little distance below the cold, wet, or snowy slopes of the highest plains there came a sudden transition to alpine aridity that supported only cacti. Then, since it was spring, they saw the middle Andean foothills green and flowering, even brilliant with drifts of yellow, lavender, and rosy pink. Below, a slow transition displayed the lower Andean foothill equivalent of the coastal desert with its gray, tan, or brown, rock-strewn mountainsides, which, rarely, swept up to a light-green crest—a severe landscape and one that was not relieved by its scattered forests of columnar cacti. Sometimes the deserts are drier, sometimes the snow fields are more extensive, but, from coast to cordillera and vice versa, there is always that fundamental contrast between deserts and snow fields.

Chapter V

THE JUNGLE

IN HIS *Exploring for Plants* David Fairchild, with his usual penetration, has said, "Never to have seen anything but the temperate zone is to have lived on the fringe of the world." And he documents his contention as follows: "Between the Tropic of Capricorn and the Tropic of Cancer live the majority of all the plant species, the vast majority of the insects, most of the strange and dangerous and exciting quadrupeds, all of the great and most of the poisonous snakes and large lizards, most of the brilliantly colored sea fishes, and the strangest and most gorgeously plumaged of the birds." And he concludes with the remark: "Not to struggle and economize and somehow see the tropics puts you, in my opinion, in the class with the boys who could never scrape together enough pennies to go to the circus. They never wanted to badly enough, that's all." I agree, except that other than purely financial considerations may sometimes deter the prospective traveler from pointing toward the tropics. The popular imagination is quite concerned about those same "strange and dangerous and exciting quadrupeds," about the anacondas, bushmasters, and other large and poisonous snakes, about insects in quantity, unfamiliar diseases, and humanity in a primitive and therefore, presumably, a decidedly unwashed condition. Although travel bureaus are rapidly dispelling this popular reaction to the word tropics, the companies selling accident and health insurance are still unconvinced and charge high premiums if you plan to spend any length of time between the Tropics of Capricorn and Cancer.

For dwellers in temperate climates the vegetation of the tropics has a great appeal. It reflects the atmosphere of a part of the world with which they are totally unfamiliar, makes an impression of unreality, and has a quality of mystery. I have spent a good many hours in the tropical houses of a number of the world's largest botanical gardens. Some of those hours were devoted to watching the reaction of the public, which is always attracted by greenhouses, to the palms, aroids, lianas, orchids, and other tropical plants that usually are so cleverly displayed as to give a fairly authentic picture of the equatorial rain forest. Just within the greenhouse door, voices tended to become hushed, comments were fewer, children's romping feet acquired a soberer pace, and the slowly circulating stream of visitors watched, half fearfully, the man-made panorama of an almost otherworldly vegetation. But, at that, they have no conception of how much more impressive the real thing can be.

During both expeditions we saw more or less of the tropical rain forests of Peru and came across many of the types of living organisms to which the quotation from David Fairchild refers. But Harvey and Bob spent a longer period in the montaña than all the rest of us put together. The following summary of their plant hunting in the Peruvian jungle gives at least a partial picture of its landscape, life, and vegetation.

By train from Lima they crossed the Andes to Cerro de Pasco, that famous copper mining center up in the clouds, where so many young North American mining engineers have served a part of their apprenticeship. Cerro de Pasco lies at an elevation of 14,380 feet. Thence, a highway leads into the montaña of the Province of Huánuco. On it you coast down the Atlantic slope of the inner range of the Andes to one thousand feet and less, where you can breathe freely in honest weight air and lose that feeling of being cold with no place in which to get warm. When a Peruvian uses the word montaña the uninitiated interpret it as meaning "mountains," whereas actually it refers to the quarter-million square miles of forested lowlands at the foot of the inner Andean ranges.

For the stranger accustomed to altitudes near sea level, the night at Cerro de Pasco is not restful, indeed scarcely endurable. When you put on enough covers to keep warm, their weight impedes the double-quick breathing that is necessary in the rarified air to supply sufficient oxygen. Periodically you awake to gasp for extra breath. Talk about "having a heart"— there is no possibility of your forgetting that you have one! To boost the circulation, it pounds away at an alarming accelerated rate, with now and then a few extra fast quarter-beats thrown in.

In that high country the copper skins of the Indians acquire a bluish cast that makes them look more than half frozen.

Actually, however, they are thoroughly accustomed to the cold, very thin air and are said to sicken when transferred to the coastal lands. The women wear their numerous, homespun woolen skirts clear down to the mud. Each successive layer is put on outside the others. No one knows how many skirts they wear. Rumor has it that none of them is ever voluntarily removed and that the only reduction in their number is the result of disintegration from natural causes! But their feet have no protection except the mud that clings to them in quantity. Those mountain folk love their freedom as far as feet are concerned and you might as well try to lasso a wild mustang and break him to harness as to attempt to put shoe leather on those mud-squashers.

Like the Indians farther south in the Andes, those of Cerro de Pasco are sprightly and travel in high gear, and are thus quite in contrast to their coastal relatives who never get out of compound low. The women usually glide along at something between a fast walk and a slow trot. Their great accumulation of long skirts conceals leg movements and Bob used to say that they looked as though they were coasting on roller skates.

After an uncomfortable night in Cerro de Pasco, Harvey and Bob hired a car, loaded in with their duffel, and started down hill for Huánuco and the montaña. The road descends rapidly along the clear headwaters of the Rio Huallaga, a stream which, farther north on its way to the Amazon, becomes a wide, muddy flood. At its source near Cerro de Pasco the Huallaga lies only two hundred and fifty miles, across the Andean ramparts, from the Pacific, but its waters must prepare for a journey of almost three thousand miles before they reach the Atlantic.

Apparently the chófer set his pace to match that of the churning, white mountain torrent. According to the delightful custom of mountain drivers in Peru he coasted much too rapidly around the sharp curves with engine shut off and clutch disengaged. Frequent admonitions to take it slower, so that the botanists might size up the vegetation along the roadsides, were graciously heeded, but only for a minute or two each time. Then the chófer would take his foot off the brake and proceed according to the popular Andean theory that the way to save

The Peruvian jungle looking toward the Andes; foreground, *Cecropia* trees
in whose hollow stems live colonies of vicious ants

The wood of this odd-looking *Bombax* of northern Peru is soft and light, but not so strong as that of the related balsa tree

A strangling fig encircles a forest tree in the Peruvian jungle

Along dim jungle trails occur strange plants, animals, and insects

Papayas have escaped cultivation and grow wild in Peru's tropics

Pumahuasi, a Peruvian jungle village between Tingo Maria and Pucallpa

brake lining is not to brake at all. When a peculiarly hair-pinnish curve appeared he would cast a quick glance at the lithograph of St. Christopher pasted above his windshield and speed on with complete confidence.

I have great respect for the faith of Peruvian chófers. However, faith without works is dead, and many of their cars need much better works, especially brakes. While there can be no objection to their custom of taking the cars to the priest to be blessed, they should at the same time be taken to the garage to be checked over. Ordinarily, cars are driven as long as they will function. When they break down on the road most of the chófers don't know how to make effective repairs. Therefore, as a prerequisite to travel on the highways of the Andes, I suggest that the visitor acquaint himself thoroughly with the insides of cars and trucks and in particular with their ignition systems.

The chófer in charge of Harvey's and Bob's transportation displayed a morbid interest in accidents. He insisted upon pointing out all spots along the highway where deaths had occurred and dwelt lugubriously on the distressing details of each accident. At one point he stopped the car at the edge of a precipice and down below pointed out the mass of distorted metal which only a week before had been a good roadster. Some little miscalculation on the part of its driver had brought the total number of casualties at that particular point to seventeen.

The larger towns along this road to the montaña appealed to them as interesting places in which to stop for a while. On that October day they were sunny, comfortably warm, and very colorful with their many-hued walls and bright roof tiles. Flowers of all sorts were cultivated and had also escaped over the garden walls. Rainfall, however, could not have been abundant because the hillsides supported only a dryland vegetation. The valley itself was green here and there with cultivated fields perched on small level benches and the riverbanks were lined with shrubs and trees.

Plants from the high puna country here met some of the more hardy ones which came up from the montaña. The "Old Man Cactus" made those same patches of cottony white so commonly seen on the cold plateaus above. Where sheep were grazing these patches suggested that a shearer had left piles of wool on the mountainside. Columnar species became more and more common down the valley. Soon the dry slopes of the hills were forested with them and with Aloes and Fourcroyas. One of the Peruvian cacti is called lana vegetal, because from it is obtained a brown wool-like fiber used extensively in the Andes for stuffing mattresses and pillows. Perhaps a bed of cactus does not sound very inviting, but it's not nearly as bad as it sounds. When the stems of lana vegetal become mature and dry the outer spiny layer is loosened, and under it appears a fibrous cortex that surrounds the central woody core. This cortex is transformed into a fluffy mass of woolly material which simulates a dry cattail head. It has a kinky quality and feels much like wool, but is too smooth to be spun into thread. As a filler for mattresses and pillows it does not pack into a solid lump as does the cotton commonly used in Peru for this purpose. In the coastal regions where cotton is grown and is cheap the packing is usually much too solid for comfort. One wakes in the morning with a pain in the neck. Other attributes of some of the small coastal towns produce the same symptoms!

The Fourcroyas are numerous here and at a distance resemble Aloes. Their swordlike leaves are cut at maturity and then soaked in water until the softened tissues disintegrate by decay. Later, the tough woody fibers are washed free from the softer tissues and hung up to dry. At first they show a greenish tinge but soon bleach to a near white. *Fourcroya* fiber serves principally for manufacture of rope and twine but also for such things as mats and sandals. The often rather remarkable suspension bridges flung across Andean gorges have from time immemorial been fashioned in part from it. In Inca days these bridges were hung on gigantic fiber cables. Today these cables have mostly been replaced by heavy wire and only the planks and guard rails are held in place by *Fourcroya* twine.

As the car still further descended the Huallaga Valley the city of Huánuco came into view. Nearby hillsides were dry and almost bare of vegetation, but the valley floor was green with herbs, trees, and shrubs, which became dense along the river itself. Characteristic trees were Humboldt's willow, *Acacia,* the widely distributed *Acnistus, Eucalyptus,* and *Schinus molle,* this last better called the "Andean" rather than the "California" pepper tree, because of its Peruvian nativity and wide distribution throughout Andean valleys and down the western river channels to the coast. An introduction that has succeeded remarkably well in the Andes is the Eucalyptus. Indeed, most of the drier regions of Peru may be said to have been pretty generally "eucalyptized," to borrow a term from David Fairchild. One looks over many a mountain valley to see old groves that give the impression that they have always been an integral part of the landscape. You sometimes wonder how such a valley might have looked before the days when the padres brought Eucalyptus to the New World.

The city of Huánuco is the meeting place not only of the vegetations but also of the peoples of sierra and montaña and their commerce. Trucks and passengers pause at this halfway point. There, goods are unloaded and distribution to the interior begins. It is a cheerful place. At an elevation of a little over six thousand feet the climate is halfway between the forbidding cold of the Andes and the steaming heat of the tropical rain forest. The middle of the day is hot, streets are deserted, and the tiendas are closed. Not only closed, but locked and double locked, the final guard consisting of an iron bar which is secured by rusty padlocks so enormous and so antiquated in structure that they appear to date from the days of the conquistadors. Not until almost six o'clock does the town really begin to live. From that hour until midnight it is gay and noisy with townsfolk and peons from the countryside, who promenade in the streets and congregate in the inevitable plaza. The latter is rather neatly laid out with trees, shrubs, and some of the annuals and perennials that are planted in parks the world around.

Unfortunately for Huánuco, as also for many other cities in South America, the old-time municipal plaza band, which was bad enough but stopped now and then for breath, has been replaced by a centrally located loud-speaker—overloud and without any oxygen requirement. The City Fathers agree with the citizens, who are certain that if a little music is good more is better; and so they turn the dial as far as it will go to the right and leave it there in perpetuity. But the crowd is cheerful and it is good to hear laughter again after the stolid silences of the Andes.

The days are usually sunny with fleecy cumulus clouds that rise from the mountain walls flanking the river valley. Their higher ridges are white with limestone outcrops. The red soil glows through a scant vegetation of shrubs and cacti. Well up from the valley floor a few farms stand out boldly green. Beyond the city the broad valley bottom is filled with cultivated fields, principally of sugar cane. Looking northward the view fades into a purple haze that overhangs the jungle. The city itself is full of color. The walls of the adobe and stucco houses are calcimined in shades of pink and blue and purple and are attractive in their very lack of color harmony. The mountain-sides farther down the valley often approach forty-five degrees of slope and are, therefore, very dry. When rain falls it runs off these slopes as from a roof, and there is little opportunity for conservation of water in the soil except where certain natural pockets catch and hold it. In them grow green islands of the pepper tree, willow, *Baccharis,* native and introduced grasses, and other herbs. A ribbon of such vegetation makes a conspicuous contour line where unusual enterprise has constructed an irrigation ditch to carry water to plantations around a turn of the valley.

A little more than one hundred and fifty years ago, the Spanish botanists, Hipólito Ruiz and José Pavón, discovered *Nicotiana tomentosa,* the giant tree "tobacco" of Peru, which was described in an earlier chapter. The years that Ruiz and Pavón spent in Peru and Chile gave the world its first comprehensive knowledge of the plant wealth of the west coast of South America. On one of their exceedingly arduous and hazardous expeditions into and over the Peruvian Andes they collected in the neighborhood of Huánuco. Some distance to the east they found the tree *Nicotiana,* and I was anxious to have seed collected from plants which I hoped would still be growing in that "type locality." In 1935, Mrs. Mexia made an effort to find them, but reported that most of the region in which Ruiz and Pavón worked had long since been cleared of forest growth and put into crops. Nevertheless, it was worth another try, and so Harvey and Bob on their journey into the montaña were instructed to keep a careful eye out for *Nicotiana tomen-tosa*. Unfortunately, nothing resembling this interesting plant was found there.

After several days of botanizing up and down the Huánuco Valley they entrusted themselves and their equipment to a truck en route down into the montaña. From casual hotel acquaint-ances they had received much gratuitous information concern-ing the snakes, *chuncho* Indians, tigers, wild pigs, insects, and malaria, all of which were supposed by the stay-at-homes to be prevalent in the Peruvian jungle where the botánicos now pro-posed to collect. Their road soon left the valley, climbed over a nine-thousand-foot ridge, and then followed the Chinchao River, a tributary stream which unites with the Huallaga before it reaches the town of Tingo Maria. Tingo was to be their ultimate collecting headquarters in the montaña.

At an altitude of about six thousand feet, the truck entered the *ceja de la montaña,* literally "eyebrow" of the montaña or the transition zone between rain forest and higher terrain. Vegetationally it is perhaps the most interesting climatic zone in the Peruvian Andes. Characteristic of the eastern watersheds, it represents the margin of advance of vegetation upward from tropical valleys to higher, cooler elevations where mists con-tinually form and produce a peculiar fog-belt flora. One of the botanically famous cejas de la montaña was this area through which Harvey and Bob were riding. It is called Carpis, the name of the ridge over which their highway ran. The forest trees were festooned with epiphytes and many shrubs of the Heath family were in bloom along the roadside. As they topped the pass and began to descend, the vegetation seemed to become gradually less dense and ultimately gave way to cultivated fields and grazing lands.

About one hour out of Huánuco they passed the *pobla-ción,* or village, of Acomayo. Beyond it for a considerable distance there were no habitations, except the occasional thatched hut of a lone mountaineer or road maintenance man, until they were well over on the other side of the divide. The highway was a marvel of engineering. In many places it hung so precariously on the sides of tall, sheer cliffs that it was hard to understand how such a shelf could have been blasted out of

the rock faces. Except on Sunday this road from Huánuco to
Tingo Maria was supposed to be one way only. On Sunday it
was assumed that there would be few or no trucks abroad and
that passenger cars could safely horn their way around the
dangerous curves. The gravel surface was kept in good condition, but the road itself was exceedingly narrow. There were
many sheer drops of hundreds of feet. It was all rather terrifying, but not much more so than some of the other Andean
highways that we all traversed many times.

In somewhat less than five hours the truck arrived at
Puente Durand, a small settlement consisting of a few thatched
cabins, which lay on the banks of the Rio Chinchao. Harvey
had a letter of introduction to the leading citizen of this hamlet,
who bought and sold coca and other montaña products and gave
food and *posada* to travelers. Here they stopped for two days.
The region round about proved to be so rich, botanically, that
they collected at Puente Durand for several days more on the
return journey.

The reason for existence of this settlement was a suspension
bridge wide enough for horses over the clear, rushing waters
of the Chinchao. It was built twenty years ago by a Dr. Durand
in order to bring to the highway the coca from his hacienda,
located in the jungle some distance westward from the left bank
of the river. Now several other haciendas also send their products across the bridge. Transportation is by horse or burro or
by Indian carriers. In early days, before the highway was extended down into the montaña, it was customary for Indians
to carry the heavy bales of coca over the steep mountain trails,
all the way to Huánuco. Each bale weighs about one hundred
and twenty-five pounds. On his back, and supported by a modified tumpline over the shoulders, a wiry little Indian will carry
one of these sacks all day long. Now the coca bales are simply
deposited in the warehouse near the bridge, to await a truck
that transports them to the larger towns and cities for distribution to neighboring countrysides. Some are sent to Europe and
the United States for the manufacture of cocaine. The plant
involved is *Erythroxylon coca,* a shrub that grows wild in the
Peruvian jungle but has also from Inca days been cultivated.
The leaves, which look somewhat like those of the laurel, are

gathered from the plants, dried, and then compressed in large burlap sacks by specially constructed presses.

The Peruvian Indians have inherited the cocaine habit from their pre-Columbian ancestors. Bringing relief from fatigue and hunger cocaine makes the Peruvian highlander capable of unbelievable feats of endurance. For days at a time he will carry heavy loads for very long distances at high altitudes. At a remarkably fast steady walk he climbs in and out of deep gorges on trails that an unburdened gringo has difficulty in negotiating at a far slower pace. The active narcotic principle is not readily released from the leaves, even when they are chewed, unless an alkaline substance is added. Therefore, the coca addict always carries a supply of moistened lime paste—sometimes in a small gourd, sometimes in a leather bag. It is said that a special kind of limestone is required for the burning of the lime oxide he uses, but just what its specific quality may be no one seems to know. In some parts of Peru, particularly in the Cuzco district, potassium obtained from plant ash is used in place of lime. The Indians are reported to have individual preferences for certain plants that are burned to provide this ash. Popular among these is the *quinoa (Chenopodium quinoa)*.

The technique of acquiring a proper quid of coca is simple. First, several leaves are folded together, popped into the mouth, and adjusted between gum and cheek. Then, with a little stick that is also carried in the gourd or bag, a bit of lime or potash is smeared over the leaves. The quid is not actively chewed in the way that tobacco is masticated by more "civilized" races, but is, only occasionally, compressed to hasten the flow of the narcotic from the cells of the leaf. It seems surprising that the use of coca does not produce unpleasant aftereffects, a hangover of some kind, but there is no apparent evidence that it does. However, Indians who take cocaine to excess have a rather greenish cast of countenance and are said to age rapidly. This must mean very rapidly, because old age, as we think of it, is rarely attained in the Andes where life is hard and even the most elementary principles of hygiene are unknown. In the Peruvian highlands the cocaine habit appears to be more or less universal, among the men at least, and to begin at an early age.

Harvey and Bob enjoyed the days they spent at Puente Durand. The few cabins or shacks were built so close to the roadside that each day a truck threatened to knock them down. It had been difficult enough to grade sufficient space for a road, let alone space for houses, because the valley of the Rio Chinchao is very narrow at this point and the road is built against the mountainside one hundred and fifty feet above the racing water. The *casa* of their host, Señor Valverde, stood, however, on a bit of level land just below the highway. He proved to be a friendly chap and displayed a considerable knowledge of the world beyond his immediate environment and even outside Peru. He and his señora made their paying guests feel genuinely welcome.

On the first evening supper was served on a screened porch that looked westward over the valley to a solid wall of dark-green jungle foliage. Rising almost directly below was the continuous roar of the river. Silhouetted against the evening sky was a single tall, slender *Bursera* tree. Its upper branches were hung with twenty or more birds' nests that in shape resembled those of the oriole but were more than three feet long. Swaying in the wind they seemed about to fall at any moment. Their occupants were dark-colored birds, with long yellow tails, which entered and left the nest through a small opening on one side.

That evening the best part of the supper was fresh, ripe papaya. To the inevitable rice, roasted yuca was added. Their host apologized because no meat was served and agreed to kill a pig the next day. The pigs certainly were very numerous and had been making nuisances of themselves by nosing into the kitchen and even into the screened porch dining room.

A large earthenware jar of fermenting wheat chicha stood under the dining table. Some of this native beer was decanted for them, although Señor Valverde said that it had not yet become quite mature. Nevertheless, it was extremely good. In its manufacture the wheat is first germinated, and when the sprouts are about an inch long the seedlings are thoroughly dried and then ground to a powder. Water is added to this powder and fermentation allowed to take place. The Indians often employ a different technique, especially as far as the grinding is concerned. Señor Valverde grinds his dry wheat sprouts in a small hand mill. The Indians are likely to grind theirs between their teeth. Every now and then in the back country one comes across a little settlement with a group of Indian women sitting about a large jar or bowl into which they periodically eject the masticated wheat. Although one knows that the chicha produced from such an unpleasant mess contains a germicidal proportion of alcohol, it is sometimes hard to forget the method of its production. It is, however, far wiser to take a chance on Indian chicha than on Andean water.

After dinner Harvey and Bob began to wonder just what sleeping arrangements were going to be made, because Señor Valverde's house appeared to be hardly big enough to accommodate more than himself, his wife, and their little daughter. A rather lengthy family consultation was held and a decision apparently arrived at. Then a candle was lighted and placed inside a tin-can candlestick, and their host asked them to follow him. With bedrolls on their shoulders they crossed the suspension bridge. As they left the shore and approached the center of the swaying, rocking bridge, the river underfoot was talking, first in deep throaty gurgles and then in quick gasping roars. Set well up on the other river bank under the wall of jungle was a small thatched hut. It contained three dirt-floored rooms—the larger, middle one, well stocked with chickens, the one to the right, a general storeroom, and to the left an annex to the henhouse that was occupied by two setting hens. With considerable protest these two were forced to desert their nests and were finally secured in the storeroom. Two dirty wooden platforms stood on either side of the henhouse annex. In the uncertain candlelight most of the feathers and some of the other debris were removed, and Harvey and Bob rolled out their sleeping bags on these platforms.

They had forgotten to leave a call with Señor Valverde but the roosters next door attended effectively to awakening them at dawn. Harvey's diary says: "Thereupon the Peruvian jungle was treated to a Wyoming cowboy's estimate of roosters in general, and our next door neighbors in particular. It was really a rather fine bit of language for such an early hour in the morning. We fooled the roosters by refusing to get up. When we finally did, and looked out the door, there was a grove of papaya trees growing all around the cabin, and some of them were heavy with ripe fruit. That gave us an idea of what we wanted for breakfast—hen and papaya fruit—and we got both."

That day they collected along the Rio Chinchao and then up a stream that flowed into it from the west. The dim trail through the tropical rain forest was overhung with small tree ferns, and underfoot were many Adiantums and other smaller fern species. The endlessness of the green vistas was immensely impressive, and they knew that for thousands of square miles to the north and east this green sea billowed and surged, almost without interruption, until it became a part of the greater expanse of the Amazonian wilderness.

They found a species of *Renealmia,* a member of the Ginger family, which one of the government officials in Lima had asked them to collect in order that it might be accurately named by experts in the United States. He was concerned with this plant because of the oil that its underground stems contained. The plants resembled the ginger of commerce and the peons called it *achira.* Like so many local names for plants everywhere in the world, this one was not specific because the same name was applied by the same peons to a white-flowered *Canna* which resembles the *Renealmia.*

The most exciting find was a splendid *Eucharis,* a member of the Amaryllis family, much larger than the species that is commonly offered in the trade. The leaves were two feet long; the flowers four inches and more in diameter, white in color, and shading to a delicate green in the throat. It grew in a dense mass, hundreds of great plants. At a distance the luminous, almost phosphorescently white flowers, like great plaques, seemed to float in the virescent light that rose from the jungle floor and was reflected from the dense background of leafy vegetation. A peon was sent back to Puente Durand for a grub hoe and a coca sack. Then they dug a hundred bulbs. That night these bulbs started by truck for Lima, to begin their long journey to California. Most of them arrived safely at the Botanical Garden and are now among our prized and coveted possessions. The plants have flowered from the beginning, but neither flowers nor leaves have attained the size they showed in the Peruvian rain forest. If grown in a "tropical" greenhouse, something which the Botanical Garden does not possess, they doubtless will return to full glory in size and form.

In addition to this *Eucharis* there was a wealth of species of many families, almost all of them unfamiliar. A large terrestrial orchid was plentiful. Its purple flowers, marked with sulphur-yellow, measured two inches across. They found a single plant of *Phragmipedium boissierianum*—quite a name for an unoffending and very handsome green-flowered orchid. Its giant "ladyslippers" looked to be far too heavy for the delicate hairy stems which supported them. Where the jungle was somewhat less dense there were a few plants of a red-flowered amaryllid, apparently a *Hippeastrum*. Later on they discovered that it grew in quantity on the hillside behind their chickenhouse bedroom.

Above the tributary of the Rio Chinchao which they were exploring the mountainsides were steep and high. Here and there they saw small cultivated fields which stood out like murals against a background of forest green. There the ancient witticism about the farmer falling out of his farm could be taken literally. In most of these cultivations coca was being grown along with potatoes, beans, and upland rice. There were some plantations of bananas and plantains, but these plants do better at lower altitudes. Papayas were omnipresent, some in cultivation but most of them gone native. Also cultivated was a sister species (*Carica candamarcensis*), not much larger than a good-sized shrub and bearing attractive small golden fruits. But the fruit was not so good as it looked. In fact it was not eaten raw but used only for cooking. Señor Valverde called it the "Spanish papaya." They also saw trees of the custard apple, *chirimoya,* and of *palta,* the avocado.

West of Puente Durand lay the region called Gaza, apparently a corruption of the Quechua word *ccasa,* meaning "cold." This region had an elevation much like that of the Carpis ridge and afforded another good example of the ceja de la montaña. They collected there later on, an expedition which Bob's diary refers to as an attempt "to pluck the eyebrow"! Quoting it further: "The Indian *arrieros* were up at daybreak, actually before the roosters got thoroughly into their morning broadcast. They brewed their coffee over an open fire near the cabin and fed their animals, while we, hoping for a very early start, hurriedly downed our breakfast at Señor Valverde's. It was eight o'clock, however, before the bestias were ready. One had escaped during the night, saddle and all, and had apparently returned to a hacienda in the mountains. There was one horse with a saddle. It was larger than the other horses and mules and so Harvey mounted him along with our raincoats, cameras, and packages of luncheon. I acquired a small animal with a heavy, padded pack saddle and no stirrups. It was a case of straddle, not sit. We had asked for a *bestia de carga* to carry our field presses. Instead, we got a husky little coca-chewing Indian. Our protests were answered by the statement that a mule would cost two soles whereas the Indian would carry as much for one sol. But at the end of the day we gave him three in an effort to ease our consciences rather than pay him for work which had proved to be much less strenuous than carrying the bale of coca which he was accustomed to tote.

"For a couple of miles our trail led north along the mountainsides west of the Rio Chinchao and then turned west up a deep valley. It was a beautiful, fresh, clear morning and as we climbed higher the jungle panorama began to unfold. Above the immense stretch of green forests the deep-blue sky was dotted with fluffy white clouds, like piles of cotton on a calm azure sea. In this land of dense vegetation, one rarely gets such views. Before long we overtook three peons carrying heavy backloads and escorting a young and rather striking looking maiden who was riding a horse. Somehow, I had the feeling that she was a bride. Her serious dusky face bore a half-frightened look as she peered from under a heavy grass-green *mantilla*. Perhaps it was my imagination but to me she looked as though she had just been dragged away from her home.

"As the horses slowly made their way up the valley we came upon a rushing stream. Its sound brought back visions of a Big Horn Mountain cascade full of trout—and then the heavy jungle trees and the great ferns choking the streambanks brought me back to the Peruvian reality. After picking our way across its boulder-strewn bed we began again the zigzag ascents. For two hours the trail ran through extremely dense forests. It was the world's roughest and steepest, not to mention muddiest, trail. I might have felt more compassion for our laboring peon if I had not been so busily engaged in keeping my mule enthusiastic about going uphill. No matter what was the condition of the trail my animal dozed and if I had stopped abusing him for an instant he would have gone sound asleep. Furthermore, even to stay on the none too comfortable pack saddle with no support for my feet was a bit of a problem, and on the steep ascents I continually tended to slide backward. After a while I began to fear that my knees would lose their grip. In fact, I more than once considered walking a bit even at the risk of losing caste in the eyes of our native companions."

Typical of the foggy "eyebrow" of the montaña the Gaza ridges were incredibly rich in plant species. Mosses and lichens mantled the trunks of the tall jungle trees. Under the dank underbrush club mosses and ferns covered the soft deep soil. Begonias were abundant, some of them low herbaceous species, others great shrubby growths, and the jungle was bright with their flowers. On every side *Calceolaria* made splotches of golden yellow. The trail and every open space was overhung with the brilliant bell-like flowers of a number of *Fuchsia* species. Always, the plant hunter's "take" from the ceja de la montaña is limited only by the size of his plant presses.

On the way to Gaza a stop had been made at the Peruvian Government's experimental hacienda where investigation of tea production was being carried on. The shrubs grew well and the quality of the leaves was said to meet with the approval of tea connoisseurs.

Below Puente Durand the highway to Tingo Maria continued northeast, followed the Chinchao through narrow gorges to its confluence with the Huallaga, and then turned north to follow the course of this important waterway. Several miles south of Tingo the valley widened to give some level terrain suitable for tropical agriculture. There the government had established experimental farms in conjunction with one of its colonization projects. Peruvian citizens were offered a parcel of jungle land and a subsidy for house building on the understanding that they would proceed to develop the land and bring it into production.

Tingo Maria was a boom town when Harvey and Bob saw it in 1938. A very busy sawmill was ripping out rough boards for wooden houses that were to replace the cooler bamboo-walled dwellings which jungle residents for generations had found to be entirely adequate for their needs. Shiny new galvanized iron was being trucked in to make hideous this formerly thatch-roof settlement. Next to the offices of the experimental farm and colonization project was the headquarters of the road gangs who were pushing the highway eastward against fearful odds toward Pucallpa, way over to the east on the great Ucayali river.

To put a modern road through the tropical rain forest over the backbone of rock which separates the valleys of the Huallaga and Ucayali requires both a lot of imagination and even more intestinal fortitude. Of the former, the Peruvians concerned have an abundance. They visioned west coast freight accumulating in Lima and eastward along the highway, the loading of this freight on an endless stream of trucks headed over the Andes for Pucallpa, and then its transport by water to Iquitos where it would be reloaded for the last time into freighters and carried almost twenty-five hundred miles down the Amazon to the Atlantic and thence to the Seven Seas. In the opposite direction they saw, some day, all the goods that Peru imports from Europe shipped by water directly to the end of this new highway. In other words, when the highway reached Pucallpa, then the center as well as the coast of Peru would possess a shorter, direct water connection with European markets. The resulting saving of time and money in the case of both export and import trade would be large. It was a project to fire the imagination. Where there is fire there is smoke, the smoke of the road crews cutting and burning their way through the jungle to turn a dream into a reality.

In 1938, the highway had pierced the jungle to a distance thirty miles east of Tingo Maria. This remarkable accomplishment was a tribute to the energy and enterprise of the government and the ability and enthusiasm of its young engineers. Even to run a preliminary survey across an almost impenetrable jungle appeared to be a superhuman undertaking. One of the surveyors was lost in the rain forest for eight days, even though he had all his instruments with him. If you don't believe this story, try to imagine yourself in a deep perpetual twilight created high above by a canopy of tropical foliage in which every leaf fights for a place in the sun; where tangled lianas hang in huge twisted masses from the branches overhead to obscure more than a limited view; where dark, smooth, strangling stems of climbing figs circle the giant tree trunks like serpents; where rain seems always to be falling on the green roof of your world and penetrating it in streams that turn the jungle floor into such a slimy morass that the forest trees must send out far-flung basal buttresses, in order to assure a firm anchorage in that ages-old accumulation of vegetable decay of which the jungle soil is made. Only bold, hardy men conquer the jungle. When they have overpowered it the fight to maintain a victory at once begins.

Starry-eyed speculators pictured great plantations lining the highway above and below Tingo. Thence, the fruits of the tropics were to be trucked out and shipped from Iquitos to the rest of the world. Tingo Maria would become a jungle metropolis which the colonists would turn into a garden spot. Perhaps. But the climate is hot, and *siestas* are long. While the colonists take their siestas the *churristate* vines, which never sleep, creep in upon the clearings. Roots of felled trees boldly send up shoots that grow into saplings overnight. In addition the jungle has a powerful ally in the hookworm which saps the vigor of the jungle's human conquerors. Harvey made a wager with Bob that the jungle would win. Bob, ever the optimist, saw a great future in the Tingo area. At the end of fifteen years, if his optimistic prediction is fulfilled, he will become the proud possessor of a new Borsalino hat. I hope he gets it.

Aside from too much rain, Tingo was a rather agreeable place in which to live. While Harvey and Bob stopped there mosquitoes were not in evidence and sleeping nets were unnecessary. They were surprised to find no malaria, either among the natives or among the many laborers' families who had come into the jungle. The theory was offered that Tingo mosquitoes were still uninfected and only awaited the advent of a malaria carrier to spread the malady so common in most of the wet areas of Peru, which lie at an altitude of less than five thousand feet. With abundance of tropical fruits, fish from the Rio Huallaga, and game from the jungle, the menus were far more appealing than the maize and potato ones of the Andean highlands.

A few hardier trippers, most of them from Lima, were already experimenting with a jungle holiday, and the government was building for their accommodation a very grand tourist hotel several miles south of Tingo. It was to be an elegant affair. The bathrooms had already been tiled and the last word in plumbing and fixtures was being installed. Their contrast to native facilities was extreme. Old jungle dwellers laughed derisively at a German settler when they saw him building a bamboo thatch outhouse, in an effort to achieve some privacy and semblance of sanitation. Why, said they, should one limit himself spatially in this manner, when God has given his people the freedom of all the out-of-doors!

This settler, the son of a *profesor* in a Peruvian colegio, had been trained as an electrical engineer, but had left a good position on the coast in order to satisfy his love for the jungle. He wished to live his life in nature's wild fastnesses and on the floods of the Amazonian sources, which roar through the Peruvian rain forest. Soon after Harvey and Bob arrived in Tingo he started off with his rifle and a crew of peons to pole up the Huallaga in a couple of dugouts. After reaching the mouth of the tributary Rio Monzon, he planned to explore that river. He wasn't looking for anything in particular; it was merely that exploring was good fun. From his point of view the jungle was beautiful and fascinating, not dangerous or unhealthy. He confessed that sometime before he had contracted the prevalent hookworm, but cured himself with peppermint. Since then he had, as a preventive, dosed himself occasionally with peppermint and had never had any more trouble.

They made the Hotel del Aguila their headquarters. The main structure and its various annexes were constructed of bamboo with a roof of palm thatch. The floors were made of planks raised on stilts some three feet above the marshy ground. The dining room was a large open porch where the elite loafers

Roots and foliage of yuca (*Manihot utilissima*), source of tapioca

Cube (barbasco) roots, yielding the fish poison and insecticide rotonone

Native dugout canoe crossing a jungle tributary of the Rio Huallaga

Our host and his mother choose the meat for the botanists' dinner

of the town gathered in the afternoons. There they stayed until late at night to exchange cheap talk and expensive drink, and to enjoy the free and very loud radio rendition of Spanish songs from the Lima station, swing music from Schenectady, and, from Berlin, world news cleverly shaded to exhibit the British Empire in a most unfavorable light. In one of the annexes the botánicos had their bunks and kept at plant drying night and day. The air was always humid and the drying was slow; therefore they had to employ artificial heat supplied by their gasoline pressure lanterns. The felt driers which they ordinarily used were replaced by heavy corrugated paper ones, and the presses were hung over the lanterns. Warm air then passed upward through the tubules of the "corrugateds" and the wet specimens dried quite rapidly. They were at once bundled and wrapped in cheap oilcloth and shipped as soon as possible by truck to us at base headquarters in Lima. There we unpacked the specimens, took care of any additional drying that seemed necessary, and started off a shipment for California.

Drying pressed specimens with artificial heat is not a new idea and we used this technique successfully in many parts of South America. Modern gasoline lanterns are exceedingly effective mechanisms for creating quick heat and they are readily portable. If gasoline in out-of-the-way places in the Andes had been as good as the lanterns, less profanity would have been used by expedition members. When there is water or other impurities in the gasoline these pressure lanterns can become as temperamental as an automobile engine fed with bad fuel. The lanterns are perfectly safe but they are not entirely foolproof. One night in Tingo, Harvey awoke to find that one of them had burned out. Half asleep he got up, fumbled around for the five-gallon gasoline can, and began refilling. Unfortunately the metal was still hot and so things immediately began to happen. Flames first shot up from the lantern and then from the can, and for a moment it looked as though the *Gran Hotel del Aguila* was going up in smoke. But the fire was quickly smothered. When the lantern had cooled Harvey refilled it, and the plant drying proceeded without further interruption. Walter and Alan had the hardest luck with lantern heat, and from Peru to Patagonia they left behind them a trail of burned "corrugateds" and charred plant specimens. They even succeeded in destroying part of a nice garden and burned up a shack or two in Patagonia.

The alternative to heat drying of specimens in moist climates is the use of a preservative. According to that technique the freshly collected plants are pressed for a short time and then placed in a tight container along with a small amount of alcohol. The alcohol prevents molding and bacterial decay of the tissues, and the plants remain in good condition for months and even for years. Unfortunately, however, the coloring material of all plant parts is extracted by alcohol and when the specimens are removed from the container and dried under pressure they become black and rather brittle. By contrast, fast heat drying usually produces plant specimens that have a quite natural appearance.

Tingo Maria with an elevation of three thousand feet and nine degrees south of the Equator is still not actually in the true jungle. The vegetation was, therefore, not of the extremely tropical rain forest type which appears in its full luxuriance along the Amazon in Brazil. Afternoons were generally rainy, but the mornings gave opportunity to collect plants up and down the Rio Huallaga and along the highway north or south. Contrary to common impression, the tropical rain forest is by no means always gay with bright-colored flowers. Actually, it is an almost tiresomely monotonous green. Near Tingo the forest floor showed only lichens, mosses, ferns, and those types of shrubs and herbs that can exist where there is a minimum of light. There were Arums, Marantas, Calatheas, wild peppers, and some showy-flowered members of the madder family. Here and there a shower of bright petals or a few showy corolla tubes lay on the ground. Then they gazed upward in the hope of determining which of the entangled treetops or lianas had shed those tantalizing bits of evidence that the roof of the jungle was in flower. Where streams, trails, roads, or clearings created openings in the dense montaña the collecting was better. Along such forest margins small species of bamboo, "Panama hat" palms, tree ferns, the ginger, and other attractive plants disported themselves. Conspicuous were the red and yellow bracts of the great banana-leaved Heliconias, which Harvey liked to call the macaws of the plant world.

The river was the center of Tingo's life. On its banks community bathing, gossipy washing of clothes, fishing, and general loitering were always in evidence. Usually there was a *balsa,* or raft, under construction. Logs for balsas were preferably cut from the balsa tree, *Ochroma,* locally called *topa.* The price of a log was one sol, or about twenty-five cents U. S. With half the weight of cork, balsa is the lightest of woods. Because of the great demand for these logs there were relatively few large trees left in the forests near Tingo Maria. The lightest wood came from the low, truly jungle country where the trees grow very rapidly and may attain a diameter of eighteen inches in five years.

Ochroma is a relative of both the cotton plant and of the tree which yields kapok. Its fruit is a large pod about six inches in length. When its segments break open a brown cottony mass of down is exposed and the pod comes to look like a rabbit's foot. In fact the first species named from Central America was called *Ochroma lagopus,* the "rabbit-foot *Ochroma."* The down is used in making pillows and mattresses. All seeds must be removed or the mice that relish them will burrow into pillow and mattress, something not conducive to restful sleep.

In constructing a balsa strands of tough bark are used to lash the logs to one another and to strong cross timbers placed fore and aft. A raised platform occupies the middle of the raft. On it cargo and passengers may keep relatively dry when the balsa shoots the rapids of the lower Huallaga. The rivermen who pole these rafts are experts and know the river well. When they have delivered a raft at the end of their special stretch of river, they return overland and await an opportunity to take down another raft. Much of the local river traffic is carried on in dugouts of various sizes, some of immense proportions. The Huallaga is always a reddish yellow flood laden with tree trunks, brushwood, and acres of soil, which is starting its transcontinental journey to help build the delta of the Amazon out into the Atlantic.

They made a number of collecting trips in the jungle across the river. One of them Bob describes as follows: "Señor

Aguila, who owns our hotel, promised to take us bright and early to the *chacra,* or small farm, of one of his relatives who lives on the opposite bank of the Huallaga. We walked to the river beyond the new government hotel and shouted at the tops of our voices to attract the attention of some peons on the opposite riverbank. Aguila ordered a dugout which, after bailing it dry, two men brought across to us. It was about twenty feet long. We all piled in and poled upstream for a while. Then we swung into the current, the two native rivermen paddling like mad with their short, hand-carved paddles. Despite their best efforts we went downstream one hundred yards in crossing about half that distance and then poled back upstream to the landing. Nearby, on land recently cleared of jungle growth, corn and bananas were planted. Aguila's relatives had built a few crude huts and set up housekeeping, surrounded by much filth. After getting his gun and cartridges the man of the family, a young clean-looking chap, joined our expedition. We struggled over all manner of logs and tree trunks on the margin of the clearing and then, on a very faint trail, plunged headlong into virgin rain forest. The hunter soon outdistanced us and we saw no more of him. Once we heard his gun far away and often he and Aguila whistled back and forth through the verdant jungle gloom.

"It was a flat, low area with many tall, large-trunked trees, the tops so overgrown with vines that we rarely caught a glimpse of the sunny blue skies above. Yes, it was a clear day at last. The lower-story vegetation was not so dense as we had found it elsewhere in the jungle and we were able to wander about at will. We did so until to me all directions were the same and I hadn't the slightest idea from which one we had come. This geographical uncertainty was accentuated when we stumbled upon a river which proved to be the Monzon and to be running in exactly the opposite direction from the one which I was prepared to have it take. Most of the time we were up to our necks in ferns and huge-leaved Arums, but collecting was poor because few things flower in such gloomy sunless depths. The tangled masses of vines and orchids which appeared on the upper parts of every tree were very enticing but climbing to them was impossible.

"Aguila disappeared suddenly and I began to think that he had brought us out with intent to lose us. Finally he reappeared, but from a totally unexpected direction. When we started back to the river he led off at right angles to the direction I would have taken. Of course he proved to be right. Upon arriving at the chacra it was too late to return to Tingo for lunch and so we sat down on the ground around an open fire in front of the cabin and prepared to sample an authentic native repast. It consisted of four baked bananas for each person. The ripe fruits were laid on the coals and left there until the skins were thoroughly charred, then peeled and passed around. They were very good, even if a bit scorched in spots. All during the meal I had my eye on a big bowl of nasty yellow-brown paste and kept praying that the family's hospitality would not include this mess. It proved to be fresh banana pulp which ferments when allowed to stand for two or three days. Mixed with water it makes quite a drink, called *chicha de plátano*. I was very jittery when the rather filthy housewife unceremoniously reached into the revolting, sticky mass and took out a goodly handful. She shook it off into a smaller bowl, added a little river water, mixed the combination with two dirty paws (they came out cleaner), threw out the larger pieces, and then handed it to me to drink. I couldn't very well refuse and so I sunk my face in the bowl and found it didn't taste nearly as bad as it looked. In fact it was really quite refreshing. Meanwhile, Harvey had been doing his best to look preoccupied and remote, but I wasn't going to let him get away with anything like that and handed him what was left in the bowl."

On another occasion a jeweler from Lima and his friend arrived in Tingo to examine for the first time "the other side of the mountains" about which he had been hearing so much. He was decked out in a fine new outfit, which no doubt had been selected after consulting the magazines to see what the well-dressed hunter was wearing. But it was a new shotgun with an outfit for loading his own shells that was obviously his most prized possession. He and his friend devoted the first two days to sitting around the bar, trying to become acclimated, loading shells, and drinking in a number of things, but particularly some pretty tall stories concerning what they might expect to find in the jungle. On the third day a sally into the wilderness was arranged and they invited Harvey and Bob to accompany them.

The expedition got under way with Señor Aguila and his murderous-looking *machete* leading off, then came the huntsman gingerly carrying his gun at what he conceived to be the correct angle, next the botánicos weighted down with plant presses and cameras, and, bringing up the rear, the huntsman's friend provided with nothing but a dread of all the things that he felt sure were going to happen to him in the terrible jungle. Señor Aguila chose a trail that led to the northwest. Periodically the party paused to listen for the sound of turtledoves. During these stops the botanists were able to make a little hay. Everyone was supposed to move as quietly as possible. But it takes long training to walk through the tropical rain forest without making considerable noise, and most of the jungle animals for a mile around them must have known what was going on. Suddenly they heard something crash off through the bush. The hunter immediately handed his gun to Señor Aguila who disappeared in the direction of the sound.

They neither saw nor heard anything of their guide for sometime and the hunter's friend became excessively alarmed. He called attention first to their entirely unprotected condition now that the gun was gone, and, second, to reports that jaguars and wild boars were common in that particular section of the jungle. Bob suggested that neither beast was likely to be dangerous if the hunter and his friend took pains not to interfere with their activities. "No, no," cried the friend, "wild boars especially are known to be very vicious; they travel in packs and kill every living thing that appears before them." Thereupon Bob further suggested that the friend had best pick out his tree, since boars were unable to climb trees. This valuable suggestion was also brushed aside. Had Bob not read that wild boars are in the habit of uprooting trees and causing them to fall, along with the contained victims?

His friend's perturbation now infected the previously rather valiant hunter who demanded that everyone be very quiet lest Señor Aguila, unaware of their presence, let off the shotgun in their direction. From that time on the two friends remained in a crouching position behind a decaying log which they apparently believed would serve as a barricade. After a considerable time Señor Aguila returned and reported no success. He and the hunters then decided to carry their expedition still farther into the jungle. The botanists, however, felt little enthusiasm for such a proposal, and it was finally agreed that they should go on with collecting nearby and that the whole party should reassemble at one o'clock, in time to return to Tingo for luncheon.

One o'clock came and there were no hunters at the rendezvous. After another hour of intensive collecting of mosses, leafy liverworts, and epiphyllous lichens, Harvey and Bob gave them up and started back. Not until late in the day did Señor Aguila and the two tenderfeet, thoroughly soaked by the regular afternoon downpour, appear at the hotel. Tired but proud, they exhibited to an admiring audience two woodpeckers and a small curassow, all three very dead and decidedly shot to pieces. That night a "hunt dinner" was arranged. The guests showered the successful hunter with compliments and repeatedly told him how good the "game" tasted. It did give a certain far-away flavor to the caldo, and later everyone was served with a morsel of bird meat. Fortunately, the understanding cook had prepared yuca, rice, beans, dried beef, fried plantains, papaya, and a *dulce,* to supplement the products of the chase.

Through a newly made friend in Tingo Maria, Harvey and Bob received an invitation to spend a few days at the Hacienda Shapajilla, about ten miles to the east along the extension of the jungle highway. Don José, the *hacendado,* and his good-looking señora gave them a hearty welcome and put them up in a bamboo-thatch storehouse near the ranch house. It was a rather large hacienda on which sixty peons were regularly employed. Some of them were Indians but the majority were mestizos, or mixed bloods. They lived in shacks on the banks of the Rio Supte at the point where it flows into the Huallaga. The peons received one sol a day in addition to their food, most of which was rice, yuca, corn, and tropical fruits in great variety, all produced on the hacienda. Fish they took from the river, and game, principally peccary, from the forest. What they caught or killed was supposed to be reported to the patron, who was then at liberty to take for his family's use as much as he desired.

Some cotton was grown but the climate was really too wet for much success with it. The principal money crop was *barbasco*. The word barbasco refers to the roots of the *cube* tree, *Lonchocarpus nicou,* a member of the pea family, and to the milky juice obtained from the pulped roots. For many centuries barbasco has been used by the jungle folk as an effective fish poison. When the peons at the Haciendo Shapajilla wanted a really big haul of fish, they "barbascoed" them. First, a bamboo wicker dam was constructed across the Rio Supte. Then, several men went upstream about a half-mile and a second party about a half-mile farther, each carrying a bundle of barbasco. Between stones they pounded the roots to a juicy pulp and tossed it into the stream. An alkaloid in the juice immediately began to diffuse in the water. It had an asphyxiating effect on any fish in the neighborhood, so that by the time they reached the bamboo barricade they were quite stupefied and floated belly up. A jolly group of nude peons thereupon waded into the water and tossed the catch ashore. The fish that were not to be eaten immediately were split in half and put in the sun to dry. When there wasn't much sunshine the product tended to become rather unpleasantly "high."

The active principle in barbasco, or cube as it is also called, is rotenone. It is poisonous only to cold-blooded organisms, or at least is not poisonous to mammals, and so there is no danger in eating a "barbascoed" fish. Rotenone acts upon insects as it does upon fish and has become an important constituent of many insecticides. When you get out the little spray gun and fill the room with a rather smelly mist the effectiveness of your activities is likely to depend in part upon the presence in the spray mixture of a trace of rotenone. The same is true of many plant sprays.

There is good material for a magazine article in the history and uses of the "fish poisons" of the tropics. Our Department of Agriculture and the agricultural departments of foreign governments always instruct plant hunters to keep on the trail of fish-poisoning natives in order to find and ship home the plant parts they employ. Before Mrs. Mexia joined our first

Andean expedition at Lima she had been for some months in
Ecuador as a collector for the Division of Plant Exploration
and Introduction of the Bureau of Plant Industry at Washington. One of her assignments was to get the plants with which
the Indians in remote regions were poisoning fish. Her intimate
knowledge of native customs and psychology and the confidence
which the Indians reposed in her made her search quite
successful.

Large quantities of barbasco have been exported from the
Peruvian jungle to Europe and the United States for manufacture of insecticides. The annual value of such exports has
been as much as $250,000. Some years ago in Peru it was
rumored, with what truth I do not know, that the Japanese
were growing the cube trees in their mandated islands or elsewhere, and that already the roots harvested from them were
competing all too successfully with those exported from Peru.
Formerly barbasco was dug from the jungle, but soon it proved
more profitable to make plantations of the cube tree. It grows
very rapidly in cultivation and after two or three years the roots
are sufficiently mature to be harvested.

There was a settlement of thatched huts along the partially
completed highway, fifteen miles deeper into the montaña. It
was called Pumahuasi, and represented the base for advance
operations of the road crews. The Quechua word *puma,* a
jaguar, occurs frequently in jungle names, and Pumahuasi
means the "lair of the jaguar." This quite unpleasant animal
is continuously hunted and its skin is commonly seen in the
native huts.

On All Saints' Day their host at Hacienda Shapajilla, Don
José, took the family and guests to Pumahuasi in his ancient
sports roadster. Nearby, Harvey and Bob found good collecting
in newly made clearings where the flora of the jungle floor,
partially freed from undergrowth, was easy to get at.

The local drunkery was the busiest place on the village
main street. There, so many of the roadworkers had accumulated that its bamboo walls bulged dangerously. An itinerant
orchestra with fiddle, banjo, and *harpa* dispensed doleful music,
and there were many unsuccessful attempts to organize community singing. The rest of the citizens celebrated the holiday

along the riverbank where they were fishing, washing clothes, drinking chicha, poling dugouts up and down, swimming— everyone, even tiny youngsters, as much at home in the water as on the land—and dynamiting fish.

This latter was forbidden by a national statute, but the montaña knows little of man-made laws. Highway construction had stimulated this fishing technique, since of course it was not possible to prevent pilferage from the roadworkers' supply of dynamite and blasting caps. The charge had to explode almost as soon as it hit the water; otherwise the fish would scatter at the first disturbance of their native element. Such close timing had led to many gruesome accidents and there were a good many arms without hands and hands without fingers in the crowd at the riverside.

Here and there along the banks of the Rios Supte and Huallaga, a tall woody grass, *Gynerium sagittatum,* formed pure stands. The straight smooth stems, light in weight, were the standard material for making arrows. To one end of the four- or five-foot lengths was fastened a foot or two of hard black palmwood, carved its entire length into sharp points and re- curved barbs. The other end was feathered in more or less conventional fashion. For bows, the same palmwood was used. The Indians hunted both fish and game with these bows and arrows. The fish were shot from the riverbank and the hunter dove in to recover the arrow and the fish that it had impaled. It was a strictly sporting proposition as well as being a far more picturesque technique than blitzbombing with dynamite.

The bow and arrow palm was known as *shapaja,* and its abundance in Don José's hacienda gave rise to the name "Shapa- jilla" given to his establishment. From it also were cut the long fronds used in the standard type of montaña thatch. While plant hunting one morning near the hacienda Harvey and Bob came upon two Indians. With machetes they were hacking to pieces the decaying trunk of a shapaja. Great, soft white grubs, often two inches long, the larvae of a large black beetle, had honeycombed the softened palm tissues, and the machetes ex- posed them in large numbers. A kettle standing nearby con- tained a mass of the writhing, wriggling larvae, and the Indians said that as soon as enough had been accumulated there was

going to be a fine, big "grub fry." These larvae are looked
upon as one of the great delicacies of the montaña and the two
Indians considered themselves very lucky to find such an abundant supply in a single palm trunk. In their grub collection a
few of the adult beetles had been included. Their addition is
said to add character to a grub fry by providing something
crunchy to bite on while the soft rich larvae melt in the
mouth!

. Fully to appreciate the Peruvian tropics a visitor should
have some knowledge of entomology. The only seriously disagreeable insects are the hymenopters which become more than
resentful when, strictly by accident, you disturb their nests.
In addition there are little black flies with a bite that raises a
small blood blister. Minute red spiders, *beta colorada,* akin to
the "chiggers" of the southern and some other sections of the
United States, can make life a burden unless early discouraged
by judicious use of sulphur. Nighttime in the montaña is always
gay with clouds of fireflies. The common species is provided
with two green headlights continuously illuminated and an
abdominal white light, which flashes intermittently and constitutes a sort of "landing light." You can't help looking for a
red tail light but probably that's expecting too much. The
bombardier beetles are always an object of curiosity. On open
ground their little burrows can be excavated, and the inhabitants made to deliver several charges of a nitrous substance
in quite up-to-the-minute chemical warfare fashion. Leaf-cutter
ants are everywhere, beating down their trails on the jungle
floor as they hasten home with neatly excised pieces of green
leaf. Often their burdens are larger than they are themselves.
The total quantity of leaf accumulation in the underground ant
galleries must be enormous. On these leafy stores they cultivate
fungus gardens to supply food for their armies of hungry
workers.

On the return trip to Cerro de Pasco and thence to Lima,
Harvey and Bob stopped off several days in the Carpis "eyebrow
of the montaña" through which they had ridden during the
journey to Tingo Maria. For lack of better accommodations in
the rain forest they were forced to put up at an Indian shack.
It was occupied by a mother and her grown son and daughter,

all of whom made it abundantly clear that the botánicos were not at all welcome. Indeed such a shelter as the bamboo thatched *casita* provided had practically to be commandeered. Their scanty supply of tinned food bought in Tingo Maria began to run low and the grudging hostess could supply nothing but hominy. She finally managed to find a few eggs but absolutely refused to provide a chicken. At each renewed demand she dolefuly repeated, *"No hay, señor,"* although there was more than one fowl wandering about the shack. In desperation they offered what in the montaña constituted a small fortune, but all they got was, *"No hay, señor."* When an Andean Indian will not sell, he will not sell.

On the Carpis "eyebrow of the montaña" most of the twenty-four hours was foggy to rainy. In other words, everything was dripping all the time. In his letters Bob referred to their days at Carpis as "fogging about in the Andes." The vegetation responded to the extremely high atmospheric humidity with larger and smaller mosses, filmy ferns, and small low shrubs of the Madder and Heath families, which together enveloped the floor of the jungle, the boulders, the fallen logs, the tree trunks, and even the branches of the trees in a continuity of deep, soft green cushions. On tree trunks and out along the branches nestled orchids, bromeliads, ferns, and other epiphytes in remarkable variety. Apart from them the most attractive plants were Gaultherias, Pernettyas, and other ericaceous species. Their glossy foliage and their brightly colored flowers make them desirable ornamentals. Unfortunately they cannot be transplanted successfully except into tropical gardens or greenhouses. Cuttings were made of a number of tree Fuchsias, of Begonias, and an unusually striking yellow *Calceolaria,* all of which were sent to Berkeley by air.

Chapter VI

WHERE THE AMAZON BEGINS

I N THE shadow of Andean snow fields and glaciers, near the
southeastern corner of Peru, begin some of the first trickles
of what are to become important among the two hundred
tributaries of the Amazon, that mightiest maze of continental
waterways in the world. Some say that the headwaters of the
Rio Marañon, north of Cerro de Pasco in central Peru, must
be called the beginning of the Amazon. Others urge the claim
of the Ucayali to be the true source of the main river. To form
the Alto Ucayali, the Rios Apurimac and Urubamba meet at
a point where the innermost of the Andean ranges looks eastward over the beginnings of the boundless Amazonian hinterland. Flowing into the Urubamba are the Paucartambo and
the Mishagua, and, only a few miles from the latter's source, a
branch of the Madre de Dios has its beginning, a beginning
that ends in the Madeira, one of the longest major tributaries
of the Amazon. In the center of these ultimate ramifications of
the Amazon's fanlike fluvial system, which begins almost in
sight of the Pacific and discharges into the Atlantic four thousand miles away, lies Cuzco, "City of the Sun," "Hub of the
Universe," ancient capital of Tahuantinsuyo, the Empire of
the Incas. In the city itself and beside the headwaters of these
Andean rivers, and on the precipitous cliffs thousands of feet
above their sunless floods, stand so many Inca and pre-Inca
fortresses, shrines, and settlements that the Cuzco area has been
called the archaeological treasure house of South America.

Going to Peru without seeing Cuzco is like going to Rome
without seeing St. Peter's. As far as the botanist is concerned
there is danger that he will linger there too long, losing his
ardor for the pursuit of plants in daydreams appropriate to this
archaeologist's Mecca. Our first sojourn there was in 1935, when
Florence and I pried about the city's narrow, Inca-walled streets,
wandered over the hill of Sacsahuaman, feasted our eyes upon
the perfection of the stonecutter's art, and, finally, tore our-

selves away to begin the collecting along the sources of the
Amazon.

We had come to Cuzco, by air from Lima to Arequipa, and
thence by train. On our last afternoon in Lima we went directly
from the audience with President Benavides to a hall where I
gave an incoherent—but, luckily, illustrated—lecture on the
national parks of western North America. Then came a farewell to the City of Kings that lasted until dawn and, finally,
the marvelous air journey to Arequipa, our first experience in
an airplane, with its spectacular termination across the nineteen
thousand-foot face of Volcan Misti.

Incidentally, this first venture of ours in the air was quite
beyond expectation; that is to say, we enjoyed every moment—
all the bumps and the slips and especially the good luncheon
Pan-American Airways always provides. This was in the days of
Ford tri-motor equipment, and something must have been
wrong with our plane, because we had an experience that certainly was not in the rule book. An hour or two out of Lima,
and, literally as well as figuratively, out of a clear sky, the plane
nosed sharply down through dense, low fog and landed lightly
on the broad, hard-packed ocean beach. Nothing was in sight
except a big truck full of gasoline cans. It pulled up beside the
plane almost as soon as we had stopped rolling along the sand.
So far as I know the passengers were not asked to leave the
plane, but most of us did, even the singularly terrified señorita
who, from the moment the wheels left the ground at Lima air-
port, had never taken her eyes off her lap and the beads that
she was counting there.

The wind blowing up the beach was terrific. Only by putting his shoulder to the blast and spreading his legs wide apart
was the pilot able to maintain his position on the wings while
he attempted to pour canned gasoline, through a much-too-
diminutive funnel, into the fuel reservoir beneath his feet.
Of course, the wind snatched away a goodly share of what he
was pouring, and soon the body of the plane and the open door
through which we had descended became enveloped in a cloud
of gasoline vapor. The passengers drew back to a respectful
distance, and stood watching what appeared to be a futile effort
to refuel the plane.

At this juncture one of our fellow passengers appeared in the door. I recognized him as a young man who had been airsick, and sufficiently affected by the altitude to require an oxygen bottle. The steward probably assumed that this passenger would be glad to rest during our emergency stop, and so had hesitated to disturb him. At any rate, there he stood in the door of the plane. As we watched him he put his hand in one pocket and pulled out a cigarette. From the other pocket he produced a box of matches. The cigarette had reached his mouth and the match was ready to be struck when, with one voice, we shouted a warning. At the same instant the steward appeared on the dead run and knocked down the match box—just in time. At the end of this pantomime another cloud of gasoline enshrouded the plane, and the young man hurried inside again. Somehow I began to feel that air travel on the Peruvian coast was a rather too informal sort of affair, and it was, therefore, with considerable trepidation that I re-entered the plane when the refueling was finally finished.

Safely landed in Arequipa at two-thirty in the afternoon we proceeded directly to Quinta Bates and into the waiting arms of Tia, the "Hostess of the Andes," beloved friend and counselor of Indian and foreigner alike. Her hotel register was a guestbook which read like a roster of most of the world's great and near great. After a chin and a drink with Tia we went to the station to verify our transportation for Cuzco, saw a little of the fine Spanish colonial architecture of a city whose climate is unsurpassed, ate a most satisfying dinner at the Quinta, watched the sunset creep up Misti's white volcanic crown, and finally, by a hair's breadth, caught our nine o'clock train for the highlands.

When we had squeezed ourselves and baggage into a minute compartment of the *coche dormitorio* and, later, succeeded in getting to bed—I on the narrow upper shelf and Florence on the equally narrow lower one—we took stock of the last twenty-four hours and realized that they had been peculiarly strenuous ones. In a short time I realized something else; a dull headache with intermittent flashes of biting pain. The train was rocking and swaying and laboring with that unmistakable vibration which means that a heavy grade is being negotiated. How heavy it was I did not at the time realize, but actually the altitude increases within a few hours east of Arequipa from eighty-five hundred feet to close to fourteen thousand. At each upward foot of altitude, the pain in the back of my neck increased until no further increase was possible, and then I partially lost consciousness. It was a fairly typical case of *siroche,* or mountain sickness, which, however, has a number of variations, all decidedly unpleasant and some of them now and then fatal. In 1939, Harvey and Bob learned that high altitude cannot be trifled with, when they witnessed in Cuzco the death from heart failure of an elderly New England woman who had been vacationing along the west coast.

We got off the train in Cuzco late in the afternoon and found ourselves at the door of the railway hotel. I was feeling too low, after my bout with siroche, to take an interest in anything but bed. Ordinarily, Cuzco's altitude of 11,800 feet should not have made me as acutely conscious of heart sounds as I was that night. All I needed, however, was twelve hours in a horizontal position, because in the morning the altitudinal adjustment had been made, and once more everything looked bright and cheerful. In the succeeding weeks of hard collecting, sometimes at altitudes above fourteen thousand feet, I felt no inconvenience, and even an exhilaration.

During those Cuzco days we lived in the Hotel Ferrocarril. It proved to be a typical railroad hotel, except that, since Cuzco is the terminus of the line, only a few trains a week arrive and depart and the freight yard is negligible in size and activity. Therefore the night was not made hideous by the bells, whistles, thumps, and bumps that have kept us awake in North American railway hotels. Our room was a corner one on the second floor, which the manager contended was forever famous because it had been occupied by David, Duke of Windsor, when he was Prince of Wales. I doubt whether our room had been his, but the three-plumed coat of arms prominently displayed in the lobby proves that he stopped in the Hotel Ferrocarril. However, ours was a clean and thoroughly comfortable room and the Prince of Wales might certainly have fared considerably worse.

By contrast with Lima, where we saw almost no flies (and this was true of a number of towns on the northern coast of

At the beginning of its long journey to the Atlantic, the Rio Urubamba's
jungle-margined flood roars through a mighty gorge

Ruins of ancient Macchu Pichu step down Urubamba's canyon walls

The Incas' terraced fields still ornament many a steep Andean slope

Barefoot Indian girls in colorful costumes and quaint flat hats swing along the streets of Cuzco, capital of their Inca ancestors

In the Andes everything, including babies, travels on patient backs

Not aigrettes but llamas, near-camels of the Andes, carrying fodder

Peru), the high country, both near and far from human habitations, was alive with them. The hotel was screened, but the flies were not to be denied and managed to get indoors in quantity. At every hour of the day, therefore, the sound and smell of fly spraying was in the air. I never determined whether the fluid was a local product or an imported brand, but it possessed a nauseating odor that was in constant competition and blended disagreeably, particularly in the dining room, with the smells of cooking. The situation was aggravated by the inherited aversion of the staff and our fellow guests to the introduction of fresh air into the hallways and public rooms of the hotel. However, the spray did the business effectively, and each time we returned to our room in the late afternoon we found that a large collection of flies had, literally, turned up their toes on window sills, bedspreads, and bureau tops. Absence of rugs and overstuffed furniture, together with constant waxing of the floors, meant no fleas, and this was a blessing. The hotel service was good, the food clean and wholesome, and altogether the Hotel Ferrocarril was a tribute to the success of the railway company's attempt to provide acceptable accommodations in what was an out-of-the-way part of the world.

That first morning in Cuzco we dressed near the windows in order to watch the Indians who were crossing the rough, cobbled, plazalike area behind the hotel. It was our initial glimpse of the bright and rather charming native costumes that are universally worn, and that represent the chief touch of attractiveness in the decidedly primitive, and somewhat unclean, ensemble of life in the Peruvian Andes. I had supposed that the mountain folk would be short, barrel-chested, and, in general, pretty powerfully built, in order to meet the physiological demands that high altitudes impose. These first Indians we saw were, however, rather slender people and not below the average height of the Peruvians in coastal cities. They were jogging along in single file on their way home from sojourns in the ancient capital of their forebears, toward those minute collections of meager farmsteads that dot the high plateaus and mountain valleys of the Cuzco region.

In one group we saw two women, one of whom carried a baby, almost completely concealed in the capacious shawl thrown over its mother's shoulders. It must have been a heavy baby because, although her step was light, the woman was leaning forward as she trotted along. The other woman was last in line. As we watched through our window we saw her stop suddenly. With anxiety in face, pose, and every movement, she fumblingly examined a small pouch that hung at her waist. Then she turned around, and, half stooping, slowly retraced her steps, searching the ground with her eyes meanwhile. Every now and again she paused, bent down, and picked up some object that was invisible to us. Although they glanced at her over their shoulders the other Indians went straight on, and long before she passed beyond our line of vision they had disappeared in the opposite direction. We felt like spectators at a play who are permitted to see only the setting, and not the development, of a simple, human drama.

The incident of the Cuzco Indian woman and her mysterious searchings would have been forgotten had she not reappeared some half an hour later, when we stood at the hotel entrance talking to the manager. With her mincing, half-running, half-walking gait, she was again on her way across the rough roadway. At our request the manager spoke to her, using that guttural, clicking, bastard Spanish-Quechua tongue so common in the highlands. She stopped in front of us with a surprised, doubtful, and slightly furtive look in her eyes. Through the manager we asked what it was that she had lost, for remembering the agonized expression on her face Florence's sympathy was aroused. After some urging the Indian woman reluctantly opened a small, dirty hand, and showed us a dozen or two parched kernels of the large Cuzco corn. The manager explained that this corn probably represented all that she would have to eat during the long journey on foot that was ahead of her. Then we understood why she had been so worried when she discovered that, through a hole in its pouch, most of the corn had disappeared. All that she could do was to follow back along her path, in the hope of picking up as many of the lost kernels as could be found. This was our first contact with the impoverished condition of native peoples in the Andes. Again and again thereafter we saw it in different settings.

I am afraid that we stared pretty hard at the Indian

woman, in that frankly curious manner that people seem to acquire when they examine other human beings whose costume happens to be different from their own. Her feet were bare, soiled, and leathery, but small and beautifully formed, as are those of most of the mountain people. She was pregnant, but not very obviously so. Her broad hips carried a succession of knee-length skirts, the outer one, made of rough, heavy, dark-blue, woolen material, flaring out at a wide angle. Over the skirts she wore a large apron dyed a brilliant magenta, a color that is popular among the Peruvian Indian women. A long, narrow, navy-blue jacket, cut in a stiff, semimilitary fashion, high shouldered and decorated along the seams with narrow, bright-red braid might, at one time, have covered the entire nakedness beneath, but did not do so now. A large ragged shawl, of yellow wool striped with red, hung over her shoulders and down her back, and was held at the neck with a big, brass breastpin. She was, obviously, a young woman and her face was still round and full, but seamed and worn with toil and priva-tion and with exposure to the severity of Andean climates. When she smiled—the self-conscious, half-grinning smile of the Peruvian Indian—we saw that her teeth were worn more than halfway down to the gums, but otherwise seemed sound enough. Hard, parched corn, and especially the dirt and grit that is likely to adhere to it, is wearing on the teeth.

The most remarkable part of the Indian woman's costume was her hat. It was half a flattened sphere, the framework made of reeds or straw over which blue cloth had been stretched. On the cloth that covered the flat top there were crossing bands of what had once been silver braid. A depression in the center of the curved surface accommodated a little of the wearer's head. The whole contraption was a foot and a half in diameter, and, according to the approved mode in the Andes, she wore it tilted forward over her eyes. In other words, her hat has served as a model for one of the current styles in headgear affected by her more sophisticated North American sisters. I know, be-cause we have one in our family. It happens to be made of black felt, but otherwise differs from the Cuzco variety only in hav-ing no roof over the flat part and in possessing more space for the head in the center of the curved part. Ours is, however,

worn tilted over one eye rather than over both eyes, thus stress-
ing jauntiness, rather than protection from the sun's rays.

We saw Cuzco in 1935, before the tourists were as numerous as they are said to be today. We rejoiced in being the only
visible transient foreigners during those October weeks. I knew,
however, that the handwriting was on the wall when a local
Main Streeter remarked, with pride and in his best English,
"On this precise day the Cuzco Tourist Association is borned."
Thereupon I learned that the fame and efficiency of Californians, Inc., had gone almost to the ends of the earth, because, in
remote Cuzco, my friend asked me to send him all their literature in order that he might demonstrate to his associates in the
day-old tourist organization how to spread the wily net of
anticipation and devise the guileful invitation.

In 1939, Harvey and Bob saw evidences of the tourist
bureau's success. The Hotel Ferrocarril was filled with North
American visitors and with Germans, who said that they were
teachers in South American schools. As a result, the botánicos
were obliged to seek accommodations in a decidedly second-rate
hostelry, which, however, was also awakening to the opportunity
that tourists present by providing a shower bath in a cold
room, with water hardly tepid. The number of souvenir vendors, and their technique, also, testified to Cuzco's increasing
tourist trade. Someone handed Harvey a printed card that advertised a "private museum" where antiquities might be viewed
and purchased at modest prices. He put the card in his pocket
and forgot about it. Then one day, when he and Bob were out
for a stroll, he recognized the street mentioned on the card.
They promptly hunted up the museum, which proved to be a
converted private residence. The proprietor was not in, but two
young women waited on them. They purchased a few odds and
ends, including an ancient stone axhead that appeared to be
authentic and worth five soles ($1.25), the price quoted by one
of the women.

A little later, when they were standing on the steps of the
cathedral in the Plaza de Armas, a boy accosted them. He said
that the young woman in the museum had been grievously in
error when she sold them the axhead for five soles. She should
have asked twenty soles, and the proprietor had sent him to

collect the balance. Harvey told the youth that they did not do business in such a manner, and advised him to be on his way immediately. In a few moments the proprietor himself appeared and, after unsuccessfully renewing his demand, became a trifle disagreeable and, finally, abusive. Soon convinced that this was the wrong line to pursue he backed down and offered to exchange the original five soles for the axhead. By this time Harvey and Bob had become decidedly annoyed, and they informed the gentleman that the transaction had been legitimate, on their part at least, and that it was now in the category of finished business. The proprietor then threatened to call the police, and they called his bluff. It was not, however, a bluff, and soon, under arrest, they were riding along Cuzco's cobbled streets in a hired taxicab, escorted by a member of the *guardia civil.*

When the desk sergeant had heard the case, he said that, of course, the defendants should have the choice of paying the full price of twenty soles or returning the ax. However, the whole matter might, if the defendants so elected, be placed before the judge, when he was free to hear the case. In the courtroom the plaintiff told a pathetic tale. These two unconscionable foreigners had entered his home, had courteously been shown his collection of museum pieces, and had purchased the property at present in litigation for almost nothing, his wife being quite unaware of its value. "Your Honor," said he, "is connoisseur enough to realize that such an antiquity is worth upwards of a hundred soles, but, being a just man, I will compromise for a total of twenty soles."

The judge after brief deliberation said that the decision hinged entirely on the question of whether or not the transaction had taken place in a private home. While he was questioning the plaintiff on this point Harvey ransacked his pockets and finally found the printed card advertising the museum and its very low prices, and presented it as Exhibit B. After one look at Exhibit B the judge's decision was made. He rose up and blasted the plaintiff. In a most excoriating speech he belabored him for conducting his business in an unlawful manner. Without competent help how could anyone expect to run a legitimate business? Where, by the way, was his license to sell antiquities?

At this point the proprietor asked that the complaint be dismissed and, when the bench agreed, he hurriedly took himself off, a sadder and wiser man. The judge thereupon descended, proffered his hand to Harvey and Bob, and made them a little speech in which he offered his personal apology, and that of all persons in authority in the fair city of Cuzco, for the annoyance to which they had been subjected. After Harvey had replied in proper fashion, making reference to His Honor as "a most excellent judge," they parted with mutual expressions of friendship and esteem. This was not the only occasion upon which members of both expeditions were impressed with the intelligence and courtesy of the civil authorities of Peruvian towns and cities.

Cuzco has been repeatedly described by returning tourists. Probably we missed seeing many of the proper things; at least it always so appears when, after enjoying in our own fashion one of the more remote or more familiar tourist rendezvous, we make the mistake of reading the things that more conventional travelers have to say about it. The ancient Inca capital reflects a mingling and blending of the flavor of Inca times, the romantic glamour of the conquistadors, and the current, but hardly modern, life of the Andes. We used to hunt for an inconspicuous spot near a populous one, and stand there trying to sort out the crowding impressions of present-day life and work in one of America's oldest human settlements. Often, watching their descendants, we tried to induce imagination to repopulate Cuzco's plazas and narrow, winding streets with the people of the past. We tried to conjure up the cortege of an Inca noble as it entered a smooth-walled stone doorway that his ancestors had built and that still stood on a modern Cuzco street corner; or, again, we made believe that we heard the pounding hoofs of Pizarro's mail-clad cavalry as, with fierce shouts, they rode down the defenders of ancient Cuzco in its narrow, twisting lanes.

Late one afternoon we took our stand near a corner of the Plaza de Armas to watch the rosy sunset light climb the towers of the cathedral. We must have been dreaming the same daydreams—dreams of Spanish colonial times, and of all the things, righteous and unrighteous, that had been done in the name of God and in favor of his earthly representatives in that very plaza—because, without warning and with the same impulse, we turned to each other in speechless amazement. Throaty trumpets were sounding a strange fanfare, the hoofs of many horses rang out quick and sharp and clear, and we heard the clash and clang of metal harness. Could all our wishing and day-dreaming have actually returned those long-gone days? Could the conquistadors, just for us, be riding again into the Plaza de Armas, as into it they had ridden so many times, back from raids on the scattered remnants of the Incas' armies?

As we gaped at each other the volume of sound rapidly increased. Then round the corner, from one of Cuzco's steepest, narrowest, rockiest streets and into the plaza at our side, rode a mounted detachment of the Peruvian army's mountain troops. We were so sensitized, so receptive to impression, that the reality was almost as unreal as the fleeting vision had been. The cavalcade approached us at a fast trot. First came the buglers, their heads thrown back to give more amplitude to their high-pitched notes, then an officer riding alone, then troopers, two and two, with shining sabers and steel helmets, then mules, with quick, dainty hoofs, carrying segments of mountain howitzers strapped on their backs, and finally more troopers. In an instant the quiet, deserted plaza was full of echoing sound and rapid, glinting movement.

There are other Cuzco memories—the second-hand market in the Plaza San Francisco, for example. During our walks about the old city we often chanced to pass through this plaza. It had always been deserted, except for llamas in groups of four or five, and dark-clad, mantilla-draped figures on the broad steps of the church that faced one side of the plaza's coarse pavement. The llamas were standing near the doors of saloons that, along with other one-story buildings, lined the remaining three sides of the plaza. Early in the morning they had carried loads of farm produce along some of the many rough trails that begin far away in the mountainous countryside and, from all directions, converge on the city of Cuzco. Now, freed from their burdens, they waited a little impatiently while their masters were fortifying themselves over against the long, homeward journey.

On this particular afternoon, however, we found the Plaza San Francisco crowded and noisy. Along the high sidewalks that ran in front of saloons and shops, llamas were standing two or three deep. Townsfolk and Indians came and went through the mouths of streets that emptied into the plaza, and the large open space itself was full of people. It was obviously a market, but a different sort of highland market from any we had seen before.

Florence delights in crowds, and the friendly give and take of street markets is always a powerful magnet to her. I remember the early winter markets in Stockholm, where we bought growing hyacinth bulbs wrapped in frosty straw; and, later, the Christmas market in Gamla Staden at night, in the snow, with the flares above the booths lighting the façade of the squat Royal Palace; the little pottery market below the bridge in Prague; the linen markets near the Tiber and, for Florence best of all, the Caledonian Market. Imagine, then, her joy when she discovered that in Cuzco's Plaza San Francisco she had found the Peruvian equivalent of her London magnet.

In parallel lines on the pavement was displayed a most amazing collection of disreputable merchandise. It was not a second-hand, it was a third- or fourth-hand market. Junk of every description was neatly arranged and displayed, or, in other cases, heaped together in piles of confusion. The owner of each collection, almost always a woman, sat cross-legged or on her heels behind her stock in trade. Offered for sale were hundreds, perhaps thousands, of bent, rusty nails of all sizes and types, old screws which long since had lost their virtue, brassy and damaged safety pins, nuts and bolts that would never again be joined together, and many more such things. Nearby lay the characteristically minute electric light bulbs of Peru, no one of which would ever burn again; cracked and broken chinaware; bedraggled fripperies of silk and lace; bits of worn tire casings. There were, in addition, piles of miscellaneous rubbish, mostly plumbing fixtures and metal fittings, so dissected and so damaged that their original form and function could scarcely be imagined.

That there were people who could be induced to buy such practically worthless and almost useless articles was difficult to believe. Being sold they were, however, and some of the buyers were almost as dilapidated as their purchases. Obviously poor of pocket, both vendors and purchasers were by no means poor in spirit. Ancient, doddery crones and shuffling grandfathers, wearing the most inconceivably ragged clothes, were bargaining for a bit of this or that with extremely animated voice and rapid gestures. The condition of their costumes was good evidence of the permanent quality of homespun, because the heavy woolen ponchos and skirts they wore seemed to consist more of holes than of fabric.

There were a great many Indians in the second-hand market, more, indeed, than we had ever before seen assembled in one place. Various of the mountain clans were represented and could be identified by larger or smaller distinctions in their brilliant and striking costumes. The shapes of their hats distinguished them most readily, but there were doubtless other finer distinctions that we did not appreciate. They were in a holiday mood, and quite willing to smile and to reply to Florence's tentative gestures of good will. She found it difficult to get much beyond the smiling stage, however, because most of the Cuzco Indians were unwilling, or perhaps unable, to speak even the small amount of Spanish that we would have been able to trade with them.

I never succeeded in thoroughly adjusting myself to the geographic, vegetational, and archaeological complex that lies to the north and east of the one-time Inca capital. Many years ago, as a schoolboy in Geneva, with my red-lined, brass-buttoned reefer and hairy, book-filled knapsack, and more than once since then, I have lingered on the Pont du Mont Blanc and watched the Rhone slip quietly out of Lac Leman and break against Ile Jean Jacques Rousseau, as it gathered power for the long, winding journey through busy cities and beside terraced vineyards, to Avignon and onward into the Mediterranean. Without following its course I had no difficulty in visualizing the landscapes it would see, the kinds of people it would watch, and the sorts of vegetation it would water—the European type of countryside. When, however, I stood beside the Andean

sources of the Amazon, nothing was familiar, neither the land
of their birth nor the wilderness they were to traverse. On
their mission to the opposite edge of the continent these violent
young rivers bathe the margins of mile upon mile of tropical
rain forest, deposit the granitic sand of the Andes on the
Amazonian plains, and wash the pigmented jungle soil down
into the vent of the continental flood, where the waters drain-
ing three million square miles of mountain and plain become
a single stream. Experience provided no background, and only
imagination could depict the complex of tall, close-growing,
perhaps beautiful—sometimes, dangerously beautiful—jungle
trees, interwoven lianas that they support, streamers of lowly,
flowerless plants hanging from their branches, the flourishing
understory of the forests, and, below, the rank growths on the
soil from which these forests spring. Seeing landscapes, vegetations, and peoples, all new to my experience, these tumultuous
waters were to journey through unreality. It was impressive and
even exciting, but also a little confusing.

There was, however, enough unreality in the immediate
foreground to occupy our minds, unreality in those snow-
crested, deep-walled gorges, rich in unaccustomed vegetation,
which the Amazon's beginnings had helped to chisel out between the miles-high ranges. At one time or another we collected along the Urubamba, the Apurimac, the Paucartambo,
the Madre de Dios, and through the country between them
and our Cuzco headquarters. The Prince, Mrs. Mexia, Harvey
and Bob, Florence and I, learned to know some of that extraordinary country more or less well. Even César, who lives and
teaches in Cuzco, saw with us parts of his homeland that were
new to him.

The plant that, above all others, I hoped to find in South
America and have an opportunity to study in its native land
was *Nicotiana tomentosa,* the tree tobacco of Peru. In the first
chapter we met this unusual species growing in the Botanical
Garden, on the day I was introduced to *Nicotiana.* Its remarkable height and bulk, and something exotically lush about its
general appearance, were impressive. From that day forth I
tried unsuccessfully in imagination to see it in its Andean
environment. I could understand how it might be a part of the

vegetation of the Huánuco area, where, on their way to the
jungle, first Mrs. Mexia and, later, Harvey and Bob hunted it
with no success. It was, however, a mystery how this soft-tissued
near tobacco, which blackened and died when a few degrees of
frost descended upon a California garden, could withstand the
rigors of these highlands in the neighborhood of Cuzco, of
which it was reported to be a native. Before we went into them,
all that I knew about these highlands was that the city itself
lay at an altitude of almost twelve thousand feet; and near it
the map showed lofty mountain ranges culminating in twenty
thousand-foot Mt. Salcantay and in other peaks as high or
higher. What was the tender tree tobacco doing in such company? We had been in Cuzco only a day or two before this riddle
was solved.

The Peruvian Government owns a few short railway lines,
and one of them runs from Cuzco into the Grand Canyon of the
Rio Urubamba. On the basis of our official credentials from
Lima the local manager of this government line gave us the
use of an *autocarril* at half the regular fare. Drs. Valcarcel
and Tello, the Peruvian archaeologists, and Bennett Greig, a
member of the British legation in Lima, an enthusiast where
Peruvian antiquities are concerned as well as an expert photographer, had been on our train from Arequipa to Cuzco. The
autocarril, a motor-driven hybrid between a railway car and a
station-wagon, seated ten or a dozen, and so we asked them
to share it with us. They were out for a few days of archaeology
at Ollantaitampu, Pisac, and especially Machu Picchu, and we
were on the trail of *Nicotiana tomentosa.*

The railway climbs northward out of the depression in
which Cuzco lies, skirts the ancient fortress or stadium called
Sacsahuaman, runs across exposed plateaus rimmed on the horizon with a succession of mighty snow-covered peaks, and then
starts downward toward the Urubamba. For a distance the first
descent is on a cliffside shelf, and the autocarril had no more
than reached it when an Indian and his two burros appeared
on the track some distance ahead. There was no room for passing toward the cliff and scarcely space enough on the outer edge,
and so the Indian decided to keep ahead of us. This was a
challenge to our chófer. From the start of the downgrade he

had turned off the gas and was saving his brakes as much as possible by using the compression of the engine. Now, however, it became a question of speed and not of brakes or compression, and certainly not of compassion for the Indian. In a moment or two we were on the heels of the trotting burros and their hurrying master, and our chófer began to enjoy himself immensely. The wiry little animals developed a remarkably fast gait, so fast indeed that soon the Indian gave up and found a spot where we could pass him. Then, without any warning, brakes and compression went on, we nearly broke our necks against the seats in front, and the autocarril almost stopped. The chófer's neck and ears showed embarrassment as we got out on the running board to see what was going on ahead. There, one of the burros was exhibiting strong evidence of irritation and resentment by doing all that his small hind hoofs could do to flatten the front of the autocarril. He would trot a few steps, stop, teeter back and forth for an instant, and then let fly a lightning kick. It was a comical sight, because he never let the car approach near enough so that his kicks could possibly reach it. Finally the chófer stopped the autocarril and the little burro slowly disappeared around the curve, still kicking. He and his mate must have found a place to leave the track, because we saw no more of them. I fear that none of us gave a thought to their owner, who must have lost many hours in searching for what were undoubtedly the most valuable of his possessions.

Extensive panoramas came into view as the track swung out around rocky promontories. To the east one blue range after another rolled higher and higher toward the horizon. To the north and west snow-covered peaks just showed above the eight- to twelve-thousand-foot walls of the Urubamba's deep, narrow gorge. At intervals we could look down into it, and we caught a hint of the amazing zonation of vegetation on its precipitous sides. Even at a distance I could see that, beginning with barren terrain at higher elevations, each thousand-foot decrease in height produced a correspondingly increased covering of green on the mountainsides, until, near and in the bottom of the canyon, the vegetation was luxuriant. The character as well as the amount of the vegetation changed successively with differences in altitude. Thus the river margins were to some extent forested, and within depressions on the more gradually sloping canyon walls trees and large shrubs extended upward for some thousands of feet. Above or on exposed areas where the cliffs rose almost from the water's edge the vegetation was thinner and largely herbaceous.

Once I had seen the depth of the Urubamba Canyon the answer to my question about *Nicotiana tomentosa* and its occurrence in the Cuzco region was forthcoming. However lofty Cuzco and the summits of nearby mountain ranges might be, the headwaters of the Urubamba were running at between seven and eight thousand feet and, a little further downstream, at six thousand feet and below. Within fifteen degrees south of the Equator such altitudes mean heat and moisture and, usually, the jungle. It was obvious, therefore, that somewhere up above the steaming river valley *Nicotiana tomentosa* could readily find congenial conditions of environment. The only point that remained to be determined was in which of the vegetational zones lying in horizontal bands on the steep, sometimes almost vertical, mountainsides would it be found to occur most characteristically. In other words, we still had to find it.

The track soon reached the upper end of the canyon. Thereafter it followed along the river, and sometimes along its very banks in places where the cliffs pushed outward toward the water's edge. In one such spot a section of the almost overhanging canyon wall had slipped, and rocks, brush, and other debris covered the rails. A gang of men was engaged, rather lackadaisically, in clearing the track. While the autocarril waited for them to finish the job, Florence and I climbed around the slide and started down the track to do a bit of collecting. As we walked along I began to look more and more critically at some of the large, treelike shrubs growing on the nearby riverbank. They had an increasingly familiar look, and the next moment I realized that we had found *Nicotiana tomentosa*.

Somehow, I was a little disappointed. Not that the plants were in poor condition, because they proved to be fine, vigorous specimens, many of them in full bloom; not that they were present in limited numbers, because they were abundant; but simply because they had been too easy to find. When, at the

beginning of the autocarril's descent, I saw those tremendous
mountainsides and their vegetation, I had foreseen a long and
laborious search for the tree tobacco, a search that might in-
volve hard climbing and the slow examination of various vegetational zones, even, perhaps, an unrewarded search—and here
were hundreds of tomentosas near the railway track, only waiting to be studied and collected. Nevertheless, it was very satisfying to see these monstrous near tobaccos in their natural surroundings. Their variability in leaf shape, flower form, and
flower color was surprising. At first, it looked as though there
were no two plants anywhere nearly identical, and we settled
down to record the evidence on paper and on film. Florence
took the notebook and wrote down my measurements and comments. I had to shout them to her, because the Urubamba,
beside whose waters we were working, was very noisy. The road
gang returning from their slide clearing must have thought
that they were listening to a family altercation. Before we were
through the autocarril appeared, and aboard it once more we
cast lingering glances back to the little *tomentosa* forest and
hoped it would not be the only one that we would come across
that day. We need not have been fearful on that score; all the
way from the point where we first found it to the Machu Picchu
ridges and below them the landscape never lacked a tree tobacco
or two, rising above the increasingly dense shrub vegetation of
the canyon floor.

All of us in the autocarril hoped to see Machu Picchu
before nightfall. The last station on the railway, some seventy
miles from Cuzco, was still a mile or two above the bridge
across the Urubamba where the trail to Machu Picchu begins.
We hired an automobile and packed ourselves into it for the
short but rough ride down the highway. The railroad is ultimately to be continued to Santa Ana, and will then tap the
valuable agricultural products of the semitropical lowlands in
the lower Urubamba Valley.

Since that day in October, 1935, many tourists have seen
Machu Picchu. I have the following stock question I ask those
of them I chance to meet, "How was the bridge across the
Urubamba?" The answer dates their visit to Peru and for almost
all of them this date is recent, because my question surprises

them. How little these pampered travelers know of the discomforts of that crossing in the good old days of 1935. When,
with faltering steps, we inched across it the bridge consisted of a
series of round poles set lengthwise, with a sagging wire handrail along one side. In some spots the platform was only three
poles wide. Now and then the wire lashings that united the
poles had broken, with the result that a piece of the flooring
was ready to spring up against your face or slap you on the
back. Everywhere the white water of the Urubamba was visible
between the poles, and in some places there were gaps through
which it seemed to reach up, eager to pluck you down into its
depths. Underfoot the manure deposited by many pack trains
was thick and sometimes fresh and slippery. The whole structure swayed violently with the shifting weight of our passage,
and trembled continuously with the pounding of the racing
river against the bridge supports.

I carried the big luncheon hamper and some collecting
paraphernalia. Florence had notebooks, cameras, and raincoats.
We progressed bravely, if not rapidly, up to the point where a
great boulder, near the center of the roaring flood, acted as
midpier for the flimsy bridge. In Cuzco we had been told that
the week before a surveyor, transit on shoulder, had fallen
from the bridge just as he reached this halfway point and had
immediately disappeared in the raging, deep-flowing waters. As
we approached the spot that had proved fatal to the surveyor
it was hard to drag our eyes away from the leaping water below
and from the ripping tide of its flow against the tremendous
boulders downstream. The surface of the river seemed to be so
close and the bridge was so narrow that I felt surrounded by
swiftly flowing water, and found myself beginning to sway and
stumble with giddiness. It occurred to me that a similar vertigo
might have been responsible for the surveyor's fatal misstep.

On the far side of the bridge horses were supposed to be
in readiness to carry us up the two thousand feet of difficult
trail to the ruins of Machu Picchu. No horses were in sight, and
the archaeologists, who proposed to make the climb on foot,
had hurried across the bridge and were out of sight on the
trail above. We therefore had no one to interpret for us with
the group of Indians who were assembling poles and lumber,

presumably and hopefully, for bridge repair. They shook their heads stupidly when we tried to find out where were the horses that we had ordered. The lunch hour had already come and gone, and we decided to satisfy what little the passage of the bridge had left of our appetites.

At this point the valley walls are precipitous and run up a thousand feet or more, almost from the water's edge. The midday sun had been pouring its heat into the narrow gorge, and we began to shed outer garments that early in the day had been all too thin. Finding a log near the margin of a small clearing, which the bridge menders had cut into the rain forest, we made a pretense of eating. The vegetation, climate, and insects reminded us again that seven thousand feet in this part of Peru means something decidedly tropical. Long before we had passed on the large remnant of our luncheon to the Indians by the bridge winged and crawling pests were raising welts on all exposed, and on most unexposed, areas of skin.

We started up the trail and found it hard going in the melting heat, for we were much too heavily burdened with clothing and equipment. The hoofs of horses and burros had loosened the dirt and rubble underfoot, and it was easy to slide backward down, or sideways off, the narrow path. Then the sky became overcast, and we welcomed the consequent decrease in the intensity of the sun's burning rays. Soon, however, rain, which later we came to expect each afternoon in the depths of Andean valleys, began to descend, and immediately the trail turned into slippery mud. The first drizzles rapidly became a heavy shower, and we sought shelter beside the trail in a thicket of large-leaved shrubs. Various kinds of stingers and biters had apparently conceived the same idea. They waited beneath the leaves and welcomed us, some silently, some buzzingly. Months later we were told that a species of poisonous snake frequented precisely the sort of trailside brush into which the rain had driven us.

As we crouched under our imperfect protection from the steady downpour and peered out toward the trail a succession of little boys passed by. Their bare feet made soft, sucking sounds as they dragged them from the mud. Their faces were thin, their clothes ragged and muddy, and their bare legs grue-

Andean snow fields look down on a remnant of Spanish colonial days

In a potato field—three shy maids from Peru with bowler hats

Potatoes of the Andes are smaller but more nutritious than ours

Indians of the Peruvian jungle—arrowheads and bows of palm wood

The massive Inca or pre-Inca stonework of Sacsahuaman has been decorated
with the initials of one of Peru's radical political organizations

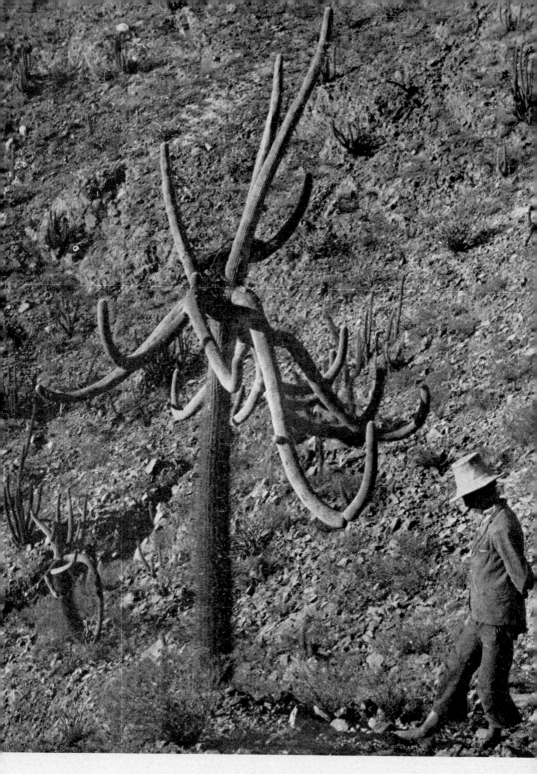

Of all the giant cacti infesting desert foothills or arid alpine plateaus of the west coast, *Browningia candelaris* is the most spectacular

some with fresh, raw sores or the pitted scars of earlier ones. They were a sorry group, and only my restraining hand on Florence's arm relieved us from a parley with them and an effort to bring a smile to their sad faces. I had hardened my heart, because I knew that once involved we would never be able to shake them off. From that time on it rained intermittently, and we made slower and slower progress up the Machu Picchu trail. I went a little in advance and, after seeing at a distance the first of the ruins, decided not to attempt to go further that day.

There have been many descriptions of the City of a Thousand Steps—of its terraces, its aqueducts, its fountains. You read of its mansions and palaces and temples, needing only roofs of thatch to make them what they were many hundreds of years ago, when, as a city of refuge, a retreat of vestal virgins, or what you will, the dwellers in impregnable Machu Picchu looked down two thousand feet to the Urubamba, a thin, white ribbon racing through the bottom of its green-walled gorge. Much has been written of the art of the Inca stonemasons who, without benefit of level, square, plumb bob, or mortar, built the Torreon, that beautiful, curvilinear, fortified tower, or laid those matched and perfectly fitted blocks to make walls and steps and windows, the like of which can be seen nowhere else in the world. Neither the written word nor the sensitized film can, however, do justice to the far-flung panoramas that surround this jungle-bordered city of stone. No other remnant of the pre-Columbian civilizations of the Andes commands wider horizons, such a world of blue-green mountain ranges, mist-hung crags, and white-mantled peaks. Machu Picchu holds a story, hidden perhaps for all time. May it not tell of lofty aspirations symbolized by this noble ruin which, in the days of its vitality, may have been the resort of men who drew inspiration from their safe, calm, lofty abode, far above the routes of war and commerce?

From the mystery of Machu Picchu comes another thought, hearteningly applicable to an interpretation of what lies beyond our current darkened and bloody horizon. It is contained in the following quotation, taken from a newspaper clipping someone gave me:

"The mystery of Machu Picchu grows with each successive

authority who writes of it. One thing, however, is certain. Machu Picchu is a totalitarian ruin. The Inca State was a totalitarian State so absolute that modern creations of similar order are nursery play by comparison. The Inca himself was a dictator so 'total' that Hitler and Mussolini, seen in proper perspective, are but petty martinets. He was judge, emperor, god. He owned every subject and every article produced in his vast empire. He prescribed, through deputies, every detail of life and action for every individual. Freedom was not merely crushed. It was an idea utterly unknown. But Machu Picchu is a ruin, barely to be held, by constant effort, from the fangs of the jungle. I find present-day comfort in this thought. Much as I admire the Incas in many ways, their system obviously was false to the eternal human values. Let other dictators, in the still watches of the night, ponder on the story of Machu Picchu!"

Another mystery has now been added to that of Machu Picchu. South of it, and almost three thousand feet higher on the walls of the Urubamba Canyon, the ruins of two sizable cities have been found. By narrow, paved trails and flights of stone steps built on narrow saddles and across precipitous slopes, these settlements are connected with Machu Picchu. Although, apparently, they do not contain such architectural achievements as it does, much of their stonework is equally good, and their terraced construction, paths and stairways, systems of water supply and drainage correspond to those of Machu Picchu and date both groups of ruins within the same period of Inca culture.

Many collections were made in and about Machu Picchu. Some of the plants we found there suggest that the Incas might have grown them as ornamentals. Certainly there appeared to be an unusually large number of showy species in, or close to, the ruins. For example, a splendid red orchid, a *Maxillaria*, was common in the terraces and on bits of open ground between the buildings. Again, there were handsome species of *Oxalis* and a succulent that looked like *Sedum* growing in crevices of the smooth and close-set walls. Finally, almost in the streets of the ruined city, the Prince found *Calceolaria tomentosa*, the giant slipperwort. We did not come across it elsewhere in the Andes, although it is known from other Andean areas. Probably the presence of so many plants of these and of other fine ornamentals in and around the City of a Thousand Steps was only coincidence, but at the time it made a different impression.

We find that in Berkeley the giant *Calceolaria* from the ancient city, like many other species from the Andes, prefers partial shade, even though in its native habitat it grows up through low brush to luxuriate in full sun. The dry air and generally reduced moisture conditions in California gardens, contrasting with the humidity of their native habitats, is doubtless responsible for the favorable reaction of many sun-loving Andean species to shaded, and therefore moister, situations in their foster home. This Machu Picchu *Calceolaria* is a distinct novelty and has attracted much attention. With us it is a perennial, at least a limited one, and in one year grows to a height of ten to twelve feet. The leaves, often eighteen inches long and almost as wide in the blade, are borne in two's on opposite sides of a thick, woody stem, which they surround with clasping bases that unite to form a cup. The striking, bright-yellow flowers, often as big as small hens' eggs, hang on the periphery of tall pyramidal inflorescences that are produced from the ends of a series of stems. Each spring a ring of new shoots starts from the crown of the previous year's main axis, grows fast, and blooms in May and June (sometimes even earlier), and also later in the year. Altogether, it is an outstanding plant in any company, but is particularly impressive when growing among the many other, relatively pygmy, Calceolarias we brought back from South America.

In 1939, Harvey, Bob, and César spent some time along the Urubamba, saw Machu Picchu, and collected as far as Echarate, well down into the lower, far more tropical, end of the valley. There they saw cultivations of sugar cane, coffee, tea, cacao, oranges, bananas, and other tropical crops. Their collections of native plants from Echarate were surprisingly similar to those that had been made much deeper in the Amazonian tropics. They found that the climate and vegetational contrasts that pass in review as one follows down the river northward are almost beyond belief. A relatively short distance separates the cold heights of Cuzco from the luxuriant tropics of the lower Urubamba Valley. In the hot, moist jungle about Echarate —malaria-ridden and infested with dangerous insects and serpents—the supreme Andean heights are almost overhead, and openings in the forest show a lofty northern horizon rimmed with perpetual snow. Two worlds as different as day is from night, stand side by side and a day's journey apart.

The Incas, from their highland capital and their terraced settlements clinging to the barren walls above the upper reaches of the Amazon's beginnings, looked with longing eyes toward the lushness of the lower valleys. By conquest they attempted to include these semitropics and their dwellers in the new order in the Andes. This proposal was largely unsuccessful. The death-laden darts that the jungle men blew from the dense shelter of the rain forest, and such natural defenses as fevers and poisonous plants and animals which their homeland erected, turned back successive invasions.

The chroniclers referred to the Amazonian tribes as fierce and warlike, but their descendants cannot be so classified. The jungle Indians, who once or twice appeared out of the forest near Echarate, were as subdued as they were filthy and diseased. They bartered bows and arrows for trinkets and were sufficiently uncivilized and unenlightened not to demand a fee when Harvey proposed to photograph them. Their lack of contact with the outside world was also evidenced by inability to speak a word of Spanish, or even Quechua, the lingua franca of the highlands. Therefore the barter that Harvey conducted with them had to be carried on in the primitive language of gesture and grimace.

There is much more to be told concerning our botanizing in the areas where the Amazon begins, and little space in which to tell it. The Prince made a difficult but profitable collecting trip to one of the headwaters of the Madre de Dios. From that inaccessible area he sent back many new or little-known plants and, in particular, a series of previously unknown species of *Fuchsia*. First and last, we discovered at least five new Fuchsias in Peru, and others that had been named and described by earlier plant hunters but that were not in cultivation. We now have a somewhat unique collection of *Fuchsia* species growing in the Botanical Garden. As ornamentals, certain of the new ones are valuable in their own right; others are proving important as parents in hybrids with well-known species. This past year one of the sensations in the local *Fuchsia* world was the appearance of a fine hybrid, one parent of which was a new species of ours.

While we were still in Peru, and more often since our return to California, César collected for us in rarely explored portions of his countryside. Of special importance was the journey that took him over the Cordillera de Carabaya to Limbani, through a remote portion of the Andes of southeastern Peru. Near the headwaters of an affluent of the Madre de Dios, and thus again where the Amazon begins, he discovered a new species of *Nicotiana*. This was a peculiarly important find because, now that we have grown plants from its seed, there is evidence that this new species is of hybrid origin, one parent being a semiarborescent species of *Nicotiana* known to grow in relatively nearby areas in Bolivia, and the other a species whose center of distribution is in the highlands of Peru. The new species has been given the specific name *arentsii* in recognition of the important contributions made by Mr. George Arents to knowledge of the history of tobacco and its culture.

That marvelous country where the Amazon begins will for many years continue to be rich in new plant treasures. They await the explorer who is willing to climb the high passes and botanize the sharply delimited zones of vegetation clothing those precipitous mountainsides that roll down from snow fields and alpine aridity to the jungle-filled river bottoms thousands of feet below.

Chapter VII

INCA TRAILS

WHEN, IN pre-Columbian times, the Incas were establishing their new order in the Andes, the importance of good highways to facilitate troop movements and exchange of merchandise loomed large in their plans of conquest or in their proposals for exploiting a negotiated peace. Many remnants of their highway systems remain, to demonstrate that whatever the new order undertook to accomplish was effectively accomplished. In engineering, as well as in statecraft, it was highly efficient. Stone-paved trails and broader paths once extended along or parallel to the Andean ranges from Quito to Chile, with branches running east and west from the main, north and south, trunk line. In terms of present-day geography, one of the important Inca routes led westward from Cuzco to Abancay, thence over Andean summits to Andahuailas and on to Ayacucho and Huancayo. This highway was old when Pizarro rode along it. In 1935 the Prince traveled over it, from Huancayo to Cuzco; in 1939 Harvey and Bob traversed it, in the opposite direction. The first of these cross-country collecting expeditions was made in the dry season, the second in the wet season.

The Prince was able to go from railhead to Ayacucho by autobus, but from that point onward most of the journey had to be made on horseback or on foot. Four years later Harvey and Bob had to do far less riding and walking. Today the entire route of the old Inca trail has been made passable for automobiles, so that one can drive all the way from Lima, through Huancayo, to Cuzco. This is only one example of the rapidity with which transportation facilities in the Peruvian Andes are being extended and improved. Incidentally, such penetration of the highlands by railroads and highways is immediately followed by an unnatural extension of the distribution of plant species across altitudinal and other natural barriers to equivalent vegetational zones far distant from their original, sometimes restricted, habitats. For example, *Nicotiana glutinosa* was once characteristic only of middle altitudes on the western front

of the outermost Andean ranges. Years ago, with the completion of the railway eastward across the summit, and then southward, the minute seeds of this *Nicotiana* were carried in the
crevices of crates or bales or hand baggage on their way over
the lofty pass and into the temperate climate of Huancayo.
There, the seed fell into congenial soil and proceeded to establish a plant species never before a part of the vegetation of that
portion of Peru. Later, again through man's intervention, the
seeds traveled farther south, to a point where the highway and
its traffic ended at the foot of another Andean range. Within
the last year the summit of this range and the country between
it and Cuzco has become free for the automobile, and *N. glutinosa*, within six months of the completion of the Cuzco highway, has approached almost to the gates of the City of the Sun.
Thus, in a few years the reports of a student of plant distribution in the Andes will be something different from those
brought back by earlier botanists who collected in the same
territories.

For his journey from Ayacucho to Cuzco, the Prince hired
a pack train. He and his native packers camped along the trail,
wherever the collecting was rich. At the start, he made his
own fire and cooked his own food. Soon, however, this proved
to be too much trouble, and he joined the packers around their
fire, and dipped with them into the common pot. Then, after
the meal was over, he brewed himself a cup of tea from his
private stock, drank it out of his own tin cup, and thus maintained a certain aloofness and dignity in the eyes of his attendants. The account of his experiences and adventures during this
overland journey was, unfortunately, lost in the wreck and
burning of a local plane that was carrying the air mail from
the mountains into Lima. His collections, sent parcel post,
reached California in good condition and contained much of
value. Of special importance was a previously unknown species
of *Nicotiana*, one of five new species of this genus we discovered
in Peru. I named it *Nicotiana benavidesii*, in honor of the then
president of the republic.

Material sufficient for many times this chapter might be
culled from the written and verbal accounts of Harvey and
Bob's expedition. As already noted, it followed the same gen-

eral route the Prince had traversed, but in the reverse direction, and at a season less desirable from the point of view of personal comfort, but more desirable as far as the condition of the vege-tation was concerned. February, in the central and southern Peruvian Andes, usually represents the height of the rainy sea-son, and Cuzco had been wet and cold. Their collecting sorties from that city provided them with a foretaste of what the roads might be like on their cross-country jaunt. At the same time the rains had brought more plants into flower in the high plateaus, on the walls of the canyons through which the Amazon's begin-nings flow, and along the banks of these rivers, than either the Prince or Florence and I had seen at other, drier seasons of the year.

The first lap of their journey took them by truck from Cuzco to Abancay. César accompanied them so far. The distance to Abancay was announced by the chófer to be approximately five hours. Thus, if the truck started on schedule at eight o'clock in the morning, they would disembark at Abancay in time for lunch. Actually, they got under way at 9:30, and arrived at 10:30 at night. Having traveled for many months in more or less remote parts of the highlands and lowlands of Peru, Harvey and Bob were not at all surprised at this discrepancy between the announced schedule and the actual time consumed.

The heavily laden truck climbed out of the Cuzco Valley. It followed a cobbled surface laid in Inca days, and had been trod by nothing heavier than the feet of relays of runners bring-ing seaside produce to the tables of the mountain-dwelling Inca nobles, by the light hoofs of llamas, or by the sandals of travelers or of sturdy porters transporting material not trusted on the backs of four-footed beasts of burden. Would that those long-forgotten, Inca road builders might see the permanence of their construction, and its ability to defy the friction of broad truck tires that prove the ruin of more modern highways! At the beginning this ancient roadway ran through high, open, par-tially cultivated terrain that was green with meadows and pepper trees, blue with lupine and *Salvia,* and yellow, in wide swathes or irregular patches, with *Grindelia boliviana* and shrubby growths of *Cassia latopetiolata.*

After crossing the high watershed between the Rios Uru-

bamba and Apurimac the road descended, much too dangerously, toward the valley bottom. The rains appeared to have
done their worst on the modern additions to the ancient roadway, but there was still room for more deterioration, as they discovered when heavy showers overtook them. With the rain came
a dense fog, that made the traversing of slippery shelves, on
steep mountainsides, a precarious undertaking. Two passengers,
in relays, were called upon to walk a few yards ahead of the
truck. It was their duty to take soundings in the deep mud,
look for slips and slides, and act as guides. The road ahead was
totally obscured by the fog, and the chófer charted his course
entirely by what he could see of the backs of his passenger
guides.

Even before they reached the waters of the Apurimac,
foaming and roaring in their deep bed, bad news came to meet
them. A traveler, climbing on foot out of the valley, stopped the
truck and insisted that the road had disappeared on the farther
side of the gorge. Then a group of horsemen appeared. They
advised the chófer to turn back at once, because he would be
unable to go forward more than a mile or two. The story grew
and grew, and finally gave a sum total which suggested that
the road had fallen into the Apurimac over such a long distance
that at least a month would be required to repair it. The chófer,
however, decided to proceed, but in a disconsolate frame of
mind. Some distance farther on, and now below the fog, they
pulled up behind another truck that had been halted by a
mountain of dirt, gravel, and boulders, under which the road
had completely disappeared. At this point the narrative is continued by Harvey:

"The passengers from the first-arrived truck were standing
around, scratching their heads, and gesticulating. The passengers on the newly arrived truck dismounted, scratched their
heads, and gesticulated some more. One courageous soul cautiously made his way over the slide and reported that another
truck was approaching from the opposite direction. Eventually,
a heterogeneous crowd was assembled, distinctly jovial and even
in festive mood. Everybody talked, everybody had a plan. Some
wanted to turn back at once, before other slides should block
all escape. Some wanted to pitch in and begin digging out—

that is, they hoped others would feel constrained to do so. Some of the more highly geared thinkers conceived the notion of having the passengers cross the slide on foot, trade trucks, and each group proceed in its original and proper direction. The whole thing was quite democratic, and worked much as does any democracy in a crisis.

"There was a policeman in one of the parties. He had a beautiful uniform, and some gold braid. More than that, he was a smart man. He looked the situation over and recognized three elements: (1) a large group of people imbued with a definite objective; (2) an obstacle blocking realization of that objective; (3) sufficient motivation, if organized and directed, to make possible expenditure of considerable energy toward removing the obstacle. Thereupon, he threw back his cape, stuck out his jaw, and barked out dictatorial decrees. All shovels were at once requisitioned. Axes were set to fashioning pikes and poles for digging gravel and rolling boulders. The passengers were organized into shifts. You should have seen the dirt move. From our side of the slide, taunts were shouted to the passengers on the farther side, with the result that gravel and boulders were soon flying from all directions. Great shouts rang down the valley of the Apurimac each time a large mass of rock was pried loose and started on its thunderous race down the steep slope."

Harvey and Bob took off their coats and fell to work. However, it soon appeared that they were actually impeding progress, because so many of the peons immediately stopped work to enjoy the strange sight of gentlemen, foreign gentlemen at that, engaged in hard labor. Then, in the hope of accelerating operations, Harvey set up a motion-picture camera and made as if to record the proceedings. Now, one might imagine that nobody would care to be recorded for the screen gracefully leaning on a shovel while others were at work, but so it was. Half the slide clearers immediately struck statuesque poses, of the tintype variety, nor could they be persuaded that Harvey wanted motion, and lots of it. Since the norteamericanos found nothing useful to do at the scene of operations, they decided to accomplish something botanical, and for two hours worked back and forth on the mountainsides beyond the slide and along the

banks of the river. There, they braved the first of many subsequent onslaughts of swarms of gnats or midges that infest the
length and breadth of the Apurimac Valley. The bite of these
insects raises a droplet of blood under the skin, and after a
bout with them their adversaries look like candidates for the
pesthouse. Liberal and continuous applications of citronella oil
to exposed parts is somewhat effective in discouraging the
minute tormentors.

After this first and most protracted halt there were other
stops for lesser road repairs. These frequent stoppages began
to irk most of the passengers. The botanists, however, were well
pleased because each halt gave opportunity for samplings of
the roadside vegetation. Gradually, the truck climbed out of
the valley of the Apurimac. After reaching a considerable elevation the road flattened out, and they wallowed across high,
treeless puna, where cold, drizzling rain fell at frequent intervals. This extensive alpine plateau ended abruptly where they
began the descent into the Limatambo Valley. They looked
down, deep in this valley, to the town of the same name, cradled
between wall-like mountainsides. The air distance seemed inconsiderable, but when they saw the many loops, curves, and
switchbacks by which their road wove its way downward, it was
no surprise to find that all of twenty-five miles separated them
from Limatambo.

Just as they began the descent darkness, with accompanying mists and fog, enveloped them. Soon the vapors became so
dense that the headlights of the truck threw back blinding light
into the chófer's eyes. There was nothing to do but turn off
the headlights. Thereafter the driver relied upon a sixth sense
and the prayers that he continually directed toward the image
of Saint Christopher, which looked down upon him from above
the windshield. For hours they slipped and slithered down to
Limatambo, and then on toward Abancay. When, at last, and
completely spent with the nervous strain of eleven hours of
rough and harrowing journey, they entered its plaza, all Abancay, except its dogs, was asleep.

The city lay in the cultivated valley of the Marino River,
a small stream that flowed past its outskirts and, some miles
below, emptied into the larger Pachachaca. The hills above

were green with grass and shrubs, and this green extended up
the quebradas and back into the mountains, where forests filled
the higher valleys. The climate was agreeable enough, with
sunny days and rainy nights, on some of which the rain was
torrential. Malaria was unknown, and there were no mosquitoes
nor any of the gnats that had made collecting near the Apurimac so disagreeable. When, however, they worked down into
the valley of the Pachachaca, the little demons appeared again
in full force.

Near the road between Abancay and the bridge over the
Pachachaca the Prince had discovered *Nicotiana benavidesii*.
This new species was distinctly limited in its distribution, for
it occurred only in the "type locality" and westward in the
valley of the Apurimac. It is a question why it does not grow
in the valley of the Marino, and upstream along the Pachachaca. Along the road they found masses of a giant *Equisetum*,
the horsetail or scouring rush. Its tall, weak, green, canelike
stalks reached twenty feet in height and leaned against small
trees or upon one another. It was, thus, in decided contrast to
the relatively diminutive species, so common in temperate climates and, actually, represents the largest of the horsetails.
It has a wide distribution from Central America southward.

Over the old stone walls about Abancay the nasturtium
(*Tropaeolum majus*) was particularly at home, although its
distribution is general in the Peruvian Andes. So charming
and unique a plant must have made a strong appeal to the eyes
of the early padres. Over two hundred and fifty years ago they
sent its seeds to Europe, whence it spread widely and was
favorably received wherever ornamentals grew. Less popular is
a sister species, *Tropaeolum peregrinum*, sometimes called the
canary bird flower. A common climber in the lower slopes of
the Andes on the Amazonian side, its dainty yellow blossoms,
spurred with green hooks, and its small, lobed leaves, add a
touch of grace and charm to the roadside vegetation.

Growing through all the valleys near Abancay the pepper
trees were resplendent in an abundant crop of red berries. The
berries were sold in the marketplace, not for decoration, as with
us, but rather for the making of a particular variety of native
beer, called *chicha de molle*. The Andean Indian does not limit

himself to maize as a source of chicha. As we have seen, he uses wheat and bananas as a base for fermentation, and even peanuts are often made into a milky chicha, said to be very nourishing. In the Abancay market the red seeds of *Bixa orellana* were a familiar commodity. As a source of dye for foods, particularly rice, the seeds of this tree are popular in many parts of Latin America. The dye is also used to color butter or oleomargarine, and the seeds have been shipped to the United States and to Europe for this purpose, as well as for dyeing confections and even cloth. The tree itself is attractive, particularly when its branches are hung with the orange-colored seed pods, reflexed to expose the red seeds within.

Harvey, Bob, and César made Abancay their headquarters for a series of collecting trips into a variety of different climates and vegetational zones that could be explored in a day's journey from the city. After each excursion there were pressed plants to be dried, and first one, and then another, stayed in the hotel to accomplish this monotonous but essential task. In the patio the proprietor and staff were engaged in bottling pop, and also something labeled mineral water; and Bob appears to have spent most of his time, between changes of plant driers, in watching the inefficient, and far from hygienic, operations of the bottling plant. Since in South America the popularity of nonalcoholic beverages is in proportion to the extent to which they have been carbonated, the operators of the local pop-works made their bottles withstand maximum pressures. They either had no gauge, or it was not in working condition, because general experience alone was relied upon to determine when the gas should be turned off. With such a system it was inevitable that, now and then, a bottle would blow up, scattering fluid and glass in all directions. Each of these explosions produced the greatest excitement; people yelled, darted about, shook fists in one another's faces; and the proprietor would always come running out to harangue his employees and threaten them with dire punishment if further explosions were permitted to occur. In due time, however, another bottle was sure to become too heavily pressured, and then the cheerful little drama was once more unfolded before Bob's eyes, to his great enjoyment.

In the mountains some ten miles north of Abancay, and at

an altitude of 15,000 feet, lies a glacier that is responsible for the presence of two nearby alpine lakes. After a stiff climb the three of them collected in the forest that filled the large que-brada extending southward from this glacier. Near the snow and ice the trees gave way to cold, desolate puna. Of special interest in the forest was the presence of *Podocarpus glomeratus*. Southward from Central America this genus takes the place of the pines, firs, and hemlocks of the northern hemisphere, and this substitution constitutes the most striking difference between the South American mountain forests and those of the north. *Podocarpus* is a relative of our conifers, and is often known as *pina,* although near Abancay the common name is *intimpa.* The leaves are not needlelike but rigid and thickened, and measure about a quarter of an inch in width. This species sup-plied most of the lumber and cabinet wood for Abancay and vicinity. The logs were dragged by horses down the long trail to primitive mills in the city. The supply was rapidly becoming depleted, and it was hard to find any straight or sizable speci-mens of *Podocarpus* in the glacier forest.

The vegetation showed that the forest climate was moist the year round, because such epiphytes as orchids, peperomias, bromeliads, leafy liverworts, and mosses were present in quantity and in considerable variety. Among plants of other types in bloom the yellow of a large-flowered *Calceolaria* supplemented the red of *Fuchsia boliviana* in adding a warm, gay note to the green of the forest. Here and there they saw an odd-looking plant with opposite leaves that made acute angles with the square green stem. It proved to be a *Sideroxylon,* and bears the specific name *herrerae* in honor of Dr. Fortuno Herrera, long the botanist of the University of Cuzco and now director of one of Lima's fine museums.

By contrast with the cool, wet, *Podocarpus* forest they found semitropical vegetation in a valley west of Abancay. Running north and south it was narrow and deep, and received full sun at midday. Its walls were stony, with loose gravelly soils. The dominant species was the Bombax tree, which grew in thin, parklike stands. Along washed-out gulleys they saw the large, tuberous storage roots of *Bombax,* dark-colored on the outside and of the consistency and color of a potato within.

Scattered among the *Bombax* were pepper trees, a shrubby
Ipomoea, and thickets, as well as solitary plants, of *tuna*
(*Opuntia*) some of which attained a height of fifteen feet.
The Abancay Indians gather tuna, or prickly pear, fruits in
large quantities, both for home consumption and to sell in the
market place. Travelers up and down the hot valley depend
upon these fleshy fruits to allay their thirst. *Jatropha,* also, was
there in quantity, and *Dalechampia,* with its lurid bracts,
climbed over the Opuntias and Bombax trees.

   Where alluvium had accumulated in the valley or in its
tributaries, there were crops of sugar cane, cotton, maize, beans,
and potatoes. The introduced castor bean had taken almost
complete possession of certain areas. Fields of sugar cane were
particularly common, and their product was accommodated in
a number of sugar mills, most of them, actually, rum mills.
The agremone poppy, always a striking plant with its silver
foliage and yellow flowers, grew happily on the margins of cultivations. From Mexico to Chile only one other tropical American weed is more ubiquitous, and that is the milkweed, *As-
clepias curassavica,* sometimes called blood flower.

   After a botanically profitable sojourn in the Abancay area,
the journey was resumed. Their route from Cuzco to Huancayo
is full of ups and downs. There are four major downs: into the
valleys of the Apurimac, Pachachaca, Pampas, and Mantaro.
In each case the descent carried them to altitudes of approximately 6,000 feet. Thence, they climbed to puna terrain that
lay at about 12,000 feet. Down from that high, steppe type of
grassland, where shepherds, mottled dark-purple by the biting
cold of the wind and rain, tend their tiny fields of potatoes and
herd their sheep or llamas, through shrubland, into brushland,
into cultivated valleys, and then up through the reverse of this
series of vegetational zones—this was the story all the way from
their starting point to their destination.

   The first stop west of Abancay was made in a shivering,
unenterprising Indian town. To compensate a little for the
dreary aspect of their community, and demonstrating a latent
instinct for the beautiful, some of the inhabitants had planted
the passion vine of the region around their habitations. Its
flowers had dark-purple corollas, shaped like teacups, with light-

colored stamens. This charming climber had been chosen from among a considerable repertoire of ornamentals that nature presented along the trail: blood-red *Bomarea, Vallea,* bluish lavender *Eupatorium, Dalechampia,* blue *Salvia, Lippia, Buddeia, Escallonia,* and many others.

After more puna travel the road dropped down into the valley of a smaller river, the Pincos. At the Hacienda Pincos, a sugar plantation on the river, Harvey and Bob enjoyed a delightful interlude in their up-and-down journey across the Andes. The owner was in Europe, and had left the establishment in charge of Heinrich Lühr. Of him they inquired about horses for Andahuailas, the next leg of their journey. Heinrich and Frieda not only agreed to provide them with horses, but insisted that they put up at the hacienda for as long as they could stay. This invitation was gratefully accepted, not only because the clean, modern ranch house, and what they suspected would be most excellent provender, was a lure, but also because the first of the days set aside for the national carnival had arrived, and during those days travel, in the highlands at least, is difficult and unpleasant.

At the hacienda *carnivales* was being vigorously celebrated by most of the eighty laborers. They knocked off work and enjoyed themselves by throwing flour and red paint at one another, dousing everyone with water, playing their flutes and snare drums, dancing in staggering fashion, and consuming all available alcohol. In general, it was for them a designated period of irresponsible licentiousness.

The hacienda lay low enough in the valley of the Pincos so that groves of oranges and large patches of sugar cane grew successfully. Below, the river dropped rapidly through increasingly semitropical countryside and finally became a series of falls and cataracts that carried its waters into the true Amazonian jungle. The entire sugar-cane crop was devoted to the manufacture of aguardiente. Liquor merchants came from great distances and carried away their fluid purchases on pack animals. Sometimes the precious gut-rot was poured into large goatskin flasks. They were secured one on each side of a horse, whereupon he looked as though possessed of three bodies, instead of one. The skins were reversed, so that the hairy side

Life in the Andes has its ups and downs, its sunshine and shadows

Peruvian Indian women, babies on their backs, leading the family llama

Sugar cane goes to the gin mill and returns as a jug of aguardiente

High Andean farms often possess only oxen and primitive wooden plows

Young scholars returning from church to the Colégio de Santa Ana, Cuzco

The Quechua Indian rarely smiles except at a fiesta. Pisac, near Cuzco

Corner of an ancient lane in Cuzco with tumble-down Spanish colonial balconies used only for exhibiting the family fighting cock was bathed by the aguardiente. Under such conditions almost any other alcoholic beverage would lose caste and acquire a doubtful flavor. However, aguardiente, that powerful distillate of alcohol and fusel oil, is proof against even the stench of goat; or perhaps the fact that, once past the lips, it rapidly destroys all the senses, including taste and smell, may explain a lack of prejudice against goatskin bottles.

The peons who worked in the cane fields and operated the mill at the hacienda receive a *copita*—in this case, a cup fashioned from the internode of a bamboo stem and holding about three ounces—of the crude, fiery beverage before going to work in the morning, and again at noon. To obtain this precious copita, they lined up much as an army lines up for inspection. This arrangement was designed to eliminate, or at least discourage, repeaters. The Peruvian Government levies a heavy tax on aguardiente and keeps an active and efficient force of inspectors in the cane-growing regions to catch contraband liquor. Selling contraband is dangerous business, because an entire mill may be closed for six months or a year upon conviction of avoiding payment of the tax.

When the days of carnivales were over, Heinrich provided good horses and a trusted peon guide for the trail to Andahuailas, and Frieda put up such elaborate lunches that Harvey and Bob forgot, for another day, that they were supposed to be on slim, Andean rations. The path from the hacienda climbed for a mile or two before it joined the main, broad trail that followed the ancient Inca highway. At the beginning they passed through shrublands but, in two hours, came out on the rough grasses of the puna. Thence, westward to Andahuailas and at lower altitudes, they crossed grazing lands that stretched far away over rounded hilltops. This segment of their expedition was memorable among all their wanderings in Peru, because the trip was made in two hours less than schedule time.

Andahuailas was set in the picturesque valley of the Rio Chimbau. Old groves of *Eucalyptus* added variety to vistas up and down the valley floor. Nearby was the village of Palavara, noteworthy because of the abundance of its fruit-laden peach trees and the elaborate, sheet-metal crosses placed in the middle of the gable of each of its houses. Every citizen of Palavara tried

to outdo his neighbors in the amount of detail he was able to
include in his cross. Some, not content with one, had put up two
or three crosses. All the peaches seemed to be of one variety,
clingstones, not very large, yellowish of skin, and of good flavor.
They were eaten raw when ripe, or cooked green, in sugar, to
be served as a dulce, or dessert.

When Harvey and Bob rode into it, on the day after the
official close of carnivales, Andahuailas had a terrific headache.
There was still a good deal of shaky, stumbling drunkenness,
some sorry-looking hangovers, and a lot of tomfoolery by the
younger set who were reluctant to call quits. They threw *bom-
bas* of thin rubber, filled with water, and shook flour from per-
forated tin cans on one another, while rouge was smeared pro-
miscuously. Some of them had hair thoroughly gummed up
with dough, from the flour-water mixture. Bob barely escaped
a shower bath when he was caught in the cross fire between a
bevy of young women on a balcony throwing basins of water at
ardent swains across the street and receiving rubber water-
bombs in return.

In Andahuailas a beautiful Spanish colonial bridge crosses
the river, like a jewel dropped beside the architectural crudities
of an Andean town. Over this bridge all traffic to and from the
south must pass. The botánicos often stopped to watch a cross
section of Andean life flowing over it—Indian women in their
bright, ragged costumes, most of them with a baby between
their shawl-covered shoulder blades (and another on the way),
and men bearing immense bundles of grass, alfalfa, sticks, or
almost any imaginable burden. One carried a half-grown sheep
that poked its head contentedly out of a fold of his owner's
poncho and watched the passing scene. Every so often he looked
down, with hauteur, upon other sheep and goats and pigs that
were being driven along beneath him.

Pig women were abundant in the street, and this had also
been true in Abancay. Leading a pig they strolled up and down,
perpetually. Where they were going, or whence they came, was
always a mystery. Harvey appears to have taken a particular
dislike to the pigs, over which he stumbled and in whose leading ropes he became entangled; and his diary contains the per-
tinent query, "Why the hell couldn't the pig stay happily at

home, while the lady of the house goes on her aimless, witless, sight-seeing tour?"

Pigsty and kitchen were synonymous in many of the homes. When a pig is fat enough to butcher, there is no looking forward to hams, bacon, sausages, or fresh loin of pork. Rather, the animal is killed and then a flock of neighbors, women and children, roll it around in the mud and scrape away at it, in an effort to eliminate some of the bristles. Thereafter it is hacked into bits and jammed into a big kettle, under which all day a fire is coaxed to burn with odds and ends of sticks and twigs carried in from hedgerows or from the mountainside. In the evening the lard is poured into five-gallon gasoline cans, to be sold, or exchanged either for something which the family needs or, usually, for alcohol. The meat, fat and lean, is dispensed among the neighbors and eaten at once, or on the next day. Neighbors who come with their plates for a load of *chicharrón* must also expect to give back a plate of the same when they kill their pig. According to such a scheme for disposing of fresh meat no refrigeration is necessary. Chicharrón tastes pretty good, if you are lucky enough to snatch a piece of lean meat.

The longest bit of their Andean journey took them northwestward, from Andahuailas to Chincheros, and during it they were in the saddle for twelve hours. Fortunately the hired horses were good ones, because most of the trail was so deep in mud that at times they were forced to leave the beaten track and ride over the puna grasslands. On sloping ground these high meadows were soggy and treacherously slippery, especially for unshod horses. Harvey's horse had developed a unique mode of descending the slick, grassy hillsides. He would pick his way carefully and surely with his forefeet, bring his hind feet well forward, ski down a bit and then dig in with all four feet to slow down his forward progress. Bob's diary describes what he calls "the skiing gait" of Harvey's horse, and the accumulating consternation which its rider displayed as his steed periodically fell away at the rear and then came up again with a jerk.

That day they rode through a lot of high country. In some of it huge erratic boulders, often as big as houses, were crazily strewn on level stretches, or hung precariously on the slopes. This boulder land had a bad reputation. Brigands were said to frequent it and levy toll on unprotected wayfarers who, after being stripped of their possessions, were murdered and the corpses hidden. Their two guides were constantly on the alert, and insisted on keeping the pack animals close to the saddle horses. However, nothing more disagreeable occurred during their passage of the land of boulders and brigands than the necessity of traversing many miles of uniformly wet, desolate, windy, and vegetationless plateau.

Toward the end of the day, descending from the high puna toward Chincheros, they looked down upon the largest plantings of maize in Peru. It is said that the name Chincheros derives from "chicha," by what rule or corruption of Quechua grammar no one seems to know. Actually that region has long been famous for its extra-good chicha. Near the town the hedgerows were ornate with the national flower of the republic, *Cantua buxifolia,* sometimes called the magic tree of Peru. A great many years ago it was introduced into European and other gardens, and was once a favorite among shrubby ornamentals in places where it could be successfully grown. We brought home selections of what appeared to be unusually good varieties of this *Cantua,* as well as of other species not so well known horticulturally.

The town proved to be a peaceful, friendly place, and might have been restful, had it not been for the extraordinarily large, and vocal, dog population. Droves of dogs greeted the horsemen when they first arrived. Immediately a series of vicious dog fights was staged in the plaza, perhaps to express the excitement that pervaded the community upon the arrival of so many visitors. The botánicos were too tired after their grueling day in the saddle to be awakened by anything short of an earthquake or a bombardment. On subsequent nights, however, their sleep was continually disturbed by community baying and howling, and Bob spent many minutes each morning in retrieving the shoes and plant driers with which he had sought to drive the dogs away from the corner of the hotel in which he and Harvey had been trying to sleep. Perhaps the large dog population was responsible for the excessive flea population. In this connection Harvey's diary contains his oft-repeated conclusion that, where fleas are concerned, it is their traveling expenses and not their board bill that most annoys the victim.

After exhausting such collecting as the Chincheros neighborhood provided they started on again. The trail made a quick descent to the Rio Pampas, and then took them past the Hacienda Pajanol, famous for its orange groves. At the end of a short ride, beyond the hacienda, they met the rapidly extending automobile highway, and exchanged horses for a truck. In it they were transported to a point where a car could be hired. After an all-night ride they entered the historic city of Ayacucho along with the first rays of the morning sun.

By automobile and train, with various stops for botanizing, they finally reached Huancayo, their destination. During this last lap they did their most important, or at least most exciting, collecting in the alpine valleys of Yauli, about an hour by train from Huancavelica. Everything was fresh and green, and most of the vegetation was at the height of its spring blooming. The natural flower gardens spread before them were more extensive and attractive than any they saw during their many months of botanizing from coast to cordillera in Peru. Here were fields of *Cosmos, Siphocampylos, Zinnia, Helianthus, Calceolaria, Mutisia,* and *Bidens,* to mention only the more abundant genera that clothed the mountainsides with a variegated mantle. Their presses were soon filled to overflowing, which meant that most of their days in Huancayo were devoted to plant drying.

Harvey and Bob had left Cuzco on February 8 and arrived in Huancayo on March 13. During those weeks they made one of the most extensive surveys of the character and distribution of Andean plants that has ever been attempted in the areas they explored. Although each night they had a roof, of sorts, over their heads, and even though they were transported by horse, or in wheeled conveyances, most of the miles they covered, there were many things that were fatiguing, disagreeable, uncomfortable, and even painful. On the other hand, there was much that was pleasant, a little that was comic, a great deal that would be a reward for any botanist, and, daily, an intimate contact with all the varied aspects of life in little-known corners of the Peruvian Andes. They will not soon forget their journey along a section of the old Inca highway.

Chapter VIII

DRIER THAN THE SAHARA

To CARL and John had been assigned an eighteen hundred mile journey southward along the coasts of Peru and Chile. First they were to collect in what I hoped would prove to be verdant lomas in southern Peru, and then to follow the spring flowering as it advanced southward down the Chilean coastal strip. By contrast with an assignment to the highlands this perhaps was not to be an adventurous journey. On the other hand, it should be full of botanical and human interest. In my behalf they would be tracing the southern extension of the Peruvian Nicotianas concerning whose distribution not much was known. In Chile they would come across other *Nicotiana* species and map their distribution southward. They would see the vast desert of Atacama and the living things, both vegetable and animal, which succeed in existing on its western margin. Below Atacama the vegetation would increase in amount and variety and culminate in the Vale of Paradise at the height of its spring blooming. They would travel by ship, by train, in automobiles, on horseback, and perhaps by airplane.

The coast of southern Peru can be even more barren and desolate than the northern one. From the port side of the coastwise Chilean steamer *Mopocho* Carl and John watched the lifeless desert hills during those first days of their journey from Lima south. They strained their eyes to catch a hint of the green film on the surfaces of the headlands and low mountains, that green film indicating the ephemeral, fog-engendered vegetation which should be waiting for them. The fog was there, so much of it that sometimes the coastal hilltops were encased in a shining gray mantle. More often it was broken into ranks of little clouds or spun out into tendrils that floated light and high over the ridges. But the green film was never there. As mile after mile of coast line passed in review they saw only the reds, the browns, the yellows of ridged outcroppings of barren rock and desert sand glowing against the clear blue sky.

The *Mopocho* swung in to the insignificant coastal towns wherever freight or passengers were to come aboard or go ashore. All the ports were open roadsteads where big, double-bowed lighters transported the freight, and fast launches the passengers from anchored ship to shore and vice versa. In these anchorages the long Pacific rollers, which were almost imperceptible when the steamer was under way, joined a heavy ground swell, and the *Mopocho* rose and fell, and lay heavily to one side and then to the other in regular but disquieting sequences. From the port of Tamba de Mora five young señoritas appeared alongside in a small launch crowded with their baggage. A bed, two trunks, a dozen boxes of assorted sizes and shapes, and a crate from which peered two bedraggled Dalmatians were hoisted aboard, and then the señoritas followed. They stood together on the deck near the head of the ladder that they had just ascended and chatted in the noisy, voluble way young people, and especially Latin-American ones, are noted for when they are on display. As the "all ashore" gong began to sound it appeared that only two were passengers and the other three were going back in the waiting launch when the last farewells had been said. Unfortunately the ground swells had increased in power and depth since the señoritas came aboard, and now the launch was bobbing up and down alarmingly and the bottom steps of the ship's ladder were alternately under water or comparatively dry. Accurately selecting the proper moment the first señorita dashed down the ladder and jumped into the arms of the launch's crew. The second was not so clever. She hesitated for an instant at the halfway mark and by the time the bottom of the ladder was reached the upward surge covered its lower steps with a flood of green water. Wet to the knees and badly frightened she managed, however, to step on the gunwale of the launch on its next downward trip and was pulled aboard. The third señorita proposed to be quite dignified. She refused to hurry down the ladder and waved away the helpful hands that were outstretched as she approached the fateful lower steps. All went well until on the very last step her high heels betrayed her and with a loud shriek she stumbled and then fell into those waiting arms which she had spurned.

Nothing intrigues the passengers on west coast South Amer-

ican voyages so thoroughly as these passages up and down the
ship's ladder by the unfortunates who have no choice but to
leave or come aboard that way. Ultimately the day arrives when
you too must go ashore. All your erstwhile friends and companions are leaning over the rail, heads of cooks and waiters
pop out of portholes, even the steerage passengers crowd as
close as possible to the scene of operations. You look upward
from the first steps of the ladder at the row of faces, and in the
eyes of all you catch nothing but an ill-concealed gleam of anticipation. With shame you recollect how yesterday you, too,
were a member of that pitiless throng and, with a wide-mouthed
grin, watched the unhappy antics of those in whose shoes you
now are standing. You yelled sham encouragements, you roared
with laughter when faulty calculation was followed by more or
less of a wetting, you embroidered accounts of what you had
seen on ships' ladders during previous voyages. All these shame-
ful pictures float before your eyes as, at the crucial moment, the
hungry sea rises up to engulf you. It rarely does, however.

Their tickets on the *Mopocho* read to the port of Lomas,
and, although the collecting had looked most unpromising all
along the coast, Carl and John decided to go ashore. There was
at least a chance that a nearer view of the coastal strip would
disclose some vegetation that could not be seen from the sea.
When they finally landed the village of Lomas proved to be
typical of the many desert communities they were destined to
see during the following weeks. The low houses, built of adobe
or wood, were flush with the cobbled sidewalks. The streets
were deep with sand and rutted by the passage of heavy trucks,
and everywhere were the small, neat hoofprints of pack burros.

The low hills that backed the village proved to be absolutely bare of vegetation, nor was there evidence that plants
had ever grown upon them. Behind the outmost ridges they saw
only a barren stony plain, infinitely arid. It was obvious that the
neighborhood of Lomas was going to do nothing for them and
that they might as well hunt transportation to the south, toward
what ought to be more fertile terrain.

After a while they found a truck about to get under way
for Yauca, a coastal town some twenty-five miles in the proper
direction. The cab of the truck was full up with two old ladies

and the chófer. The body of the truck seemed rather well filled also. There were household goods, produce, and general merchandise, with a top dressing of bunches of bananas. But, since two passengers had already located themselves on top of the load and since the truck driver was willing, Carl and John climbed up among the bananas.

The chófer shouted, the passengers replied, and in grinding low gear the truck began to churn the sandy streets of Lomas. They ended abruptly in a steep, gravelly bank up which the heavily laden vehicle pitched and rocked. The bananas skidded about and the passengers settled themselves deeper into the particular depression each had selected. The steep pitch ended in the ancient uplifted beach. Ahead there was not the slightest semblance of a road, nothing but an incredible jumble of large rock masses, flattened sand dunes, and big and little boulders. Every truck that passed that way must have picked out its own special route because double ruts led in all directions. On every hand was evidence of the severest kind of wind erosion, and none that rain had ever fallen. Wherever there was a comparatively level stretch all fine earth material had been swept with the wind's gigantic broom into dunes and piles, which lay against the low hills and spilled down into the narrow quebradas. Under its high, gray, fog canopy the wide expanse of rough desert was a scene of gloomy grandeur.

On the poor excuse for a road it was a long twenty-five miles from Lomas to Yauca. Except at one spot they were lifeless. In the bottom of one wide, sandy quebrada the runoff or seepage from the fog-covered hilltops nearer the sea supported a thin growth of stunted trees and scraggly underbrush. In the scant protection of this wind-blown grove a bit of a house had been built, and a family lived by selling from a pitifully meager stock those supplies of food and drink that travelers in the wasteland might require. The road down into this inhabited quebrada was so nearly vertical that the truck with set brakes slipped and skidded over the loose, sand and gravel surface. After a few miles the landscape changed. Stiff sandstone cliffs replaced the rounded contours of low hills and gave the scene more character. High conical piles of partially decomposed pinkish granite lent some color to the distant view.

Yauca proved to be a three-streeted village. Chinese owned the one modest hotel, an old, one-story, sometime whitewashed adobe. The roof was made of bamboo shoots covered with laced matting, for in this rainless land protection from the sun alone was required. The entrance opened directly on a narrow hall with the doors of the two guest rooms at its upper end and a combination bar, dining room, and store at its extremity. Beyond was the kitchen with its characteristic adobe fireplace.

Beside the village they found a green oasis where a small stream issued from the coastal hills to irrigate fields of alfalfa, truck crops, and small orchards. The sight of vegetation was a welcome one to the two botánicos, and along the margins of the cultivated areas and on the hillside behind them they hoped for native plants to collect. They were disappointed. Just as near Lomas, so here there was nothing, not even vestiges of vegetation of former years. In the violent overlighting of the clear desert afternoon the Yauca hills were stark and harsh, and even the lengthening shadows and softer light tones of early evening did little to dissemble the crudity of their outlines.

The next morning Carl and John decided to push on south again, to Chala. Their arrival in Yauca had provided a much-needed source of gossip and thus had been well advertised. Local owners of automobiles were waiting for the *yanquis*. They must have held a meeting and agreed upon a price for the trip to Chala, a price just short of outrageous. Each chófer when approached refused to bargain. Profanity and the stamping of feet produced only a grin and the statement, "That is the price, señores." There was nothing to do but pick the car with the best-looking tires and the driver who looked most intelligent. Duffel bags, plant presses, and fiber cases went into the back seat. A small ragged boy, out for a ride, perched himself on top of the luggage and the two still embittered botanists climbed in beside the driver.

The road ran through the village toward the sea and then to the left up onto a bench that sloped gradually down to the beach. By contrast with the roads they had traveled for two days this one was remarkably good. Indeed, it was so good that the paying passengers began again to complain about the fare. They called attention to the fact that if this were a hard and difficult

road there might be some excuse for charging such an exor-
bitant sum, whereas actually it was almost a highway. The
chófer looked at the protestants, smiled pityingly, held up a
graceful hand, and said, "Paciencia, señores, paciencia."

For a mile or two the road traveled parallel to the beach
which was three hundred yards away and one hundred feet below. The road surface was good enough to justify thirty-five
miles or a little more, but to a Peruvian chófer it was a challenge to step on the gas, and soon the car was pitching and
swaying at fifty. Without warning and as though the car had
gone out of control they curved sharply to the right and
careened away on a mad dash toward the sea. The urchin in
the back seat screamed with excitement, the chófer smiled happily, the botanists grimly watched their end approaching. The
car seemed to sail over the slanting surface of the drifted sand
and miraculously missed outcrops of rock and hummocks built
up around both them and the occasional bits of strand vegetation. Finally they glided past the last obstruction and found the
hard, packed sand of the seashore.

The beach stretched ahead for three miles in a wide cres-
cent and ended abruptly in massive cliffs on which the surf
broke high and white. The driver stepped up the speed and
swung his car back and forth to follow the water's edge where
the surface was most firm. The tide was coming in fast and apparently he was gambling on reaching the end of the beach before the waves drove him back into the soft sand where the car
would soon be trapped. Perhaps the chófer had a little private
bet with himself on the outcome. Anyway he won, but not until
he took another long chance by turning sharp left at the edge
of the cliff and putting the car at top speed up an almost vertical goat path. Pulling with every ounce of its power the poor
car, bouncing and jolting, struggled on and finally flattened
out on the road that they originally had been following. There
seemed to be no justification for the interlude along the waves,
but Carl and John were so relieved to have it over that they
did not argue the point with the chófer.

The almost level inland plain across which they now ran
was plantless, but in the distance there were low mountains
encouragingly green. The road grew worse and worse as it

turned again toward the sea. It crossed many small, deep quebradas where the car plunged down one side and up the other
in alarming fashion. As they rounded a sharp turn a deep gorge
lay ahead. In it and on its sides hundreds of laborers were at
work on a cut and fill which was to span the deep depression.
The car was stopped for a few minutes to allow the botánicos to
watch the work. The chófer explained that this was a segment of
Peru's contribution to the Pan-American highway.

Anyone who has flown over the jungles and mountains of
Central America and those of the upper west coast of South
America must agree that the proposal to build a continuous
highway through them, thus linking all parts of both Americas,
is probably as extraordinarily difficult a project as man has ever
conceived. But it will be done, and before we know it rolling
down to Rio under one's own power will be an old story.

A bad detour carried them around the road work and
brought them out to a section of the completed Pan-American
highway. As the car met it the chófer relaxed with a contented
sigh and opened up the throttle. The highway was wide enough
for two cars, surfaced with gravel, and beautifully engineered.
There were dozens of small quebradas or larger ravines sunk
into the desert floor, and the road crossed them on neat, func-
tionally simple stone bridges that blended well with the landscape. The turns were carefully banked and the car took them
at sixty miles an hour. Well on in the morning, thankful to be
alive, they rolled into Chala and bade farewell to their chófer
and his car. There were no recriminations when the fare was
paid, for every sol of it had been earned.

Chala was a town of not much more than one street. It
sprawled along a slope of the coastal hills down to the sea, with
a few buildings on the water front and more along the main
street which, ankle-deep in brown sand, parallel the beach. On
the omnipresent plaza fronted a decrepit, wind-blown church
and the office of the military police. The one hotel, "American,"
was owned by a gentleman of mixed parentage, mostly Spanish-
Irish. His first suggestion was a small room opening off the wide
patio. Apparently it had been unoccupied for some time except by the miscellaneous livestock and chickens that were

parked in the patio. After some persuasion a clean, large room on the street side of the hotel was put at their disposal.

The hills behind Chala were green from a distance, but when John and Carl got into them they found that grazing animals had long since done their worst. Still, there was some collecting, and after the days of lifeless desert they fell to with enthusiasm. Just at the line of juncture of the coastal plain and the hills, between lichen-encrusted boulders, they came upon thin rosettes of long, slender, deep-green leaves. From the centers of some of them a tenuous, foot-long flowering stem had been pushed up. Topping each were two or three deep wine-red, tubular flowers. It was obviously an amaryllid and the first of that charming plant group which South America had exhibited to them. Often thereafter, on the coastal mountains and in the Andean foothills to the south, they were to find equally attractive relatives of this first amaryllid.

On the lower slopes of the hills were two species of *Oxalis,* the sorrel, one of which grew abundantly but was rather inconspicuous and small-flowered. They found only a few plants of the other *Oxalis,* but it was a more attractive species with large, creamy-white to pale-yellow flowers. Like most of the other species of this genus that we brought back from South America this one proved to have little ornamental importance in competition with the attractive races already listed in garden catalogues. It is always a bit dangerous to introduce *Oxalis* species because they may become undesirable weeds. By wide distribution of their many minute seeds and a tendency to spread by underground stems they can rapidly and all too effectively occupy garden space not assigned to them. After a time some of them become difficult to eradicate.

Above the amaryllids and *Oxalis* the hillsides steepened rapidly. They were green and the collecting was fairly rewarding, but nothing to become excited about. On the whole Chala's vegetation was rather disappointing.

Dinner at the "American" was served at 8:30. The guests sat with the proprietor and his family at a long table on a balcony overlooking the ocean. At its head was the venerable padre of Chala, and at the foot Señor O'Donnell, the proprietor. All had scarcely been seated before loud shouts of "Dolores! Do-

lores!" were raised. In a moment or two the soup appeared in
Dolores' small, brown hands. She was a short, chunky, dark-
skinned, twelve-year-old girl, a member of the family that did
most of the work in the hotel. Her mother was laundress, her
elder sister was cook, she was waitress, and a younger sister was
chambermaid. This hard-working group of four owned only one
pair of shoes and they were not Dolores'. Her bare feet had worn
a smooth path from the cook shack, up the wooden stairs, and
onto the outdoor dining room.

The next day Carl and John decided to retrace their steps
ten miles or so in the hope of finding better collecting on the
first green hills that they had passed on the ride from Yauca.
Their hope was largely realized. The lower slopes of the fog-
drenched hills and the nearby sandy plains yielded an abundant harvest of plants. Of these the most colorful was the blue-
flowered *Nolana,* quite like the garden one. We found many
other Nolanas and near Nolanas on the dry coasts of Peru and
Chile. Most bore flowers in shades of blue, and the yellow-
brown sand they preferred provided them with an effective
background. A few of the Nolanas were white-flowered and exceedingly attractive. I believe that something rather important
might be accomplished if the fancier would attempt selection
and crossing among the Nolanas we collected. A series of such
desirable plant characters as dwarfness, compact habit of
growth, lack or intensity of color, and extreme floriferousness
are available, but in the wild races they are never combined in
one strain. It should not be difficult to bring them all together
and produce something new or something at least better than
the Nolanas we sometimes grow. Perhaps such innovations or
improvements would attract attention to this genus which deserves far more popularity than it at present enjoys.

Just as in northern, so here in southern Peru, the presence
of fog-determined vegetational oases in a coastal strip as arid
as any place on the earth's surface is a constant source of surprise. Each time we came upon such lomas as those north of
Chala we had to pinch ourselves all over again. Their composition was quite varied. The blue *Nolana,* a low, woody borage
and a tuberous *Solanum* with white or bluish flowers were the
dominant species while a near *Grindelia* and a few different

legumes were also common. In addition, there were sparse grasses, some cacti, a wild tomato, one or two inconspicuous members of the Lily family, one valerian, an *Oxalis* or two, and a *Tigridia*. The species which we think of as weeds were uncommon; indeed, nothing but a few such plants as *Capsella,* the shepherd's-purse, and *Erodium,* the crane's-bill, were to be seen.

The morning was more than spent when they had worked back to the antique station-wagon they had hired for the day. The chófer, yawning with hunger, politely inquired what had kept them so long, and clearly showed his contempt for grown men who spent their time digging up plants and putting them between pieces of paper. All three, however, agreed on the immediate necessity of finding food. After some discussion they decided to seek it in the nearby village of Atiquipa. Inquiries there disclosed neither hotel nor restaurant, but a hospitable housewife was finally found who fed them all the omelets, fried rice, and tea they could consume. The total charge was twenty cents U. S.!

According to established custom a siesta was now in order, and without discussing plans for the afternoon the chófer immediately retired for a sleep in his station-wagon. The restless gringos were not so inclined. They succeeded in routing out an old villager who agreed to guide them into the low mountains to the south. The old man, accustomed since childhood to climbing the hilly terrain near his home, set off at a stiff pace that taxed the capacity of the somewhat overfed botanists. The lower hillsides were worn almost bare by the feet of the villagers and the hoofs of their stock. Only in the bottoms of deep quebradas was there any vegetation. Then the slopes became rapidly much steeper and scattered shrubs and herbs began to appear. This so-called *chaparralita,* or little chaparral, plant association consisted of low, dense composites, a shrubby yellow *Calceolaria,* and small stunted trees probably related to the mesquite. The open ground was surfaced with a compact, lawnlike sheet of prostrate grasses and herbs, mostly a red-flowered clover. This began to look like a real collecting area and they pushed upward in high hopes of finding a lot of plants not seen before.

Then, suddenly, a thousand feet above the sea they came into the fog. At one moment it was merely the gray, gloomy roof of the world, at the next it was an all-enveloping, milky white mist into which everything began at once to disappear. The nap of sweaters and the inside and outside surfaces of spectacles were instantly covered with millions of tiny droplets. The vegetation at the same time became denser. To tear a path through the high brush meant the bringing down of cold cloudbursts at every step. The clayey surface soil was completely saturated. Rivulets ran down the steep cattle paths to fill the many depressions left by the hoofs of grazing animals. In the openings of the brush the soaking, grassy slopes were impossible for wearers of hobnailed boots that had picked up a slick coating of wet clay. All this would not have mattered if there had been anything to collect. The plants were there, new and interesting ones, but only one or two of them in flower. Buds were just forming and it would be a month or more before the sun, breaking through a thinning fog mantle, would stimulate their development into flowers.

As we have already seen, seasonal conditions constitute one of the major problems of the plant hunter. On the semiarid lower slopes of these south Peruvian coastal hills and mountains Carl and John were too late. At intermediate altitudes the vegetation was in flower, but not very rich in species. Above, where moister conditions permitted the growth of the most varied and distinctive array of plants, they were much too early.

Two pretty wet and discouraged botanists turned about face and began to slide and fall down the mountainsides. The old man had long since vanished in the mist and probably was waiting far above for them to reappear. As they came out from under the veil of moisture the sun was hanging low out over the misty Pacific. It warned them to hurry down to the village to begin the return drive to Chala. They knew that it was essential to reach the relative comforts of, and especially the dry clothes at, the hotel before the penetrating chill of the foggy coastal night was upon them.

The drive was uneventful but too fast for comfort. Beware of an old station-wagon on a rough Peruvian road! You may be prepared to have the absence of functioning springs keep your

Chilean seaside vegetation near Valparaiso—pink Alstroemerias and *Oxalis* among white-flowered *Mesembryanthemum;* above, leaves of *Puya*

Rodolfo puts a tiny swamp species of buttercup in the plant press

A *Cruckshanksia* in porphyry scree at 10,500 feet, Chilean Andes

A Chilean village landscape in the coastal hills—Vale of Paradise

The Chilean honey palm in Valparaiso's chaparral-covered hills

Rocky outcrops of the Chilean coast ranges glow with Alstroemerias

Largest and most beautiful of the Chilean Alstroemerias, *A. violacea*

thigh muscles achingly taut, but don't forget that when your head hits the solid wooden top of the station-wagon it is something quite different again from banging into the padded roof of a sedan!

Halfway back to Chala the road was full of cattle. At the chófer's first toot the hard-bitten *vaqueros* who had been riding in front of the herd turned around and tried to clear the road. With shrill shouts and pistol-like cracks of their short, heavy lashes they pushed through the cattle. Slowly a tortuous path began to appear. Down it the chófer guided the car with its horn at full roar. For a desert chófer who rarely could find valid excuse to use his horn this was an opportunity not to be overlooked, and he made the most of it. The unfamiliar and deafening noise increased the terror and fractiousness of the poor animals and largely counteracted the vaqueros' efforts to clear the road.

At last, however, the cattle were left behind and then the car passed the hacendado to whom they belonged. His señora was with him and together they made a charming picture. He was a big man with a bright, colorful poncho over his shoulders and rode a bay horse, light-footed and nervous. The shy, petite, dark-haired lady was mounted on a large black mare and sat daintily on her high sidesaddle. In the early evening they arrived at the Hotel American and tied their horses at the hitching post beside the kitchen door.

Years ago Chala had been an important cattle-shipping center. Herds of range-fed steers were driven down to the port from the more remote mountains near the coast and from the distant Andean foothills, to be shipped on the hoof up and down the coast by water. Most of them went to the nitrate fields of northern Chile. There the aridity is complete and extensive. By contrast, on the south Peruvian coast a dozen watercourses flow down from the Andes, cross the dry plains in deep channels, breech the coast range, and finally reach the sea. Along these rivers, and especially where they run through coastal hills, domesticated animals and the wild, cameloid *vicuña* have always found abundant pasturage. Correspondingly, the condors wheel above the coast range in numbers said to be far greater than can be seen in the high Andes that lie to the eastward. The

great birds, carrion feeders, live well on the carcasses of cattle
and vicuña and on the bodies of dead sea birds washed up on
the ocean beaches.

In the early morning before they left for their collecting
in the Atiquipa hills a small freight steamer on its way south
had been lying at anchor in the so-called port of Chala. On it
they proposed to voyage along the Peruvian coast to Chile, stopping only if coastal hills and plains clearly showed more vegetation than they had yet seen. Imagine, then, their disappointment when, as the station-wagon negotiated the last curve
around a sandy hill and Chala and the ocean came into view,
they saw no steamer. There was nothing in the harbor but a
collection of chunky lighters, rolling and bobbing in the long
Pacific swells.

During the evening they took stock of their situation after
listening to all kinds of advice from the other guests in the
hotel. It was obvious that this year the season for plants was
going to be an early one, at least in the lower altitudes. Therefore they must go south fast or the vegetation of the generally
less foggy Chilean coast would be gone before they reached it.
Apparently there were only two ways to get on to the south.
The first meant an overland journey of one hundred miles or
more by automobile and muleback to one of the more important ports where southbound ships might call—in other words,
the traversing of still more of the desolate waste land they had
seen. The roads would be terrible, the transportation charges
worse, and at the end of the journey only a chance of catching a
steamer. The alternative was to fly to Arequipa, and then go by
train down to the port of Mollendo where almost all coastwise
shipping was certain to call. They flew, the next day.

At Mollendo they went aboard the southbound *Orduña*
of the Pacific Steam Navigation Company. After the *Capac* and
the *Mapocho,* here was luxury. They enjoyed it to the full during the two days' run along the last bit of Peruvian and first
stretch of Chilean coast to the port and city of Antofagasta.
First or last, all of us on the two expeditions had these wonderful, if brief interludes, on fine English or American liners. They
will always be bright spots materially on the calendar of months
during which relative privation and hardship were our lot.

As we have seen, the coast of South America from the point where the continent stretches farthest west, almost at the border of Ecuador and Peru, to the southern limits of the latter republic must be called a desert. But this desert does not end at the Peruvian border. Rather, it continues on into Chile along eight hundred miles of coastline. At the beginning it broadens greatly to the east and in certain areas approaches the absolute in terms of aridity. Behind Antofagasta, Chile shows its maximum width, approximately two hundred miles. This eastward bulge is Atacama, a dry, salt-encrusted waste thousands of square miles in extent.

In years gone by fabulous fortunes were made on Atacama from *salitre,* the Chilean saltpeter, that was only waiting to be scraped from her desert floor. Arica, Pisagua, Iquique, Tocopilla, Mejillones, Antofagasta, the nitrate ports, are names to stir the memories of men who loaded the clean, white salt into the holds of their ships and carried it back to revive or enrich the heavily cropped soils of the Old World.

The whole of Atacama's great extent is rainless and waterless, and therein lies the explanation of the vast surface deposits of sodium nitrate. Such an accumulation of salts represents complete evaporation in the dim past of an impounded arm of the ocean. Perhaps tremendous masses of seaweeds were imprisoned in the ancient inland sea and added their organic remains to the saline layers. Possibly guano beds of a size and extent to dwarf those found today on the nearby coasts and islands were involved in the origin of the deposits on the floor of this great desert. Be that as it may, Atacama's past and present aridity is responsible for the production and preservation of her saline wealth. For Chile saltpeter is highly soluble and therefore could have accumulated in such quantity on the Atacama desert only in the almost complete absence of rainfall.

Although a much smaller city Antofagasta is like Valparaiso in some ways. Both are too big for their present-day commercial importance. Most of the members of the two expeditions stopped in Antofagasta for hours or for a few days and agreed that it was an unusually bright, clean, and attractive place. There was a good hotel-pension, a homey place, like a large private villa set in a garden full of flowers. It was managed by an attentive and polyglot Yugoslav and his Brünhildean German wife. One day everything would be quiet and peaceful at the Hotel Aleman; the next, a big ship would come into the "harbor" of Antofagasta to erupt yanqui tourists who swarmed over the hotel for the few hours they had to spend ashore. They were very typical—consuming a great many tall drinks, asking questions, and looking exceedingly spruce and clean in their new, and somewhat inappropriate, tropical clothing. Antofagasta had a remarkably fine series of parks or parkways, all well cared for. A good-looking park or even small private garden on the arid margin of the nitrate desert of northern Chile is something of a triumph to achieve. It means importing soil—at the Hotel Aleman they claimed that their garden soil came all the way from Japan—and bringing water two hundred miles from the Andes.

The immediate vicinity of the nitrate deposits is plantless not only because of lack of moisture but also because of a lethal concentration of salts in the upper soil layers. Just west of the nitrate desert, however, the hills and low mountains next the sea show vegetation during the foggy season. Therefore the two botanists should find something to collect, perhaps not close to Antofagasta, but certainly somewhat farther south. Local information suggested that Taltal would probably be the most important center of operations and they decided to go there at once. By sea Taltal is a little more than one hundred miles south of Antofagasta, but by the railroad, which they used, the distance is half as much again.

The Longitudinal Railway extends north and south through Chile a total distance of two thousand miles with numerous branch lines, most of which serve the ports. Railhead in the north is somewhat above the coastal city of Iquique. Thence the railway runs on a line roughly parallel to the ocean along the high, more or less level, plains that lie between the coast range and the Andes. The desert of Atacama represents the northern part of this wide valley, but well south of its great nitrate fields the railway still traverses only arid terrain.

A train ride in northern Chile is likely to be a hot, dusty, and generally disagreeable affair, although the service is remarkably good. Always the wind blows hard and steadily. For hundreds of miles it has blustered across the floor of the desert and thereby acquired a high temperature and a load of sand and dust. A part of this load is deposited in the cars, which become hazy with a fine suspension of superdust. It can work its way through the stoutest cloth to irritate covered as well as uncovered skin. Despite the intense dryness enough moisture must cling to one's skin so that the dust particles are held and fused upon the body. At any rate, in a short time you look and feel like a glacé fruit. When a sudden movement cracks the glaze, you shiver!

From midday onward through the stifling afternoon the desert flings at your eyes a blaze of hard, yellow light reflected from its shining, salty crust. As the sun begins to fall below the rounded hilltops of the coastal ranges, soft pastel contrasts, miragelike paths of shadow, begin to float across the barren plains. Gradually they increase and flow together to spread a gray-brown mantle over all the cooling sands. The last streamers of golden light strike horizontally from the serrate crown of the western hills. Toward the Andes the sky is delicately flushed with a rosy light. Slowly the shadowy eastern horizon is rimmed with a deep band of pink and lavender. Then, as the eastward rolling earth thrusts more and more of itself into the pathway of the sun, the pink horizon flows skyward on the surface of an increasing cloud of aquamarine. The light fails fast, the desert comes to bear a dome of dull turquoise, and Atacama's day is at an end. Through the pale-blue sky the stars begin to shine and gather brightness as their background deepens.

Along the railway across the desert are many isolated stations. Whom or what they serve, one never discovers. Usually there is only a single building, rarely more than two. But the train always stops and each time something is loaded and unloaded. Invariably a poorly dressed, deeply tanned, and windblown woman stands in a doorway. She carries a baby on her hip and children cling to her skirts. With a hand shading her eyes against the desert glare she intently watches the operations of the train crew at the baggage car. Without the train there would be no food or water at these desert stations. Small wonder that she watches it so intently. She must be certain that it leaves behind that which will supply the simple needs of her family for the days until it returns again.

After riding all day across the desert Carl and John got off at the junction for Taltal. Their train on the branch line did not leave until the next morning and they spent the night at a nearby village. In the heyday of the Chilean nitrate trade, before men learned to fix the nitrogen of the air, this village, like so many other desert settlements, had been a busy place. Now, its reason for existence largely gone, it was almost completely deserted and the strong, rough desert winds were wearing it away and tearing it apart.

Next day in the Quebrada de Taltal they began their first serious Chilean plant hunting. In past time heavy rains had cut this deep gorge in the coastal hills. Today its streambed rarely carries water and it was entirely dry on the October morning when they saw it. But hillslopes high above were covered with vegetation. Here again was that now familiar but still almost unbelievable contrast between arid lower altitudes rising from an incredibly dry desert floor and the moist, fog-drenched, green hilltops.

John's diary gives a first hand account of what they found on the margin of the desert and on the foggy hillsides above it:

"At lower and mid-altitudes, the cacti were abundant. Massive candelabra-like *Cereus coquimbanus*, called *el quisco*, grew everywhere and overtopped a whole series of lesser spiny relatives. Where this great cactus extended its distribution upward into the foggier, moister regions, festoons of lichen hung from its long tough spines. Sometimes the red stems and flowers of a parasitic plant changed its green surface to an unnatural color. One particularly large quisco was almost completely covered by a vigorous, climbing nasturtium, *Tropaeolum tricolor*, sparkling with brilliant, red and orange, orchidlike flowers. Between the rocks we saw our first plant of *Cruckshanksia*, that curiously beautiful genus of the Rubiaceae or Madder family, which was often to thrill us in our Chilean collecting.

"This species, *Cruckshanksia pumila*, was the smallest and the only annual member of this striking genus that we came across. The plants were compact and, in rocky crevices, made small rounded tufts, three to six inches high. Their bright-green leaves formed a clear, fine background on which were displayed the large brilliantly yellow bracts that surrounded the relatively inconspicuous flowers. In Cruckshanksias the small, true flowers are borne several together in the center of a flat, colored disc formed by much modified leaves or bracts, which, at first glance, can readily be mistaken for petals. The individual flowers were about one-half inch long. At the base slender tubes, they flared out at the tops to form little, five-pointed stars. As we got up from our knees after analyzing this first *Cruckshanksia* we looked ahead and saw that a few rods higher in the quebrada the rocks were everywhere painted yellow by this low annual. Collecting promised to be good.

"We turned up a narrow, rocky gulch to the north and began to climb a bit. On this hillside the first plant seen in any abundance was *Balbisia,* which happens to be a member of the plant family to which the Geranium belongs. This *Balbisia,* or *Ledocarpum* as it was called by the early writers on Chilean botany, was a tall, rounded shrub, reaching when mature a height of six to eight feet. At this season of the year, the gray-green bushes were heavy with bright-yellow, erect flowers, about an inch across. In the loose soil below this decorative plant we noticed a small lupine with pale, yellow and white flowers. For some obscure reason, we could find only a single plant of this tiny *Lupinus microcarpus.* There was also a beautiful lilac-colored species of *Cristaria,* a genus of the Mallow family which is very widespread in Chile. Along the edges of the steep rocky slopes we began to find several little, hairy, white-flowered plants of a borage, *Cryptantha.* They called our attention to the similarity between elements of the Chilean lomas flora and the annual flora of the coastal hills in California.

"We worked our way along the rough hillside for a while and then suddenly our path was blocked by a huge mass of *Loasa bertrandi* that was climbing through the tall cacti. The bright-green, shiny leaves of this *Loasa* and its beautiful white flowers, striped with bright yellow and red, make you keen to strip great streamers of it from the spiny cacti and get busy putting them in the presses. Such a desire is almost immediately curbed. How stupid to be so careful to avoid the obvious spines of the cacti! They are just spines and only make puncture wounds in one's flesh. But this white-flowered serpent of a plant, with its marvelously glossy leaves, what a vicious thing it is! Each hair, those glistening white threads on stems and leaves and flowers, is a stinger of such authority that the pain from the worst nettle sting is less than a pin prick by comparison. Loasas can be collected, but heavy gloves or large forceps must be used.

"Here, in the coarse scree above the trail we saw our first Chilean violet. It was a tiny, reddish rosette, with half-inch-long, slender, pointed leaves, closely packed in geometric fashion to produce an intricate design. Small, red and white flowers peeked out beneath the lower leaves of the flat-topped rosettes. In color this reddish leaved violet so closely matched the rocks in which it grew that we had to crawl on hands and knees, with eyes close to the ground, in order to find enough specimens for the plant press.

"After we had our specimens, we decided to collect a hundred seeds. At first glance this proposal appeared to be easy of accomplishment. One capsule should yield eight to ten seeds and so, if we found a dozen plants with ripe seed capsules, we would have our packet of one hundred seeds. However, closer examination of the plants revealed a problem. There were only two kinds of capsules—green ones, which grew out parallel to the scree surface, and already opened ones, which were directed sharply downward. In other words, the seed was either too green to collect or it had been completely shed. Then we carefully pulled up a plant and examined the stump of its little tap-root. Sure enough, there was a dark, slate-gray seed on the surface of the adhering mass of pebbles. A moistened knife-blade tip secured it. The top layer of pebbles was then gently brushed away, and two more seeds appeared. After two hours of pebble hunting we finally accumulated our one hundred seeds.

"Then we climbed higher along a small tributary quebrada into an open shrub vegetation. Through it we walked for a time without seeing anything of special interest. Then, without preliminaries, the openings in the scrub took on color and we were suddenly looking at *Alstroemeria violacea,* one of the most attractive plants that grows on the west coast of South America.

By this time we had climbed almost into the fog and just over-head was its swirling, cottony cloud of grayness. It began to send out tentacles all about us, and in a few more steps we were lost in its cool, soft embrace. In this fog-swept zone, the character of the vegetation changed completely and all plant life grew lux-uriantly. Below, the plants existed only in dry, rocky soil and de-pended for moisture upon some hidden supply of ground water or the combination of nightly fogs and the low evaporation rate. It must have been the latter combination of factors which determined the continued existence of such shallow rooted plants as *Cruckshanksia,* the rare lupine, and the other species of annuals. In the upper, fertile, fog-swept zone, the same fac-tors obtained but with much greater emphasis. The fog was ever-present and a fine mist bathed the soil and everything above it. Under the apparently benign influence of this thick, wet mantle many beautiful and interesting species grew on the high hillsides. There were many low annuals reminiscent of home; for example, a *Bowlesia,* so like a California relative that it was hard to believe that they were distinct species. It spread its pale-green leaves and opened its tiny white flowers in the half shade of a group of columnar *Cereus.* Nearby grew a few plants of *Pectocarya dimorpha,* another genus well known in California. Its inconspicuous, four-parted, spiny-edged fruits were ripe, but we could find no flowering specimens to put in press.

"Higher up we found two Calceolarias, the first, *Calceo-laria paposana,* a straggling shrub with erect branches which bore an abundance of yellow flowers. It was quite common among the large rocks in the very bottom of a high, narrow ra-vine. The second *Calceolaria* was extremely rare and grew only where fog moisture had collected in little rocky depressions. We saw only three plants. This species produced a few big, bright, orange-red-spotted flowers and large, pale-green basal leaves."

The two botánicos had gone to Taltal primarily because *Nicotiana solanifolia,* a tobacco relative, was reported to grow in the vicinity. This shrubby species is the only *Nicotiana* of north Chile and its distribution is restricted to hills near the coast. It's a choosy plant and demands just a certain combina-tion of soil and atmospheric moisture, of sun and of fog shade.

When we grow it in Berkeley the California summer climate and sunshine has a discouraging effect and the plants mature slowly and flower sparingly. It is a perennial, and year after year we hoped to find that it had become acclimated. But it never has, and the information that Carl and John brought back from Quebrada de Taltal dims our hope of growing it successfully in the Botanical Garden in Berkeley.

As they worked up toward the foggier heights a few plants of the sought-after *Nicotiana* began to appear. Stunted, scrawny, and poor as to flowers, these plants were, apparently, just able to survive in the bottoms of small, rocky, exposed gulches where they found some moisture in the subsoil. Much higher up, at about eighteen hundred feet, where the fog was thick and wet, the same species was quite a different thing. The plants were five feet high, straight and strong and covered with big, gray-green, heart-shaped leaves; and the stems ended in stately, foot-high pyramids of pale, yellow-green, tubular flowers which shone through the fog with a faint, delicate light. Obviously this Chilean species of near tobacco wants plenty of moisture in the air and in the surface soil when it gets ready to do its growing and flowering. This means that to grow it successfully in Berkeley we will have to wait until the California wet and dry seasons decide to reverse themselves or else we must try to create artificially the equivalent of a north Chilean coastal fog.

Taltal itself is a small, sprawling seaport, considerably decayed in appearance. Dry cliffs lie behind the town, rocky headlands to the west, and a bight opens to the north. At Taltal, Rodolfo Wagenknecht, a Chilean collecting assistant, was scheduled to catch up with them. Because of a misunderstanding he had been waiting in Iquique as they sailed by that port on the *Orduña*, bound for Antofagasta. Telegrams back and forth finally put Carl and John in communication with him and they expected to find Rodolfo waiting for them when they returned to Taltal after their first day's collecting on the nearby hills.

A round of the few hotels in town brought no results; none had seen or heard of Rodolfo. Then they tried the office of the *carabineros,* those singularly able and effective Chilean policemen. They were received courteously by a lieutenant and two plain clothes men. In their best Spanish, Carl and John tried to explain their quest and to ask for assistance. Unfortunately the Germanic character of Rodolfo's family name seemed to create an atmosphere of doubt and even of some distrust. They were promptly ushered into another room where the officer in charge kept the national and international black lists. Their appearance must have belied his first notion that they were criminals of international importance. At any rate, after looking them over very carefully the officer began to compare their faces only with the Chilean "Man wanted" photographs. When they had come through this test successfully the carabineros appeared to be entirely stumped. Finally some bright officer suggested that they should be sent to the Governor of the Department of Taltal.

On the way to the office of his Excellency, Carl and John decided that the time had come for thorough identification and exoneration. From the recesses of his person Carl thereupon extracted their trump card, held in reserve for just such emergencies. It was an elaborate greeting from the sovereign State of California to the President of Chile and "too whom it may concern." In a lower corner of this formidable document was the Great (golden) Seal of California, and generous lengths of blue and gold ribbons ran diagonally from the seal to an upper corner.

The effect of this decorated parchment upon the governor and his carabineros was immediate and fully up to expectation, even without presentation of the Spanish translation which alone would have made it intelligible. But despite the change in their status which had been thus suddenly created no one knew what to do next. It then appeared that from the very beginning nobody had had the slightest idea what Carl and John really wanted and the more they had explained the less their Spanish was comprehended. At this juncture someone suggested an interpreter.

The little procession started out again, two North Americans who only wanted to find their German-Chilean assistant and two thoroughly puzzled carabineros. The "man who speaks English" proved to be the British vice-consul in Taltal, who was also the local agent of W. R. Grace and Company. He immediately grasped the problem and proceeded to make a speech to the carabineros. Their faces registered increasing enlightenment as he went along and were wreathed in smiles when he finally dismissed them with the assurance that all would be well. He seemed certain that Rodolfo would turn up shortly and pointed out that once he arrived he would have no difficulty in locating Carl and John after all the official excitement they had created in Taltal.

According to the vice-consul the neighboring hills were in far better condition for botanizing than anyone had any right to expect them to be at that season of the year. He said that in an average season the sun would long before have begun to pour down all day and every day on the Taltal hills and plains, and immediately most of the herbage nurtured by the coastal fogs would have become bone dry. Normally the fogs lay over the Taltal coast only until early spring. By contrast, this year they had continued to roll in during the late spring and as a result the October vegetation was greener and more extensive than he had ever before seen it.

He had lived on the west coast for thirty years and was able to give them some significant and amusing contrasts between Chilean life, past and present. Among other things he told how in early days the floors of all better homes had been covered from wall to wall with thick carpets, almost ankle deep in pile. In them the fleas found a congenial home and multiplied excessively. There were overlapping families, clans, tribes, and even nations of fleas that rose from these carpets to contend with one another for favored locations on the fair, thin skin of the foreigner from northern climes. Finally even the residents, long inured to insect attentions, began to protest, with the result that Chilean floors became what they are today, mostly bare and well waxed.

The next day, when Carl and John had taken all the plants they needed from Quebrada de Taltal and were ready to move southward, Rodolfo appeared. After some discussion with him they decided to go by train to Copiapó, an inland city on the southern edge of the desert of Atacama. Establishing a tem-

porary headquarters there they would be in striking distance
of Andean foothill as well as coastal collecting grounds.

The monotony of their eighteen-hour train ride across the
desert was somewhat relieved by distant, indistinct glimpses of
the great Andes, whose outlying ranges stretch nearer to the sea
as one enters the central zone of Chile. Increasingly the wide
plains were uplifted into low cross ranges and isolated peaks.
As they approached Copiapó there were occasional patches of
prostrate, flowering vegetation in the bottoms of shallow draws.
The city itself lay cradled in a valley through which ran one
of the few small rivers that succeed in crossing the Chilean
desert to the ocean. As the train skirted the rim of this valley
preparatory to winding down into it their eyes, for the first
time in weeks, came to rest upon the grateful green of riverside masses of Lombardy poplars and weeping willows. It was
a small, artificial forest, the uppermost trees silhouetted sharply
against the brownish scarps of the opposite valley wall.

They had left Taltal with presses full of recently collected
and thus very wet specimens. Therefore their first duty at the
hotel in Copiapó was to start plant drying. They were now
some distance back from the coast, and so the sun shone all day
long and the air was hot and dry. Soon the floor of the hotel
patio was mosaicked with dark-gray blotters and tan rectangles
of corrugated cardboard, all heavy with the moisture that, in
the presses, they had begun to extract from the Taltal plants.
In the warmth and dryness of the patio this moisture soon left
the driers and back they went between the plants.

They had planned to devote the first two days in Copiapó
to nothing but plant drying. But the unexpectedly long hours
of hot sunshine made possible three changes of driers in one
day, and so the work was done and the completely dried, pressed
plants were ready on the second morning to be mailed to Valparaiso for storage. Some of the credit for this shortening of the
drying schedule should be given to Yasna, nine years old, Yvo,
eleven years old, and Yeri, five years old, the granddaughter and
grandsons of the Yugoslav hotel proprietor. For them the tiresome business of first laying out hundreds of wet driers and then
gathering them all in again after they were dry was a novel and
entertaining game. As the plants in their folded paper covers

went back into press the youngsters insisted upon seeing every one. When any especially pretty flowering specimen appeared they chorused, *"linda, bonita,"* and laughed happily.

The first collecting trip out of Copiapó was to Caldera on the coast. They went by automobile rather than by train in order to collect whatever was to be found along the road. Instead of a road, however, they traveled a medium good mule track. Great numbers of pack animals had used it over the decades during which their backs were the only means of transporting ore to the coast and foodstuffs back to the mines in the Andean foothills. No one in his right mind would ever have attempted to drive an automobile over such a trail. But as we have already learned, west coast chófers are entirely inured to hardship and hazard, and thoroughly understand that everything in this world is relative—in other words, the "road" to Caldera might be better but, on the other hand, it might be worse.

After a few miles they left the irrigated valley behind and the car climbed out onto the dry plains. To one side lay the village of Toledo, dominated by a barren mountain whose loose, sandy slopes are constantly shifting. As they move a series of thunderous groaning noises is produced and the mountain is therefore called *El Bramador,* "The Roarer."

As the car careened crazily from side to side the desert landscape took on an inexpressibly wild and desolate appearance. The land began to fall away toward the coast in a jumble of ledges, spurs, and isolated masses of rock. The driver headed his machine between and among these constant hazards with steady and practiced hand. His three passengers bounded up and down between the defunct springs of the seat cushions and the car roof, which was greasy and worn by contact with the heads of many previous unfortunates.

Near approach to the sea was signaled by a hint of moisture in the air and by the flowering of desert shrubs and herbs in the few flat, open spaces between the great boulders. The dominant plant was the lilac-flowered, yellow-green leaved *Cristaria,* which they had first seen near Taltal. With this attractive plant grew abundant blue Nolanas, Loasas, provided as usual with stinging hairs, and some species of *Argylia.* The rather scattered collecting led them on and on until passing over a last rise they saw the tumble-down town and the port of Caldera, and beyond it the dull-blue Pacific stretching out with ever-diminishing color to the foggy western horizon.

They had gone to Caldera because nearby there were two collecting areas of some fame and importance. In one, Quebrada del Leon, I wanted them to search for a species of *Nicotiana* which had been reported to be growing there. It was said to be related to, or identical with, *Nicotiana solanifolia* which they had found in the coastal hills to the north. The second collecting ground was the Morro de Copiapó, a tall headland jutting out into the sea just south of Caldera.

Following their exhibition to the carabineros in Taltal of the beribboned greeting from California, Carl and John had become well and favorably known characters on the north Chilean coast. Only a minimum of persuasion was therefore necessary to convince the carabineros in Caldera that government horses should be provided for the collecting trip to Quebrada del Leon. The number finally agreed upon was two. Unfortunately it then appeared that one of them must be ridden by an officer who was to go along in order that the party should acquire a thoroughly official and dignified character. This meant that two more animals had to be found. After much scurrying about by Rodolfo, who because of his Spanish and knowledge of the people and their customs had from Taltal onward become tour guide, the owner of two miserable mules was cajoled into renting them for the following day.

Next morning horses, officer, and mules appeared before the hotel at an hour much earlier than they had anticipated on the basis of previous experience with such transportation arrangements. The horses were fine, strong, well-gaited animals, but the less said about the mules the better. Of all depressed, ramshackle, bony-backed, cross-grained, and thoroughly unreliable quadrupeds, these Caldera mules were the worst. By virtue of seniority Carl obtained the horse, and this left the mules for John and Rodolfo, who were also to carry the plant presses and other collecting equipment.

It proved to be a distinctly divided trip. The horses trotted, the mules walked, and soon the horsemen were out of sight. At the edge of the Quebrada del Leon, the party was finally re-

assembled. A considerable disappointment awaited the three
botánicos, for most of the vegetation in the Quebrada consisted
of perennial species and only a few of them were in flower.
However, the *Nicotiana* I wanted to know more about was
actually there in quantity and some of it in flowering condition.
They collected it and photographed it, but were unable to find
mature seeds. I would willingly have exchanged a pinch of seed
for all the pressed specimens and the photographs they made!

Of the few other plants which were flowering, the most
conspicuous and unusual was the giant *Oxalis* (*O. gigantea*).
The other *Oxalis* species they had found in the north had been
small, more or less delicate herbs, or, in other words, quite
corresponding in stature and character to the various kinds of
wild and cultivated sorrel we know in the United States. By
contrast, this Quebrada del Leon *Oxalis* was a six-foot tall,
semiwoody perennial, with yard-long, slender, snaky branches;
something quite beyond expectation for *Oxalis* and in general
a decidedly peculiar-looking species. The leaves were sorrel-like
but very small for such a large plant. The flowers were bright
yellow.

When they had collected this and a little *Oxalis* with
orange-yellow, scarlet-tipped petals and a few other more or less
interesting plants there was nothing more to do. With blas-
phemous references to the luck of the seasons—too early here
and too late there—they mounted horses and mules, and while
the afternoon was still very young began the ride back to
Caldera. The two horsemen again forged ahead and in a few
minutes were lost to view. The mules reacted to the homeward
journey, not by any improvement in their gait, but by developing a complete unwillingness to permit their riders to get on or
off their backs. This was a disappointment because in the morning John and Rodolfo had seen a number of trailside plants
they wanted, and had planned to collect them on the way back.
They did stop once or twice, but it took so much time to leave
the rearing mules and to escape hoofs and teeth when they tried
to regain their saddles that any hope of real collecting had to be
abandoned.

That evening two of the three botanists were painfully
aware of their long, jolting ride on bony muleback. Neverthe-

The lemon-yellow pouches of this Peruvian *Calceolaria* are held erect

Peru is hospitable to many such cosmopolitan weeds—*Argemone mexicana*

When grown in shade, this 20-foot Peruvian *Calceolaria* (*C. tomentosa*) luxuriates in the Botanical Garden in California

This treelike Peruvian tobacco relative (*Nicotiana tomentosa*) grows in little
forests along the racing waters of the Rio Urubamba

In Peruvian "meadows on the desert" we found *Begonia octopetala* growing in
moist clefts of hilltop boulders

less the collections had to be arranged and notes on them jotted down. Before the grogshops closed they bought two bottles of authentic *pisco* for the officer who had ridden with them to Quebrada del Leon and return. This expression of appreciation was enthusiastically received and doubtless their healths were drunk by all the Caldera carabineros.

Rodolfo had hired a launch to take them next morning to Morro de Copiapó. They met it at the foggy dockside about seven o'clock. It was an old but sturdy craft and not too offensively odorous even though it had long been used for fishing. Along the coasts of Chile and Peru the fishermen are on the fishing grounds before daybreak. Only a few hours after it has left the water their catch of *congrio, corvina,* and other delicacies of the Humboldt Current, carried over the shoulder on a strip of rawhide, is offered for sale in the streets of coastal cities. Almost perfect freshness is one of the reasons why fish, especially corvina, is such a popular item for tourists on the menus of west coast hotels and restaurants. The fishermen have a steady job but a poorly paid one, and therefore the chance to earn eighty pesos by taking some gringos on a half-day excursion is very attractive.

The launch was powered by a big gasoline engine that drove them rapidly over the quiet surface of Caldera's inner harbor. They rounded a sharp, lighthouse-topped promontory into the rougher waters of Bahia Inglesa and hugged its southwest shore. Breakfast was then in order and exceedingly welcome. The younger of the two *launcheros* produced the ubiquitous five-gallon oil can. This one was a quarter full of ashes, with the lower part of one side cut away to provide a draft. With wires, a grate or grill had been hung down in the can. A bit of kindling under the grate soon produced heartening odors from the spout of the coffee pot. When it had boiled and been removed the halves of good Chilean breakfast buns went on to toast. By contrast with most South American "continental" breakfasts, the coffee and rolls were present in abundance.

Variations in the origin and topography of the Chilean coastal strip can best be observed from the sea. North of Tocopilla, near Chañaral, south of Taltal and elsewhere, lofty, almost perpendicular cliffs and headlands rise from the very water's edge. At other points, for example, to the north of Caldera and from Caldera south to Huasco, there may be a terrace uplifted above the sea or a series of mighty steps that end in the coastal hills two or three miles from the beach. The power of the Pacific surge is magnificent, and that morning on the protected side of Bahia Inglesa they watched mountainous breakers crashing against the steep scarp of the eastern terrace. The sea was almost calm in the protection of the Morro whose massive bulk grew rapidly larger, straight ahead.

They went ashore on a rocky ledge of the great headland. The launch immediately turned back into the bay so that its crew might do a little fishing while the botanists were at work. The vegetation, reputed to be very interesting, did not come up to expectation. In addition it was once more too early in the season for the flowering of the shrubs and herbs that grew on the upper levels of the cliff sides. But to reward them for their climbing *Alstroemeria violacea* was there. They had seen it first at Taltal. But here, under the brow of Morro de Copiapó, they saw it in its full beauty. The many stems which come up from the long, slender, fleshy roots were not so tall as those of the familiar yellow-flowered *Alstroemeria aurantiaca* or of the so-called chilensis hybrids. They were, however, stiff and strong with many broad, highly varnished, dark-green leaves. At the stem apices were the flowers, six to twelve of them.

Although a luminous blue-lavender color is their most unusually distinctive and attractive feature, the shape and size of the flowers is also outstanding among Alstroemerias. The petals are broad, somewhat ruffled on the margins, and together form a wide spreading salver-formed flower. The narrow bottom of this lavender-blue cup is colored yellow to orange with a fringe of long, narrow, purple stripes. Altogether, *Alstroemeria violacea* is a novelty which probably has never been in cultivation; it is a distinct and valuable acquisition and will be much sought after.

We have grown it successfully from seed in the Botanical Garden in Berkeley. It begins to flower in eighteen months and requires no special treatment. Fortunately it has retained in cultivation all the desirable ornamental characters it showed in the wild state, something that by no means always happens. Many a well-formed, floriferous, and otherwise desirable, new or little-known species has been introduced into cultivation by plant hunters who came across it in some extremely remote part of the world and who esteemed it highly. Grown at home in the garden it too often becomes a leggy, gangling, weak-kneed affair that spends its strength on thin stems and leaves and has only strength enough left to produce a few disappointing flowers.

Below the higher levels where this fine *Alstroemeria* was growing they found a number of interesting plants in the dry bed of a brook and in loose rock along the cliff's base. There was a lilac-flowered species of *Astragalus,* a member of the Pea family, both in flower and fruit. This stage of plant maturity is the one always sought by the plant hunter because the complete reproductive history of a species can then be preserved in the dried, pressed specimen he collects. Without fruits as well as flowers the specialist who, months or years later, will attempt to give the specimen its correct name may be checkmated.

They also found two species of *Cristaria* different from the ones in the north. There was, too, a low, white-flowered *Schizopetalon,* of the Mustard family, botanically the most interesting plant they saw near the Morro. The petals were lacy, and in general the plant was almost a miniature edition of one of the swamp orchids of the northeastern United States. On a steep, sandy slope was a large patch of another *Alstroemeria,* quite a different one from *Alstroemeria violacea* but with considerable charm. It lay prostrate in the sand and was covered with small, clear-yellow flowers that almost hid the scant foliage. In the loose earth it was easy to dig the fleshy roots which in most Alstroemerias are buried deep in heavy or rocky soil.

The broad vista of sea and sky well repaid them for a hard climb to the summit of the Morro and offset to some extent their disappointment over the meagerness of the collecting. The fog masses which in the early morning had enveloped sea and shore were drifting slowly inland past the high headland upon which they stood. The surface of the sea, illuminated where the sun's rays struck through the mist, was a clear, mild blue, flecked now and then with white where the long, deep

Pacific swells crested and broke. Almost at their feet the launch with the two fishermen at their tasks lay at anchor in the calm protection of the promontory. Far out to sea, wheeling and diving, thousands upon thousands of sea birds—gulls, pelicans, cormorants, boobies, and petrels—gave animation to the horizon.

The return trip from the Morro de Copiapó to Caldera was exceedingly rough by comparison with the early morning voyage. The ground swells had lengthened and deepened and ran somewhat at cross purposes, so that it was difficult for the helmsman to gauge their course and effect. Some that looked harmless enough would suddenly throw the launch high in the air and then drop it at the wrong angle into an abyss. On the first of these occasions the older launchero, dozing in the warm sunlight on the cabin roof, was tossed across the boat and almost overboard. Thereafter he was more alert. After they passed the lighthouse the more protected bay gave some relief, and the landing at the Caldera wharf was accomplished without much difficulty.

For the plant hunter the neighborhood of Copiapó, at about 27° South, and that of Caldera, on the coast at the same latitude, marks the southern limit of the north Chilean desert. The hills surrounding Copiapó are dry, and the sandy wastes behind them that stretch away in all directions are barren. But each mile that one travels southward from this margin of the true desert marks a minute increase in moisture. It may be that only one twenty-fifth of an inch of rain falls each year, but even this small alteration in moisture conditions makes it possible, in favorable seasons, for a transient vegetation to appear. Thus, south of Copiapó, such a minimum will bring about the germination of grass seeds, and if there chances to be an additional shower or two soon enough thereafter, then the brown hills are covered with a green mantle, a thin one but sufficient to provide temporary forage for grazing animals.

The railway runs southward from Copiapó through a perceptibly decreasing aridity, in terms of vegetation at least. Gradually you begin to realize that there are a few more cacti per acre. Increasing numbers of low shrubs wage a ceaseless but successful struggle with drought and wind. Ever so gradually do the distances between the individuals which combine to produce this shrubby vegetation decrease. As the main line turns westward from Vallenar toward Coquimbo and the sea an ever more continuous green covering smooths and softens the rough silhouette of the increasingly massive coastal mountain ranges.

Between Vallenar and La Serena the railway builders encountered difficult terrain. They had to cut long, steep grades, many of which terminate in tunnels. The train constantly winds in one direction and then in another, twisting sharply from side to side and often doubling directly back upon itself. Because of the difficult grades and the relatively low-power engines, the train proceeds at a snail's pace. Furiously barking dogs rush out from adjacent haciendas. Sometimes they are content with such protest. Others, more intelligent or hungry, run alongside the dining car for miles, expecting and occasionally receiving scraps of food. For a moment or two you find amusement in watching the loping dog and his sidelong, fleeting glances toward the dining car. Then your attention is attracted elsewhere. Assuming that the dog has long since become tired out and discouraged you again glance idly out of the window and find to your astonishment that the same dog is still running beside the train. Some people claim that these dogs continually follow the trains back and forth from one hacienda to another. When they are finally overwhelmed with weariness they drop out near a likely looking establishment. Then, if it does not come up to expectation in the matter of food, they pick up the next train in the opposite direction and run back to their original headquarters.

With one of its sources in the snow fields of the eighteen-thousand-foot Cerro del Volcan, almost on the Chilean-Argentine border, the Rio Limari runs swiftly to the west, and after it has left behind the interior city of Ovalle enters the Pacific south of La Serena. In its valley west of Ovalle occurs the northernmost known stands of the famous *palma chilena, Jubaea spectabilis*. This stately palm, indigenous to central Chile, is found from the Rio Limari to the Rio Maule in the south, or through less than five degrees of latitude. Always a conspicuous element in its landscape, to me it is most attractive when it rises from a shrub-filled valley bottom and is seen against the tan surfaces of the distant Andean foothills.

The largest specimens are said to attain a height of almost one hundred feet. The trunk is swollen for one-half to two-thirds of its length and then above that point the diameter decreases rather abruptly and thereafter continues upward without diminution until it terminates in the long, much-dissected leaves. The heavy leaf crown often forms an almost complete sphere. In the coastal cordillera, at altitudes below one thousand feet, palma chilena was in years goneby an important element of every landscape. In the neighborhood of Valparaiso and for a hundred miles south it once existed in extraordinary numbers. Charles Darwin speaks of a census taken in 1830 on the lands belonging to a hacienda near the town of Petorca, which was abandoned after some hundreds of thousands of palms had been tallied. Today its numbers have everywhere been greatly reduced; indeed, some of the local botanists speak of the possible extinction of this most attractive and typical Chilean plant.

Man has, of course, been responsible for its partially complete disappearance. Unfortunately for this palm, the abundant sap has a high sugar content. Boiled down it yields *miel de palma*, palm honey, which is a commercially valuable and highly esteemed sweetmeat in Chile. To obtain the sap the palm must be cut down in early spring. If possible, it is felled uphill so that the top will be higher than the cut end. Then a cross cut is made below the crown of leaves and the flowing sap is collected. A fresh slice of wood is periodically removed in order to maintain a constant flow. The exudate continues for six to eight weeks, and a total of from seventy-five to one hundred gallons of sweet sap is often secured.

How significant in the history of the race the palms have been, still are, and doubtless always will continue to be. They have rivaled every other plant in their importance and utility to man. Over great areas of the tropics and semitropics the date or the coconut palms are relied upon to provide food, drink, clothing, and shelter, as well as being among the most valuable articles of commerce that their areas produce. Among native

Chilean plants *Jubaea spectabilis* is certainly pre-eminent, at least in terms of the value of its products.

Carl, John, and Rodolfo completed their Chilean coastal journey at Valparaiso early in December. Soon thereafter Carl returned to the United States, and Florence and I arrived from our three months in Argentina. The unusually dry season along the entire coastal strip of Peru and Chile made collecting less profitable than it should have been. On the other hand, I sometimes wonder what would have happened if the collections of dried specimens, seeds, bulbs, and other plant parts that came into Valparaiso had been any larger than they were. It took us many weeks to care for them and prepare them for shipment to California.

Adding together the results of what we did in 1938 and those obtained in 1935 by members of the first expedition we have been able to bring back to California the most comprehensive body of information concerning the vegetation of the north and middle Chilean coast that has ever been assembled.

Chapter IX

VALE OF PARADISE

CHILE IS a long country. Not less than twenty-six hundred miles, the airline distance between San Francisco and New York, separates Arica on Chile's northern border from Tierra del Fuego, its southern extremity and the southernmost point on our sister continent. North Chile is desert or semidesert, south Chile is extremely wet and rather cold, and between them is our Vale of Paradise. A semicircle based upon the Pacific, whose fifty-mile radius includes Santiago, Chile's capital, and whose center lies in her only important port, Valparaiso (literally "Vale of Paradise," whereas the city is only a part of it so far as this chapter is concerned), encloses what for Florence and for me is the land of brightest sunshine, of clearest atmosphere, of gentle fragrant breezes, of charming flowers, and of peaceful landscapes. Here someday we will return and live each hour fully in a round of labors undisturbed and simple joys, surrounded by smiling, gentle faces and served by willing, patient hands. We stopped for many months in this Vale of Paradise and we liked it.

As do most North American travelers we first saw the city of Valparaiso from the sea. While the Grace liner *Santa Lucia* poked her nose carefully between the lines of lighters, slipped inside the great mole, and was slowly warped to the dock, we studied the terraced hillsides that are Valparaiso. At first sight, Valparaiso seems to be merely a narrow coastal plain which, after running back from the sea wall only a few city blocks, comes to a full stop against precipitous cliffs and steep ridges. On this coastal plain you wander along not too narrow, well-paved, rather well-kept streets beside stores, banks, office buildings, apartment houses, through plazas larger and smaller. If your time ashore is limited you are unlikely to wander far from the main plaza, Plaza Sotomayor, which you entered soon after leaving the dock. On one side of the entrance is the customhouse and opposite it is the new railway station to which the citizens of Valparaiso point with pride. They have reason to be enthusiastic about it because the old station was something quite deplorable. Incidentally, this new station was reported considerably damaged by the great storm of last summer which drove ashore several of the ships anchored in the harbor and attacked all seaside buildings with destructive winds and waves. Before the present breakwater was built, Valparaiso harbor had for more than two hundred years possessed a bad name among mariners who, at the first hint of the gathering of a winter storm, promptly forsook its almost open roadstead and rode out the storm on the open sea well off the coast.

The plaza contains many shops filled with the trifles that tourists buy. The characteristic "come on" in these Valparaiso tripper emporia is a window display of pseudo-Easter Island wooden images that are not only undraped but also prominently decorated with anatomical grotesqueries, both fore and aft. Here in the plaza we exchanged our American greenbacks for Chilean pesos. Had we listened to the representatives of travel bureaus who came aboard just before we docked, we would have seen practically nothing of Valparaiso. These gentlemen strongly urged us to spend no time in Valparaiso but to get on the train and ride for three hours to the Chilean capital, Santiago, where an escorted tour of the city, luncheon at the best hotel, and so forth, would be provided, all for a quite sizable consideration. They insisted that there was nothing to see or do in Valparaiso and much of interest in Santiago. And, however fond we are of shabby, comfortable Valparaiso, I must confess that up to a certain extent this information is correct.

Instead, we made a short excursion away from the central plaza, down the Calle Condell which runs along the inner edge of the coastal plain. Every now and then we passed a small, somewhat tumble-down ticket office next the sidewalk, and behind it an elevator-like car that runs on tracks and a cogwheel almost straight up the hillside to a small box perched high above. Into that box an ascending car suddenly disappears, while at the same instant a descending one pops out. This is one of the famous *ascensores* or outdoor elevators on which most of Valparaiso's population goes home at night and down to work in the morning. If you live in Valparaiso you will almost certainly have your office or shop down on the coastal plain; while your home will hang along one of the terraced hillside streets so far above that the only thing to do is to take the elevator up, and down—the fare, a fraction of one cent each way.

Steep, cobbled roads wind back and forth up the rocky sides of the ravines which break the continuity of the hillsides and, above, cross the series of terraced residence streets that follow the contours of the hills. On these abruptly ascending roads the up and down traffic of foot passengers, strings of loaded burros, private automobiles, taxis, autobusses, and trucks, weave in and out with noisy good nature. A little boy with packages to deliver from a store below kicks a tennis ball up the hill to make his journey really worth while and thoroughly interesting. A greengrocer with his stock in trade on a burro's back comes to a sudden stop at the shrill call of a housewife; and behind him brakes squeal and grind, horns protest, the bus driver springs from his *gondola* with imprecations and a wooden wedge to fortify his brakes. From the level streets below it is impossible to appreciate the construction of the city of Valparaiso or to see anything of what is going on above. But we became well acquainted with these goings on, because for days and weeks on end we went, sometimes twice a day, from our hotel on the coastal plain near the Plaza Victoria up into the Valparaiso terraces and back again.

In addition to the collections of dried plants, seeds, bulbs, roots, and cuttings which we were making in the Vale of Paradise, we were periodically receiving more of all these kinds of plant material from the other collectors who were scattered a distance of from two to five hundred miles both north and south. On receipt of these shipments, we unpacked them, sorted them, cared for them in a variety of ways, and ultimately saw them and our own collections boxed and shipped to California.

The handling of thousands of plant specimens requires a lot of room. It is always a mussy, usually a dirty job. We first began the work in our hotel room and before each day was over the tables, dressers, beds, and finally the floor, were entirely covered with plants. Every now and then we found ourselves pinned in a corner, unable to move for fear of stepping on something valuable. At least once every twenty-four hours everything had to be cleared up in order, first, that we could get a little sleep and, second, that the maid could come in and at least go through the motions of cleaning up the mess. After a week of this sort of thing tempers were short, not much had been accomplished, and we decided to try to hire a vacant store to use as a workshop. At this juncture our friend the "General" came to the rescue, just as he did on so many other occasions.

The General, Dr. Edwyn P. Reed, one of the best-trained medical men in Chile, is an Anglo-Chilean, whose father came from England to Valparaiso many years ago to teach geology and natural history in the Naval Academy of Chile. Mentally and physically he is one of the most vigorous men I have ever known. Better still, he is wonderfully good company and all that a real friend could possibly be. His title was bestowed upon him as the result of a chance remark. With us he always exhibited a mischievous enthusiasm for coming out with something that would shock Florence, and he was continually going as far as he dared in recounting stories or using expletives acquired from the officers of the American and English ships docked in Valparaiso, with whom he has had a long and wide acquaintance. On a particularly warm day he greeted us with, "It's as hot as Jesus Christ and General Jackson!" So "General" he straightway became.

The amiable General promptly solved the problem of where to deal with our plants by offering us the use of a large balcony in his home up on the Valparaiso hillside. He and his Chilean señora have had twelve children, of whom seven are living, all boys and all crack swimmers. To house such a large family and particularly to provide sufficient space in which the explosive spirits of the boys could expand, he bought a large residence which had once belonged to a wealthy Englishman. Twenty-nine rooms have been no more than enough to accommodate the family, the servants, billiard tables, studies, museums, and so on.

On a wide first-floor balcony overlooking his fine garden, the General let us establish ourselves. There were big tables on which our specimens could be spread out, and corners where Florence examined each sheet to see whether there was seed that could be taken from the dried plants. All about we accumulated great piles of corrugated boards and pieces of felt; with these we dried our collections and completed the drying of those that were sent in to us too wet for packing and shipping. Once and often twice a day we had to change the plant driers and then carefully lay out the moist driers on all garden paths. When the hot Valparaiso sun had done its work and the driers were thoroughly dry again, we had to pick them up one by one and put them back into the presses or store them on the balcony against the evening dew. If anyone requires convincing evidence of the effect upon hips and shoulders of increasing age and weight, let him first place carefully on the ground and subsequently pick up two or three hundred pieces of heavy felt.

The drudgery of what we did for many weeks on the General's balcony was each day lightened by our pleasure and interest in the plants we spread out before us. Sometimes they were our own collections made the day before or perhaps many weeks before. Each plant brought back a memory of a bit of landscape and often some experience amusing or the reverse. When a shipment came in from the collectors, we began to feel real enthusiasm for the work. The first question was: Did he get the particular thing he and we hoped that he would come across in that special area where he had been collecting? This question led to a quick search through the specimens, but we had to curb our impatience at once for fear of mixing up the plants and then set about a slow, methodical examination of each one. Until we came across the desired plant, and we almost always did, a certain suppressed—and on Florence's part a not-too-well-suppressed—atmosphere of excitement prevailed. Then we would relax, apply ourselves to the old routine, only now and again commenting on some specimen that attracted our attention. From time to time one of the collectors would come in to headquarters at Valparaiso and before long we would all find ourselves being drawn toward the balcony. There he would go through his collections and give us the details associated with the collecting of each specimen.

During the past twenty-five years I have spent a good deal of time in examining the specimens of *Nicotiana* which, along with those of all other genera of plants, are to be found in the great herbaria of the world. An herbarium is, of course, a collection of dried, pressed plants, and in the larger herbaria every section of the globe is well represented. To each specimen is attached a label on which the collector has written the date and place of collection, a variety of information concerning the conditions under which the plant was growing, notes on plant characters such as color of flower, which may disappear when a plant has been killed and dried, and any further data he may have secured. The botanist, or the interested layman, can obtain from an herbarium a remarkably accurate picture not only of the character and composition of the floras in every part of the world, but also of the environmental conditions that characterize any particular area.

At the beginning of my herbarium work I came across specimens of many species and varieties that were not represented in our living collection of *Nicotiana* in the Botanical Garden in Berkeley. Most of these dried Nicotianas in which I was particularly interested had seed capsules containing seed; but in the majority of cases the specimen had been collected so long ago or had been so thoroughly poisoned against destructive museum insects that the seed which I took from them failed to germinate. To insure my botanical colleagues against similar disappointments I decided to take seed from the dried plants, not only of *Nicotiana* but also of all other genera, in every case where it appeared to be mature. This proved to be a rather large order, which Florence cheerfully and effectively filled. Rarely was the seed large and easily taken from the dried specimens without injuring them; more often it was small and in many cases minute, as, for example, in the species of *Calceolaria*. Then with the greatest of care she had to seek and find the mature seed pods among the dry and brittle flowers and leaves, and open them carefully to extract what seed they contained. Sometimes the seed pods were so hard and woody that a hammer had to be used to open them. To extract the seed without damage required a nice appreciation of the weight of the hammer head and the amount of strength being employed. Florence can feel well repaid for all her efforts in the matter of seed taking, because since our return to California many requests have come in from botanists for the seeds of certain particular groups of South American plants in the, obviously very vague, hope that we could supply them. If Florence had not systematically taken seed from all the dried specimens where seed was available we could not have complied with these requests.

In my youth, our family spent each summer in northern Wisconsin. In addition to fishing, one of the favorite family occupations was blueberry picking. In openings in the pine forests there were acres of blueberry bushes and we had soon charted all the most important patches within easy walking distance of our summer cottage. I happened to be the only child in a combined family of fifteen. When we undertook a blueberry excursion I was supposed to pick only from those bushes that were lowest. This was because I was, relatively speaking, nearer the ground and, if only the higher bushes required the attention of the rest of the family, a minimum of stooping on their part would be involved.

Nevertheless, I would have thoroughly enjoyed blueberry picking except that constantly in my mind was the aftermath. This consisted of picking over the blueberries and examining each one on the chance that the small stem had remained attached to the fruit. After a successful family foray in blueberry areas the succeeding day or two was devoted to this process of picking-over. The entire family assembled about large baskets of blueberries and each one dipped in and proceeded to examine his handful, this sequence being repeated indefinitely. To lighten the labor and to reduce the amount of incidental conversation which would have interfered with the effectiveness of the operation, one member of the family, almost always my father, was assigned the task of reading out loud to the group. The only respite came when the reader paused for breath or a drink of water. I was sustained in my duty through the long hours of picking-over primarily by loyalty to my father who was troubled whenever he was interrupted in his reading. This was bound to happen when older members of the family noticed that I was becoming at all derelict in my duty—a dereliction caused by pleasant visions of pies into which ultimately the blueberries would become incorporated. Even this anticipation could not, however, banish from my mind the experience which I knew I was going to have during the succeeding night. After a day of picking-over, my dreams pictured a series of backgrounds, usually battlefields or steep hillsides, on which I was constantly threatened by larger and smaller blue spheres which approached me at tremendous rates of speed. Part of the night I spent dodging these missiles and during the rest of it my dreams involved an exhaustive examination of a great collection of blue balls, which continuously moved before my eyes and arranged themselves in a variety of constantly altering patterns.

After Florence had concentrated each day for many weeks on seed extraction and examination she confessed that her sleep was similarly troubled. Before her eyes passed constantly in review a succession of seeds of various sizes, colors, and shapes. Sometimes she found herself approaching a large object that ultimately proved to be a gigantic seed pod which, when she attacked it, proceeded to disgorge a large number of round objects that chased her for miles across imaginary countrysides. Even after two years her remembrances of her activities on the General's balcony are inseparably connected with such dreams, just as are my remembrances of blueberry picking forty years ago in northern Wisconsin.

Interrupting our round of duties with the specimens were many longer and shorter collecting trips into the Vale of Paradise and beyond. One of the most profitable was a journey made with the General into the valley of the Rio Aconcagua and up it to the pass through which the Transandine Railway runs to Argentina. This and other collecting experiences in the Chilean highlands will be described in a subsequent chapter. Altogether, we saw the vegetation of central Chile from early spring in November to early fall in March.

Most of our shorter botanical journeys were made with the General in his car. He is an all-round naturalist, a keen observer, and has a considerable knowledge of the vegetation of Chile. His own special interest is entomology. He inherited from his father a large and valuable collection of the insects of temperate South America, to which he has made many important additions. When he took us to collecting grounds he always had a butterfly net over his shoulder and a killing bottle in his pocket.

To the north and south of the Vale of Paradise the coast

range consists primarily of high hills, but between Valparaiso
and Santiago and for a considerable distance north of an imaginary line connecting these two cities the hills become mountains. In this portion of the Cordillera de la Costa the topmost
peak, Cerro Cache, rises somewhat over seven thousand feet
above sea level, and there are ten or more other mountains
whose altitudes exceed six thousand. The most famous is La
Campana, or the "Bell Mountain," a few miles northeast of
Limache, which is one of the most climatically delightful,
garden-filled towns in the Vale of Paradise. In 1832 the young
naturalist, of H.M.S. *Beagle,* Charles Darwin, climbed the Bell
Mountain. It had attracted his attention as an isolated portion
of the Cordillera de la Costa which rose more or less solitary
from the broad coastal plain. One hundred years later the Valparaiso Scientific Society prepared a bronze plaque commemo-
rating Darwin's visit and with appropriate ceremonies placed it
permanently near a spring where, on the slopes of La Campana,
he had spent the night.

The varied character of the vegetational habitats which
these mountains in the Vale of Paradise provide leads one to
expect a correspondingly varied plant population and this
expectation is abundantly fulfilled. The peaks themselves are
covered with upwards of four inches of snow during the southern winter and a part of this white mantle may extend down to
the three-thousand-foot level. Rains that fall, but often sparingly, preceding and following the snow, add further moisture
to the rocky soils of the mountainsides. In summer the lower
altitudes are regularly bathed in fog, while the peaks and high
ridges are drying out in the bright sunshine and clear atmosphere. In the quebradas and on the gentle, lower mountain
slopes, especially on those facing south where soil moisture is
longest preserved, some of the characteristic trees of heavily
forested southern Chile reach their northernmost limit of distribution.

In midsummer the higher elevations, the broad valleys,
and the exposed plateaus have become almost arid; but there
are still many deep moist quebradas in the Cordillera de la
Costa in the bottoms of which slow-flowing rivulets meander
around huge streambed boulders, and on whose sides tall trees

Florence, the author, Alan, Rodolfo, and Walter on the General's balcony

A Chilean rodeo; the calf has escaped from the two pursuing huasos

An outdoor bakery is an important part of Chilean farm life

This is a familiar scene on every Valparaiso street

John, Sr. Garaventa (Chilean botanist and expedition collaborator), and the General (Dr. Edwyn P. Reed)—Bell Mountain in the background

A fearsomely spined cactus (*Eulychnia* sp.)—coast of central Chile
Lavender Godetias carpeted the coastal valleys near Concepción

festooned with Spanish moss rise high above a dense undergrowth. On north-facing slopes where maximum exposure to
sunlight produces maximum evaporation, or on mountainsides
too steep to hold a heavy layer of fertile soil, this forest is
abruptly replaced by the *monte* or dense chaparral. This is characteristic of thousands of square miles in the mountains of
central Chile just as it is of similar terrain in the far western
portions of the United States.

Of all the coast-range mountains in the Vale of Paradise,
Las Vizcachas, some six thousand and fifty feet in altitude,
yielded for us the largest and most varied collections of plants
of ornamental as well as botanical interest. The mountain is
named for the elusive *vizcacha* whose shrill piping cries echo
along the most inaccessible rock slides and cavernous defiles in
the evening afterglow, or as the dawn first touches the highest
peaks of the Chilean ranges. A larger edition of its relative,
the *chinchilla,* the vizcacha resembles a rabbit in shape and size
but differs from it by possessing the large, fluffy tail of a squirrel.

In a hired auto we drove to the village of La Dormida
which lies at the foot of Las Vizcachas. Ultimately we found
the house of the man who had been engaged in advance to act
as our guide and horse wrangler on the mountain. His name
proved to be Diogenes and those who had at birth bestowed it
upon him must have possessed clairvoyant powers. Although
carefully instructed some days before of our need of riding
horses and pack mules Diogenes had apparently made no effort
to procure them. We immediately proceeded to work up a
violent rage on the subject and after a number of hours a few
animals were finally rounded up.

Some child psychologists contend that a baby repeatedly
pitches his nursing bottle over the cribside, and creates other
equally distressing disturbances, solely to observe those facial
and other contortions which its fond parents or other attendants
are certain immediately to exhibit. Sometimes I wondered
whether, in an analogous fashion, the native Chilean or Peruvian did not consistently disappoint us in practically everything
for which we were forced to depend upon him, primarily in
order that he might enjoy the fine exhibition of rage and disgust

with which he had learned that the gringo, when thwarted, would always oblige.

At four in the afternoon we finally began to ride up the lower slopes of Las Vizcachas. For the first two thousand feet Diogenes led us along the side of a deep quebrada in which such handsome trees as *el boldo, el peumo* (*Cryptocarya peumus*), and *la patagua* (*Crinodendron patagua*), formed the dominant feature. The vegetation also included *siete camisas* (*Escallonia rubra*), other shrubs, and a multitude of ferns as a dense understory of the open forest. The common Chilean *Escallonia* is locally called *siete camisas* or "seven shirts" in allusion to the readiness with which the bark of this shrub scales off, to be soon replaced by another loose integument.

Along the margins of the quebrada where its forest was, on the more exposed and thus drier slopes, replaced by monte, the fountainlike sprays of a near-bamboo formed impenetrable thickets and also filled small openings in the forest itself and the bottoms of little-exposed, side ravines. Often the upper surfaces of these brownish green thickets sparkled in the sunlight with hundreds of the deep orange-red flowers of a species of *Mutisia*. The climbing species of this genus of the Sunflower family are familiar and attractive elements of the landscape in not-too-dry, brush-covered areas both in Peru and Chile. Rather straggling vines, requiring support, they prefer to aggregate their plant bodies under shrubs or small trees with long arms clasping the branches and pushing out into the light, among the leaves of the supporting plant, only the extremities of leafy flowering shoots. We collected a number of new flower-color varieties, or possibly species, of *Mutisia* and have added them to those already in cultivation. Unfortunately we found only a seed or two per plant, and sometimes none, because the insects had always been there before us. Apparently eggs are laid within the flower and as the fruits begin to mature the larvae follow suit and devour all the ripening seed. The Mutisias are easy to grow and require no special treatment beyond provision for adequate support of the long, floppy shoots which push up in quantity from the soil surface. As we rode upward the forest became thinner with more and larger openings where the sunlight could reach the earth through its green canopy. In these sunny spots we saw the first of the Alstroemerias which were to make memorable our collecting on Las Vizcachas.

In recounting our plant-hunting experiences along the northern coast of Chile and in the Andean foothills behind it we mentioned a number of species of *Alstroemeria*, and particularly *A. violacea* which was one of the real prizes of our South American plant hunting and is, perhaps, the most beautiful plant in all Chile. On the slopes of Las Vizcachas *Alstroemeria haemantha* first appeared. In contrast to some of the North Chilean species which were relatively low growing, these plants were tall and stately, the long straight stems clothed with slender, bright-green leaves and terminated by clusters of ten or more golden yellow, broad, bell-shaped flowers. It preferred well-drained, rocky soil and was never abundant.

When we reached the three-thousand-foot level on the west side of the mountain we had left the quebrada up which the climb began and had started the weary ascent of steeper treeless slopes on a rough and zigzag trail. Somewhat higher a small grove of trees appeared which Diogenes informed us would be our first *descanso* or resting place. There we dismounted and loosened the saddle girths on the tired animals to help them regain their wind. The bit of scattered woodland consisted of small trees of *Quillaja saponaria,* a member of the Rose family, whose bark is highly prized because of its richness in a soaplike substance. Beneath these trees, species of *Berberis,* Escallonia, and Cestrum formed a loose underbrush. The descanso provided a welcome relief for riders as well as horses and we walked about examining the vegetation, stopping now and then to look upward toward the peak far above our heads and the steep slopes just below it. On them we detected here and there faint films of pink laid upon the prevailing tan and gray of dried grasses and rocky ridges. Next day when we reached the high slopes these pink patches proved each to represent hundreds of square yards of rich, rocky soil covered with *Schizanthus hookeri.*

Diogenes insisted upon a second descanso after we had climbed only another thousand feet. Here on the open mountainside, in veins of loose, rich, black soil, first appeared *corymbosa,* the alpine and subalpine species of *Nicotiana,* which we

were particularly in search of. It is an unpleasant little plant
with a multitude of glandular hairs on its epidermis which are
ready at a touch to exude a sticky, resinous, strong-smelling
gum. It had a prominent place in our South American plant
hunting and will be encountered in subsequent chapters. We
were soon again to find it, this time higher up on Las Vizcachas
and in greater abundance.

Our proposed camping place for the night was what had
been reported to be a relatively level area immediately below
the peak of the mountain; but we began to despair of reaching
it before dark because Diogenes called for a descanso twice more
before the climbing was over for the day. We really could not
protest because our guide was obviously concerned not for his
own comfort or ours, but solely for that of the animals in his
charge.

The first plant we saw in the early morning light was a
superb species of *Argylia* entirely new to us. This genus belongs
to the Bignoniaceae of which our most familiar garden representative is the trumpet vine. In the lomas flora along the north
Chilean coast, which has been described in a previous chapter,
we had already found another species of *Argylia,* as well as a
third species in the Alta Cordillera. This Las Vizcachas species
was much the best of the three. Over patches many feet square
and usually in broad pockets among huge boulders it spread a
continuous, deep-green, varnished carpet over the mountaintop
scree. From this shining surface rose short flower stalks on
which were borne numbers of large, tubular, trumpetlike
flowers whose mottled corollas came in shades of yellow, orange,
and salmon.

For ornamental purposes, herbaceous perennials are always
much sought after, and this high-altitude *Argylia* falls in that
desirable plant group. It forms a long, rather thick, partly
woody, partly fleshy main root from which at the soil line
numerous horizontal branches arise. The beautiful foliage will
in cultivation probably prove to be essentially evergreen. In
every sense this plant appears to have potential ornamental
importance, and we have been growing it from seed along with
its coastal and higher Andean relatives. Germination takes place
only a few days after sowing and although the young seedlings

are handled without difficulty, a little later on the young plants are very touchy as far as water is concerned and must be kept distinctly on the dry side. The soil in which Argylias are grown should from the beginning correspond to that of its native habitat in being particularly well drained. Our experiments, however, have been with the ordinary Berkeley soil which is rather heavy. We have found that, if half-mature plants from pots or flats are planted with a little gravel or sand in the bottom of the hole, the moisture-retaining quality of this soil does not appear to do any damage, although now and then the half-fleshy root will decay in it. The wet and open Berkeley winter may be unacceptable to *Argylia,* which should prefer a more rigorous climate, including a period when the ground is snow-covered.

With the General we visited a number of nearby haciendas that were owned by some of his numerous friends. We were entertained more than once at one of the largest of these baronial establishments, which lies some miles southeast of Valparaiso. One Sunday I stood with the patron of this hacienda in an open field behind his large, rambling, one-story, patio-enclosing ranch house; immediately behind us to the east was a range of low hills, and far in the distance in front of us light-gray fog masses marked the shore of the Pacific. I asked him to point out to me the extent of his land holdings. He thought for a moment and then said, "My property begins in those hills to the east, and it runs to the ocean on the west, but just how far it extends north and south I cannot show you." Later in the day we rode over a part of his domain and found that for convenience the numerous employees on the estate were concentrated in more than one little hamlet. This dispersion enabled them readily to reach outlying agricultural operations instead of having to travel a number of miles to and from the headquarters of the hacienda. Since it was Sunday, the entire population was on display at the hacienda buildings and in the villages.

The botanist, when he is in a land whose vegetation is either unknown to him or otherwise interesting, is a bad person to entertain on a country estate. He is quite certain to neglect his social obligations and will unexpectedly wander off to see what he can find beyond the confines of the living room and the formal garden outside its windows, returning late for dinner and with muddy feet. And so John and I, at the instigation of the General, wandered away from our host, the patron, who was showing the party from Valparaiso around the hacienda buildings and gardens; and we left Florence and Laura, the General's señora, to complete the tour. Doubtless they did quite well without us.

We had in mind a little plant hunting in the hills that formed the eastern border of the great estate. There the General promised to find for us some extra fine specimens of *Puya,* one of the most impressive and decorative of all Chilean plants. The genus *Puya* belongs to the Bromeliaceae or Pineapple family and has representatives, mostly near the coast, in both Chile and Peru. They are essentially plants of arid terrain and grow successfully on barren ocean cliffs and on rocky shoulders thrusting out through the thin soil that covers the coastal mountains; they form one of the most characteristic elements of the vegetation of the Vale of Paradise.

As usual the General did not disappoint us, for as soon as we approached our destination we began to see on the skyline above the low ridges a serrated fence of unequally spaced, dark-green posts which, on closer approach, looked more and more like the gun swabs of Civil War days standing at attention. They were, actually, the flowering stems of Puyas which rose five to eight feet, each one from its own round green bed of long, leathery, straplike, sharp-pointed leaves whose edges are dangerously keen as well as spiny. For over three-quarters of their length the flower stalks run up clear; and then abruptly comes a compact, cylindrical head eight inches in diameter, in which are closely set hundreds of inch-and-a-half long, half-inch wide, vaselike flowers.

The Puyas that the General found for us that day showed silvery gray-green stems with flowers colored a somewhat unfamiliar but nonetheless attractive shade of light blue-green. Farther north and nearer the sea we found the still more decorative species or variety in which the equally tall flowering stem and its apical subdivisions in the inflorescence are brilliant scarlet, while the flowers in the tight heads are a bright, shining steel-gray. These massive Chilean pineapple relatives deserve more attention as garden plants than they have hitherto obtained. Now and then they are grown in California and fill a garden corner impressively, give height to a slight eminence, or provide an accent point on the margin of a large rockery. But they could successfully and appropriately be used in far more California gardens. Some of the best Chilean races of *Puya* have been offered for sale as seed or young plants by a few English horticulturists, and grow well in parts of Devonshire, Cornwall, and Wales. In Berkeley we have grown them from seed collected in a number of different localities in central and northern Chile.

After a noon dinner with the patron and his family we drove a few miles to one of the villages. It consisted of a small store, a chapel, and a number of houses for the workers. One of the patron's sons was in charge and he kept bachelor hall in a remarkable covered wagon or caravan provided with such large wheels that it was necessary to put up a large flight of steps to reach his front door. All the villagers and numerous visitors had gathered in this little community on that Sunday afternoon because a traveling mission was to hold services in the chapel.

Both here and at the headquarters of the hacienda displays of horsemanship were arranged for our benefit. First, the Chilean cowboys or *huasos* did a little plain and fancy riding. Few of the farm laborers were dressed in the full cowboy costume, but all of them wore the typical Chilean poncho and since it was Sunday they had on their best variety of poncho. The poncho adds a great deal of animation and color to a Chilean rodeo because, as soon as the horseman gathers speed, this red, green, or variegated shoulder covering begins to rise, front and back, and flaps vigorously in the wind. The riding exhibition soon changed into something different. Horsemen in twos and threes began to rush at and jostle one another, not with intent to unhorse an antagonist but rather to demonstrate how, by clever manipulation of the horse and pressure applied at the right point and right moment, a rider's course could be effectively altered.

Late in the afternoon we returned to the main buildings

where an impromptu but more or less typical Chilean rodeo had been arranged. This performance reminded us of the more elaborate affair we had seen some years before in the Santiago section of the Vale of Paradise. On that occasion we had been invited to go with the Santiago Scientific Society on their annual excursion. We accepted in the expectation that the party would inspect some nearby region of particular interest either for the botanist, zoologist, or geologist. On the appointed day some twenty members of the Society and guests left Santiago in the middle of the morning in a gondola, provided by the Government's Department of Education. After riding through the Santiago countryside for an hour and a half we arrived at the outskirts of a large hacienda. It was then explained to us that, primarily in our favor, the Society had decided to devote the excursion to attendance at a rodeo which was being held on this particular day by the patron of the hacienda we were approaching and by other large landowners of the vicinity. It was to be the one great event of the year for the country people for miles around and involved a two- or three-day celebration, of which the rodeo itself was the culminating attraction.

In a pasture near the hacienda buildings a semicircular line of booths had been set up. Outside of them ran a long railing to which many of the *huasos* had tied their horses. Some of the booths were outdoor bars, and others were hucksters' establishments where a variety of odds and ends could be bought. Some were small dance floors roofed over with branches and leaves, while a few booths served as picnic places and were provided with tables and benches. In one of these last our party established itself and then promptly dispersed to take part in the festivities and enjoy the extremely merry and animated scene.

This was our first opportunity to watch the Chilean native dance called the *cueca* which was actively under way in all the dancing booths. Some small acquaintance, subsequently gained, indicates that above all else it is an extremely vigorous form of entertainment. It is a dance that requires the maintenance of a certain rhythm and full acquaintance with a complicated series of figures, while the feet keep up a continuous combination of a shuffle, a certain amount of clogging, and a lot of heel-and-toe work. The music is provided by a violin and small harp, and the dancers receive encouragement from the spectators who continuously pound their feet and clap their hands. At the start of the dance, the gentleman and his partner come out on the dance floor and each raises one hand above his head. In this raised hand is a handkerchief, preferably a green or a red one. After a moment of moving of their feet to catch the rhythm, the couple begins to engage in a series of stampings, kickings, and hoppings, sometimes face to face, sometimes back to back, sometimes whirling about. The tempo of the dance depends upon the amount of alcohol that has been consumed, particularly by the musicians; and like all country dances the only factors that determine the duration of each round are the strength and the breath of the participants. At the beginning and end of each performance the dancing couple quaffed extremely large glasses of cider, to which had been added a certain amount of wine. It appeared that from the sale of this beverage those in charge of a dance floor and the musicians received their remuneration.

Our whole party, dressed in city clothes, attracted considerable attention, and Florence and I received the larger share since it was soon noised about that we were norteamericanos. In line with our consistent attempt in South America not to remain merely spectators but to enter, as far as possible, into the national customs and enthusiasms I attempted to take part in the cueca. This was decidedly an error of judgment, because not only did I know nothing of the dance save what I had observed in the last half hour, but I had also entirely failed to appreciate some of the ceremonial niceties connected with the performance. Thus my appearance on the dance floor and my selection of a charming country girl as my partner at first aroused great enthusiasm among the spectators. This was soon followed, however, by an embarrassing silence, particularly on the part of the musicians. It finally occurred to me that buying a drink might ease the tension. A motion of the hand was sufficient and I was promptly provided with a quart-size glass of chicha. I immediately handed it to my partner and the applause indicated this was the proper gesture. I expected, of course, that another glass would then be provided for my consumption, but not at all. My partner, after having taken a generous drink, handed the glass back and I soon discovered that I was supposed to drink, from the original glass, with all present, while an attendant stationed at my elbow refilled the glass as often as required. Apparently our quaint custom of passing along the word that somebody is "buying" also exists in Chile. At any rate in a few moments I was faced with the probability of having to share the glass with some half-hundred Chilean agriculturists. I am ashamed to say that hygienic inhibitions soon became so strong that I ignominiously retired, after providing sufficient funds for the entertainment of the entire company; and I decided to pursue my study of the cueca in private rather than in public.

Our party of scientists had, as I have said, made headquarters in one of the picnic booths. After my unfortunate experience with the cueca I retired to this booth to find that the party was preparing to eat luncheon. A rather strong wine punch made its appearance first and full glasses were served all around; but having just come from the consumption of a considerable amount of alcohol my enthusiasm for more was not very great. Thus, when the second round was being served it was discovered that my first round had not been entirely consumed. When I made it clear that I really did not care for anything more to drink, my half-filled glass was promptly poured back into the large pitcher containing the punch supply. This last blow was on the point of taking away my appetite, not only for the drink but also for food, when a messenger arrived with an invitation for Florence and myself to be guests of the patron of the hacienda at a special luncheon which he was giving. At first we declined since we were already guests of the scientific group. They, however, strongly urged us to accept. We thereupon accompanied the messenger and the two or three other members of the scientific party, who also had been invited, to the great ranch house where we met the patron. He proved to be a man of about thirty years, good-looking, charming, and cultured. He was dressed in the height of *huaso* fashion, including tight-fitting trousers reaching to the shoe tops, which from shoes to knees were covered with heavy leather leggings. Under a short, black velvet jacket he wore a white silk shirt, and over the jacket a small bright poncho made of soft, finely woven wool on which large roses were embroidered in silk. We were subsequently told that such a poncho was probably an heirloom and might be worth as much as three hundred dollars. His hat was the typical, broad-brimmed, low-crowned felt affair, decorated with a brilliant hatband from which extended strands of wool tipped with colored woolen balls, and reminiscent of an Andalusian type of headgear.

We found him on the pathway leading to the door of his wide-spreading ranch house with a servant engaged in unbuckling his high leggings. He told us that he had seen our pictures in the Santiago paper and when our scientific party arrived had immediately identified us among the Chileans. He was a bachelor and it was soon apparent that he had made the rodeo an occasion for inviting a number of his gentlemen friends from the city. After we had been introduced to the other guests the whole group began to wander off to a nearby grove of trees where a large luncheon table had been spread. Not until we were all seated—some thirty-five of us—did it occur simultaneously to Florence and to me that she was the only woman in the party.

From the character of the decorations and table service we saw that this was not a picnic but, rather, a decidedly formal luncheon, even though most of the ranch owners and some of the city guests were dressed in huaso costume. A flock of waiters and waitresses in white jackets, aprons, and gloves stood behind the chairs. At each place were bottles of both white and red wine and no invitation was necessary to start it flowing as the first course. Thereafter came a series of courses, the principal one being a choice of barbecued beef, sheep, or young goat. All the men knew each other quite intimately but they vied with one another in trying to make us feel a part of the occasion. Their courteous and friendly attentions were particularly directed toward Florence to whom they explained the intricacies of a Chilean *asado,* the barbecuing of meat, and from whom they repeatedly asked for an expression of our reactions—hopefully pleasant, of course—to Chile and its inhabitants. Many toasts were drunk including one to the United States and another to the success of our plant hunting in Chile.

Indeed our healths were proposed so repeatedly that finally we hesitated to raise our eyes for fear of catching those of someone across the table who would immediately propose a health. In a weak and thoughtless moment I referred to the various ceremonies connected with the drinking of a *skol* in Sweden. I was then called upon to stand and demonstrate the ceremony— eye to eye, glass up to the third vest button, drink, glass down to the fourth vest button, and so on. Before I knew it I found that I was being asked to carry on an individual demonstration with most of the others present.

With an eye to the effect upon me of adding thirty-five healths to those which I had already drunk Florence thoughtfully created a diversion by inviting the entire company to visit us in California. This shifted attention from me and at once resulted in an enthusiastic exchange of calling cards because, following her invitation to our home, each of the men present promptly invited us to his, accompanied by the correct, and by no means insincere, "my home is your home." Most of the men produced calling cards which began to accumulate in a pile in front of Florence's plate. Some wrote their names and addresses on pieces of paper. I observed that one fat and jolly gentleman, the uncle of the patron and owner of a nearby hacienda, was proceeding to write his name on a one-hundred-peso note. This did not appeal to me, but I was seated so far from Florence that I had no opportunity of suggesting that some way be found not to accept uncle's very thoughtful attention. She was, however, quite equal to the emergency. When the one-hundred-peso note with the gentleman's name attached reached her she promptly proceeded to write her name on another part of it, and with salutations returned it to its original owner. This was received with great applause by the assembled company.

When the last health had been drunk we left the table and proceeded to the rodeo. A circle of level ground about an acre in extent had been surrounded with a barrier made of eight-foot uprights heavily surfaced inside with saplings and brush. A small segment was similarly walled off with openings left at either end of the wall to give access into the larger area. Within this segment twenty or thirty lively calves had been driven. For the patron and his guests there was a small high grandstand behind the calf corral and across from us, on the far side of the circular rodeo field, was another, larger grandstand for the country people.

When the patron and his guests were seated the mounted huasos who were to take part in the rodeo arranged themselves in a line in front of us and acknowledged the patron's presence by removing their hats and bowing. Then they lined up with their horses backed against the outer side of the calf corral. At a signal from the patron the rodeo began. Two huasos left the line, saluted the patron, rode into the corral, forced their way among the noisily protesting calves, and proceeded to "cut out" the animal of their choice. When they had succeeded in forcing him to one of the exits from the corral the excitement began. The calf promptly attempted to break away into the arena, whereas the huasos had something quite different in mind. They proposed to drive the calf three times back and forth along the circular barrier without permitting him to escape them, the performance being carried on at top speed. While one huaso began to drive the calf with whip and yells, the other member of the team rode at the calf's shoulder and attempted to keep the animal running continuously beside the barrier. Just before the calf reached a point in front of our grandstand he had to be turned about and started back in the opposite direction. This job fell primarily to the huaso who had been riding beside the calf. Putting on a burst of speed he advanced a half-length ahead of the calf and, turning his horse sharply at right angles, rode head on into the barrier. This immediately checked the forward progress of the calf which, if wise, turned directly about and began to retrace his steps. Thereupon the huasos reversed positions: the one who had been riding at the calf's shoulder now pursued the calf and the other one took the shoulder position. Just before reaching the calf corral they engineered another about-face and so reversed their positions again. When they had successfully repeated this performance three times the calf was permitted to escape through an opening just beneath our grandstand. The two huasos then returned to their positions in the line and were greeted with groans or cheers, depending upon whether or

not the calf had escaped them for a moment or two or whether
they had or had not successfully demonstrated certain refinements in the correct technique, which we were unable to
appreciate. With varying fortunes all the other huasos, in teams
of two, carried out a similar performance.

For the spectator the excitement was almost continuous
and for the huasos it must have been a strenuous hour and
a half. The calves were big, tough, fast, and very fractious, and
knew their own minds from start to finish of each round. Obviously it needed much practice, as well as a special timing and
perfect co-ordination between horse and rider, to turn the calf
without letting him get away. Most of the huasos in the rodeo
were older men, large and powerful, and, in some instances,
seemingly too heavy for the horses they rode. The best strains
of Chilean horses have a certain amount of Arabian blood and
appear to be rather light in the legs. One particularly large cowboy, when he drove his horse into the barrier, must have put
too much weight on its front legs; at any rate the horse stumbled and the rider was thrown. He got up almost at once, caught
his horse, mounted it, and completed the sequence of three
turns back and forth. We noted, however, that he did not return to his place in the line, and we learned afterwards that he
had broken his hip in the fall. How he managed to remount his
horse and carry on is hard to understand. When the rodeo was
over prizes were distributed with much enthusiastic comment
from the persons seated in both grandstands.

After the rodeo our original party gradually reassembled
and prepared to return to Santiago in the big gondola. The
afternoon had turned out to be rather warm and everyone had
consumed a certain amount of alcohol, with the result that we,
at least, looked forward to a peaceful, sleepy ride. However, just
as the bus was ready to leave a Santiago policeman appeared
and asked for a lift. He was in full uniform and presumably
had been sent out to the rodeo to see that order was kept. As
soon as he had seated himself next to the driver we realized that
he had succeeded in enjoying himself along with the carrying
out of his official duties. In a loud voice and with many gestures
he began to explain to the driver that from his point of view the
rodeo had been an exceedingly successful affair. Certain mem-

bers of our party were much amused by the policeman's remarks. This encouragement produced a result that was a little
unexpected, at least to Florence and me. Struggling to his feet
in the swaying bus and supporting himself with an arm around
the post that ran up behind the driver's seat our friend the
policeman proceeded to give us an impassioned oration. He
began rather slowly and deliberately but gathered power and
enthusiasm as he went along. From time to time he yelled loudly
and gesticulated wildly with his free arm and even, now and
then, forgot the necessity of the support which the other arm
gave him. On such occasions he lurched violently back and
forth but always succeeded in keeping on his feet. It was impossible for us to understand more than a fraction of the policeman's remarks. We were told, however, that he was extolling
the ancient and modern virtues of his native land, recounting
Chilean history in a somewhat garbled fashion, and in general
making the Chilean eagle scream. He left us as the bus approached the suburbs of Santiago.

First and last, we lived for two months in Santiago, Chile's
capital. A considerably larger city than Valparaiso, it is also
more active and vigorous, with most of the best hotels and shops
in Chile. The foothills of the Chilean Andes begin to rise rapidly behind Santiago which lies at an altitude of a little over
fifteen hundred feet. In the wintertime these first ridges of the
Andes, as well as the far higher, serrated backbone of the continent on the horizon, are snow-covered; and in summer when
the snow is gone from the lower ridges you plainly see the great
range, covered with perpetual snow, standing out sharp and
clear. After living awhile in Santiago the visitor almost unconsciously glances up each eastward running street to catch a
glimpse of the city's tremendous, snow-capped Andean back-
drop.

We always stopped at the Hotel Savoy and, in favor of se-
curing the maximum amount of light and air, selected a front
room on an upper floor. The hotel faced one of the main but
not wide streets, along which flowed a continuous stream of
traffic and on which one-way streetcars were constantly running.
The noise was pretty bad but we managed to adjust ourselves
to it except when it continued too far on into the night.

A certain proportion of the Chilean population is much addicted to gambling. Late at night when other, more sophisticated opportunities for wagering failed, the die-hard remnants of the sporting fraternity gathered to bet on streetcar numbers. Four or five car lines originated on our street, later to branch out into other parts of the city and suburbs. Thus a sequence of different numbers might be expected to appear. This desirable condition of affairs plus proximity of the hotel bar resulted in a gathering every few nights on the sidewalk beneath our windows. From ten to twenty men would assemble, place their bets in rather loud voices, and then in noisy anticipation listen for the approach of a streetcar. As soon as it was spotted the number would be shouted out by the keenest sighted. A great uproar followed as the winners congratulated each other vociferously and the losers very audibly commiserated with one another. At first there was a certain novelty about this performance and we would hang out of our windows to follow the course of the betting. The novelty rapidly wore off as need of sleep asserted itself. We therefore provided a pitcher of water on the window sill and when once well awakened proceeded to pour it over the assembled gamblers. This treatment was temporarily effective and was accepted quite good-naturedly by those below. I felt constantly worried, however, because in the rather dim light it was difficult to determine whether or not a policeman was among the group. If this ever occurred he must have accepted our technique of noise abatement as good-naturedly as the gamblers because we never received any official reaction. However, nothing permanent was accomplished by the sprinkling method. Within a few days much the same group, to judge by their voices, once more took up headquarters underneath our window.

In Lima, Valparaiso, and Santiago, the largest cities on the West Coast and the ones we know best, there are almost no florists' shops worthy of the name, and as few nurseries. This is largely due to the poverty of all the working classes who cannot afford to buy plants or flowers except occasionally, and then only in the markets or on street corners. In addition, the relatively few wealthy people grow flowers for cutting in their

Agaves and *Cephalocereus* dispute with Bob an Andean foothill trail

Effect of back lighting on Andean cacti (*Opuntia* sp.) and Harvey

Chilean cacti flowering in the Botanical Garden, Berkeley, California

One of the many woolly as well as spiny Peruvian cacti in flower

In the highlands of southeastern Peru this powerful cactus (*Trichocereus* sp.)
makes an effective fence around homes and corrals

Still legible after 15 years is this Peruvian patriot's cactus lament:
Peru, beloved native land. Fate one day attacked you in the bosom cruelly with
the sword and I am downcast but not humiliated. My lips quiver in agony.

large gardens, which can be maintained at little cost because labor is cheap and the climate is optimum for plant growth.

The one or two flower shops we saw in Santiago contained nothing of interest. We had been collecting so many, for us, new and desirable ornamental native Chilean species, many of which grew wild and in profusion almost on the florist's doorstep, that it was hard to understand why he filled his windows with the tame and far less attractive plants that can be bought, but not so cheap, in any flower shop in North America. Of course, this was a simple-minded attitude on our part. The public in Chile, in the United States, and everywhere else is not going to pay money for native plants which theoretically can be, and, alas, actually are to be, obtained for nothing more than despoliation of the neighboring landscape. Then, too, such plants are local and familiar, and a person has a right to expect something a bit foreign or peculiar in the way of flowers if he is prepared to pay for them. Originally, of course, all the commercial plantsman's novelties, and the old favorites too, came from the wild. It is what has happened to them since their introduction into cultivation in the way of selection for a variety of desirable characters that makes them salable, in preference to their wild relatives. Still, I did continue to protest inwardly against popular Santiago florists' assortments of small South African and other foreign cacti—grown in Germany and imported under the barter system; for on the foothills of the nearby Andes anyone could find just as attractive and far better grown members of this prickly fraternity.

The racing season in Santiago is eagerly looked forward to. The Club Hipico is a large and elaborate establishment, and the grandstand has a magnificent view of the snowy Andes. Until public gatherings were banned because of a threatened outbreak of plague we went a number of times to the races. I shall always remember one of these occasions. At the Savoy was an Italian manufacturer whom we had met on the steamer from San Francisco to Valparaiso. All over the world he sells the hat-manufacturing machinery which he builds in his Milan factory. One day at lunch Guido announced excitedly that he had discovered a fellow countryman who knew someone who had horses at the race track. This, of course, meant that he should be able to get some hot second-hand tips on the afternoon's races. I agreed to the proposal that we should go and also try our luck, but insisted that our total combined investment should not exceed twenty dollars. This amounted to about six hundred Chilean pesos. After paying transportation to the races and entrance fees to the grandstand we had more or less five hundred left.

Florence urged the desirability of taking an open horse-drawn vehicle rather than a taxicab. In foreign countries, horse carriages are cheaper than taxis and women usually prefer the slow-moving hack because it gives them a better chance of doing a little window-shopping. On the other hand, in my experience, it usually includes a distinctly salivary current of air from both horse and driver and attracts usually unintelligible but obviously personal comment from the youth on the sidewalks. However, I have ridden in them through a number of the world's capitals and am inured to their hazards and discomforts. Despite my best endeavors to walk only on main thoroughfares where taxis alone should exist, a cruising horse-drawn equipage rarely fails to appear at the moment we need transportation; and Florence hails it with such delight and anticipation that I have not the heart to protest.

At the race track Guido sought his Italian friend. Just as the first race was beginning he returned, looking worried, to tell us that he could not find his friend. In the interval between the first and second race he tried again without success. We therefore decided to do the best that we could without expert advice. Scanning the list of entries for the third race we read that the owner's colors in one instance included orange. Since orange was the color of the dress that Florence happened to be wearing we decided to bet half our pesos on the horse carrying this color. Such a method of picking a winner appealed to me as the surest and quickest way to exhaust our stock of money, and thereafter we would be able to view the remaining races in peace and comfort. When Guido placed the bet he discovered that our horse carried extremely long odds. This further convinced me that we had selected an entirely erroneous system. I was therefore the most surprised member of our group when our horse won handily. Collected by Guido, our winnings

totaled a good many pieces of Chilean paper money which we
bestowed about our persons.

Our selection for the next race was based upon Florence's
discovery that one of the horses had a name that vaguely suggested that of the city in which she was born. To put an end
to the suspense as rapidly as possible, I suggested that we bet
all that we had on the horse of Florence's choice. The odds in
this case were not so much in our favor—but our horse won.

At this point I began to be considerably interested. To test
our system without additional risk I advised against betting in
the next race, knowing full well that this would not deter Florence from making a selection. When this selection won I knew
that something had happened to us, and I insisted that all our
winnings be placed on Florence's choice for the following, the
next-to-the-last, race. Her selection was as arbitrary as before,
but once more we won.

Since we had pyramided all bets, our accumulation of low
denominations of Chilean paper money was enormous and filled
every pocket and Florence's handbag. For the last race we decided upon the grand plunge. We would bet all our winnings,
plus the residue of what we had originally brought with us
(less only the cost of taxi fare back to the hotel), upon a horse
of Florence's choosing. She promptly pointed out that one of
the horses was wearing colors which could be interpreted as
blue and gold, the official colors of our University of California.
We assisted Guido in concentrating our multitudinous pesos
into two large rolls which he placed in the side pockets of his
coat, and keeping his hands on them he walked out of the grandstand to the betting booths below. He returned betimes,
wreathed in smiles and with the announcement that at last he
had met his long-sought Italian friend who had given him the
hottest kind of a tip on the last race. Instead of betting on Blue
and Gold, therefore, he had placed our money on another
horse. It is hardly necessary to state that Blue and Gold won.

Most of our days in Santiago were spent at work in the
Museo de Historia Natural, which is to be found in the Quinta
Normal, a park about a mile from the center of the city. A good
many years ago Dr. R. A. Philippi, the most famous of Chilean
botanists, during his long term as director of this museum,

planted around it an interesting and unusual collection of trees and shrubs. Many of the species he planted became well established and grew rapidly in the exceptionally favorable climate of Santiago. Although long since abandoned as a botanical garden, a considerable number of fine, mature specimens of native and introduced trees are still preserved.

We did our work in the botanical section of the museum, and particularly in the two or three rooms in which the collections of dried plants are housed. These collections have a great importance for the students of the floras of the Andes and the Chilean coast, because preserved in them are the original plants which Philippi collected during his many extended journeys north and south throughout Chile.

Many of the plants he collected had previously been unknown and so he was at liberty to give them names and to describe them. Philippi's descriptions of these new species were published in Chilean and other scientific journals. Subsequently other botanists collected in the same areas where Philippi had made his collections and oftentimes, as we did, succeeded in finding many of the plants which Philippi first named. Usually Philippi's published descriptions of the new species he had found were sufficiently detailed and accurate so that other botanists have been able either to identify the plants they collected as equivalent to his, or to be sure that their plants are themselves new and unnamed and undescribed. But sometimes there is considerable doubt and then it is important to be able to see the actual dried specimen which Philippi named, called the "type" specimen. This was particularly important in my case, because Philippi had collected and described many species of *Nicotiana;* and, being on the ground and having an opportunity to do so, I wanted to see the original specimens in every case and be able to describe them myself, photograph them, and make drawings of them. I had also been asked to examine type specimens of other plant genera by research men working on them in the United States and in England. The Director of the Museum, Don Ricardo Latcham, was extremely kind and co-operative, as was Señor Espinosa, who has the herbarium in charge. We were given a table at which to work and the privilege of examining all the specimens in the cases.

Unfortunately, little money has been made available by the government for the care of collections of all sorts in this museum. Despite the best efforts of the staff, the dried plants have not been fumigated against museum insects as thoroughly as they should have been, and in general they have not received the attention that such valuable collections deserve. In the case of the plant groups on which we were working, we suggested that we would be glad to undertake a systematic cleaning and arrangement of them. It seemed to us a small acknowledgment of all the kindness and courtesy we were receiving; but it proved to be a considerable piece of work. Sometimes the specimens were a little mixed because of the combination of more than one collection in a single paper container and because the specimens were unmounted. This made it necessary to refer to the original descriptions of the plants and endeavor by means of the localities which were attached on bits of paper to the plants, together with the numbers that sometimes appeared on slips of paper, to organize the specimens correctly.

In the case of the Nicotianas and some of their relatives—*Petunia, Salpiglossis, Nierembergia,* and *Fabiana*—we made intensive studies of the priceless specimens which we spread out before us; and I found that many of the questions I had been asking myself about the plants Philippi had described were being answered. Florence made many drawings of specimens that were of special interest. From time to time during our days in the botanical section of the museum other foreign botanists appeared and were equally delighted at the chance of seeing at first hand just what Philippi had collected so many years ago among the plants with which they were working.

Don Ricardo, the director, is an archaeologist and has made many important collections, particularly on the northern coast of Chile. He had on display in the museum remarkably complete evidences of the life and culture of the ancient peoples who, if they did not live there, certainly buried their dead in the deserts of north coastal Chile. I was especially interested in the corn that Don Ricardo has found there in what he believes to be twelfth-century burials. The remarkable thing about Don Ricardo's corn was the fact that it consisted largely of a variety of popcorn. Those pre-Inca inhabitants of Chile who grew it had evidently learned that application of heat would cause the kernels of this kind of corn to explode and become transformed into delicate white material. They must have highly esteemed this popped corn or for them it must have had ceremonial significance, because Don Ricardo almost always found little bowls or cotton bags filled with it beside the mummified bodies. Some of the ears, midget ones with every kernel in place, were also found in the graves, and Don Ricardo was good enough to give me a fine one along with a few pieces of the popped corn.

After our return to California I put this ear of ancient popcorn in one of the Inca bowls that adorned our living-room table. Along with other South American antiquities we exhibited it to our friends and recited our little story of where it had been found, and so on. As friends always do under such circumstances, ours took a courteous if not too sustained or intelligent interest in the objects we showed them. They showed some special interest in the little ear of corn but, alas, only because they wanted to test the firmness with which the kernels were fixed upon the cob. I suddenly discovered that there were more kernels off the cob than on it, and promptly withdrew the corn exhibit from circulation.

One cold, wet winter evening it occurred to me to try an experiment with these kernels of pre-Inca popcorn. I placed a few on a tin pie plate and put the combination on the electric range in the kitchen. Much to my surprise that corn, which had been gathered perhaps a thousand years ago, popped as readily as did last year's crop that had come in a box from the shelves of the neighborhood cash-and-carry store. Today a tin pie plate on an electric stove; yesterday the campfire or primitive hearth and a flat stone or a clay bowl! I thought that I caught a glimpse of those faces dimly seen in the flickering light of that fire which burned so long ago, the strong features, the high cheekbones; and in the shadows I thought I saw the long, brilliantly embroidered robes of cotton, the bright scarves of llama wool, the feathered headdresses and the golden breastplates.

The next morning I took the newly popped corn to my eight o'clock class at the university. The lecture was supposed to be concerned with the microscopical anatomy of the living cell, but I found a spot at which my experiment of the previous

evening could be dragged in and its result displayed. At the
end of the lecture a number of those students who are always
willing to humor the vagaries and enthusiasms of the professor,
gathered round the lecture desk to examine my popped corn.
One asked permission to sample a few kernels. Since this appeared to be a natural request and one that might sustain interest for a longer period in my popped corn, I willingly agreed.
The rest of the students came closer and watched the mastica-
tion with interest. At first the experiment seemed to be going
well, but suddenly a horrified expression appeared upon the
face of the experimenter; he violently expelled as much of the
popcorn as he had not already swallowed, and showed signs of
desiring to be rid of all of it. It suddenly occurred to me that
since the corn had originally been in a museum it might have
been impregnated there with poison to discourage insect attack.
Fortunately, however, the unpleasant outcome of the student's
scientific curiosity was due to nothing more serious than cam-
phor with which, as I somewhat tardily recollected, the ear of
corn had been sprinkled before shipment to California. During
the remainder of the semester I sensed a certain reserve in the
camphorated student's personal attitude toward me, and it came
into my mind that he actually thought that I had perpetrated a
practical joke. At any rate, since that episode I have strictly
confined my lectures and demonstrations to the announced subject of the course.

During our days in the Vale of Paradise we met Sr. Gaul-
terio Looser who is one of the best known amateur botanists
in Chile. For many years he has collected Chilean plants, of
which he has a small but well-kept and valuable herbarium. He
generously shared with us many of his duplicate specimens and
gave us much important advice about collecting areas and the
seasons during which they could be most profitably visited.

One exceedingly hot day early in December he and I made
a collecting trip into the dry, hilly, plateau country that lies a
little northwest of Santiago. I wanted to find out whether the
subalpine species of *Nicotiana* came down from the foothills of
the Andes east of Santiago into this lower altitude; and also
whether the coastal species so often found near Valparaiso extended their distribution any great distance eastward. Except in

the mountains where, of course, it is considerably later, the main
blooming period of native plants in central Chile occurs during October if the season is a normal one. The rain, which falls
only during the southern winter—from April or May to September or October—rarely amounts to a total of more than
about fifteen inches each year; but in dry years the rainfall may
be reduced to only seven or eight inches. Unfortunately for
the vegetation and thus for us also, the two years during which
we collected in Chile were both dry ones. As a result the countryside in which Looser and I were to botanize so relatively late
in the collecting season showed few plants in flower.

During our many months in Chile I was repeatedly reminded of California, and on this occasion I could readily have
imagined that I had been suddenly transferred to the foothills
of the Californian Sierras in summer. I saw the same intensely
brilliant, vivid blue sky. There was the same brittle quality in the atmosphere, the same warm brown mantle spread
over hills and valleys and plains—a mantle striped in the same
fashion with thin bands of green to show where declining
streams or deep, shaded canyons alone supported a vigorous
growth of trees and shrubs.

The region we were in was familiar ground to Looser
where he was certain that some years before he had seen plants
of the Nicotianas that I sought. At first we tramped along rough
country roads leading through broad valleys in which small isolated farms were scattered here and there. Then we began to
follow cattle paths out into the uncultivated, hilly countryside.
In the bottoms of deeper valleys and along the lower contours
of north-facing slopes we saw clear evidence that an herbaceous
spring vegetation had been in bloom a month or two before.
Now, the plants were dead and dry, but their rapid desiccation
and the lack of rain since their blooming had preserved them in
remarkably lifelike condition; ghosts of their former splendor
so perfectly intact that often it was possible to identify them
long after death.

On this mummified vegetation there was an abundance of
mature fruits, and Looser and I filled many envelopes with seed
of some of the handsome Chilean plants which in early October
I had seen in full flower nearer Valparaiso. It was easy in imagi-

nation to transform the brown landscape into its spring background of green, on which would be painted sky-blue fields of the Chilean lily called "the glory of the sun"—sky-blue fields that would be rimmed and veined with the rich dark blue of *Conanthera,* and in the lush valleys a mist of delicate lavender *Godetia.*

From time to time bulbs of *Leucocoryne—ixioides* and other unnamed species, all of which are called "the glory of the sun"—have been introduced into cultivation. Some years ago Clarence Elliot, the well-known English plant hunter, dug many thousands of *Leucocoryne* bulbs from the hillsides of central Chile and grew them in his Thames Valley nursery. Both he and certain California horticulturists have greatly improved the average wild plant of *Leucocoryne* by repeated selection for vigor, flower size, and flower color; and fine strains of this fragrant, blue-flowered lily are now available. For me these improved strains have not nearly the charm that their wild relatives possess. We saw them growing close together and blooming by the hundreds, perhaps thousands, in more than one part of the Vale of Paradise; and a single glance revealed a wide range of variation in all plant characters, but particularly in flower color. Beginning with pure white or cream there was a graded series of soft pastel lavenders and blues which culminated in the brilliant, hard sky-blue which is the horticulturally popular, but to me least attractive shade for *Leucocoryne.*

The Conantheras are all Chilean and are by no means as well known elsewhere as the Leucocorynes, or as they deserve to be. From a rosette of leaves they send up a number of thin, wiry, foot-long flowering stems; these are topped with four to six half-erect, nodding, intensely dark-blue, broadly bell-shaped, inch-wide flowers. In their natural environment the Conantheras seek full exposure in well-drained soil and so appear within rocky outcroppings and along gravelly rifts in the heavy soil which *Leucocoryne* prefers.

In Berkeley we have grown many thousands of these small but charming and horticulturally useful bulbs which came from lower altitudes in central Chile. The culture of all of them is much the same and we have had success with them when properly grown.

The dusty heat didn't seem to bother Looser but it bothered me considerably. Perhaps this was because I had been doing my walking and climbing at higher altitudes, where the atmosphere is more stimulating and where the heat is tempered by tag ends of vagrant breezes that carry a breath of cool freshness from the snowfields over which they are borne. Finally, I had to ask for a respite and we decided to stop and eat an early lunch. It was not too easy to find the shady spot which I, at least, longed for, because the hillsides in the more mountainous and more arid country we had begun to traverse were covered with nothing but columnar cacti; and the valley bottoms were overgrown with tangles of spiny shrubs among which I recognized species of *Acacia, Adesmia,* and *Proustia.* We therefore struck off to the west toward a stream which, true to Looser's promise, we found on the other side of a ridge. Although it had long since completely dried up, its sandy bed was bordered by a few small trees whose roots doubtless found subsoil stores of moisture along its course.

I picked out the shade of the first of these trees and was on the point of settling down beneath it when Looser warned me off. He explained that my tree selection was the much feared *litre (Lithraea caustica)*, from contact with which many people receive a quite serious dermatitis. It belongs to the Anacardiaceae, a family of which our poison ivy *(Rhus toxicodendron)* of the Eastern States and Middle West and the equally dangerous poison oak *(Rhus diversiloba)* of the Pacific Coast are also members.

Further down the drywash we found shade under a young and not too vigorous specimen of *Peumus boldus.* When well grown this Chilean tree is attractive with its deep, compact crown of dark-green leaves, which in shape resemble those of the California live oak. The crushed leaves emit a pleasant, spicy fragrance. When we were entertained in Chilean homes we learned to expect a choice of after-dinner beverages—coffee or *boldo,* the latter a cup of boiling water in which a dried leaf or two of *Peumus boldus* was steeping, sometimes with a smaller leaf of lemon verbena added. We always chose boldo, partly because it was a novelty, but mainly because it was remarkably refreshing and sleeplessness did not lie in its cup.

As we consumed the contents of our knapsacks Looser told me about the occurrence in central Chile of a few small, isolated areas, some of them only recently discovered, in which grow many of the plants otherwise found only far to the south where the climatic conditions are entirely different. The most famous of these vegetational "islands" is the so-called "forest" of Fray Jorge which, like a green oasis, lies surrounded by the semidesert of the north central Chilean coast some three hundred miles above Valparaiso.

The vegetation of this dry region is not abundant, and the low growth-form and the compact structure of the plants that compose it show an obvious adaptation to drought conditions. It is, therefore, more than a surprise to find in the midst of such a vegetation a small forest made up of fairly sizable trees, with numerous ferns on the forest floor, and vines connecting it and the tree crowns above. Even more startling is the fact that almost all the elements of this out-of-place forest belong exclusively to southern Chile where they grow in abundance in a uniformly cool, wet climate. For example, at Fray Jorge you find such typically south Chilean plants as *Aextoxicon punctatum,* a tree of the Euphorbiaceae or Milkweed family, *Mitraria coccinea* and *Sarmienta repens,* two beautiful vines, and even *Nertera depressa,* "bead plant."

As we broached our lunch we fell to wondering how these vegetational islands came into existence. One explanation might be that in past time the climate of southern Chile with its heavier rainfall and lower temperatures must also have been the climate of middle and, at least in part, of northern Chile, which today is so dry and warm. Moreover, the fact that the Fray Jorge plants are identical—species for species—with those which today grow farther south means that from a geological standpoint the change in central and northern Chile from a cool, wet climate to a warm, dry one, must have occurred relatively recently. We reasoned this out in the following way. Suppose such a distinct climatic alteration had taken place at an early period in the earth history of that part of the West Coast of South America which we today refer to as central and north central Chile. Then evolutionary processes, which are always at work everywhere, would certainly, during the long interim, have pro-

duced visible changes in the form and structure of those groups
of plants that survived the climatic alteration in the environment. But today the relics, like the forest at Fray Jorge, of the
vegetation which we assume to have once covered central and
north central Chile show no such distinction in form and structure—no adaptation to their present warm, dry surroundings—
when compared with the same species in the south. It seems fair,
therefore, to say that the climatic alteration that took place up
the Chilean coast occurred too short a time ago to permit evolutionary processes to do their work. . . . It was, however, too
hot a day to prolong this somewhat academic discussion, and
Looser and I soon replaced it with a siesta, to which in Latin
America the hour following luncheon is universally dedicated.

Toward the end of our discussion and just before the siesta
my attention had wandered toward a group of plants that grew
on the opposite side of the dry stream. As, from a distance I
had suspected, they later proved to be plants of *Nicotiana
acuminata,* the coastal species, and precisely what we had been
looking for all the morning. Growing in almost pure sand on
the banks and in the dry bed of the stream, the Chilean habitat
of these tobacco relatives corresponded to that of the places near
the coasts of California and Washington where this typically
Chilean species is now and then to be found. The seeds of the
tobacco plant and its relatives are extremely small and light
and have rough, catching surfaces. Lodged in and under the
feathers of some of the birds that annually make the tremendous
round trip from almost the northern to almost the southern extremity of the western edge of the two Americas, the seeds of
Nicotiana acuminata have been carried to the Pacific Coast of
North America. Many years ago I saw for the first time this
Chilean *Nicotiana* growing in small quantity but quite happily
in the dry, sandy, summer bed of Niles Creek which empties
into the southern end of San Francisco Bay. Later I found it
north of San Francisco, again in dry, sandy soil, on the banks of
Napa River. Others have collected it near the mouth of the
Columbia.

On the Australian continent there are a number of native
species of *Nicotiana,* each of which has a somewhat distinct geographical center of distribution. The early plant hunters found

these different Nicotianas only in or near these centers of distribution. Today, however, some of the species have spread considerably beyond their original domains and have intermingled extensively. As already mentioned, this recent plant migration undoubtedly took place during the period when the cattle industry was beginning to assume importance in parts of Australia and when herds were driven across country for great distances in search of pasturage or to market. On the rough, shaggy coats of the cattle the small, clinging seeds of trailside plants of *Nicotiana* were caught and then were transferred from their original habitats to others far distant; and there, now and then at least, they fell on fertile soil and, if the climate was favorable, grew and even flourished.

Man has consciously, and for a variety of good reasons, shifted plants back and forth from one part of the globe to another, but some of his plant introductions have been entirely unconscious ones. In ancient times and down to recent days ships were ballasted with rocks, rubble, and soil, gathered up on the shores of those distant harbors where their cargoes were discharged. When in some other port another cargo was found the sailors threw the ballast out to add to the debris accumulated near a home or foreign dockside. With each exchange of ballast between the ports of the world went seeds of a variety of plants. Many of them were cosmopolitan weeds of ancient lineage, but some were hardy representatives of a local flora; and all of them that could survive in any of the climates to which they had been given free transportation grew and bloomed and shed their seed on the ballast heaps. As such "ballast weeds" a number of South American *Nicotiana* species have appeared in various warm-temperate portions of the world; and often they have extended themselves far beyond the port to which they were originally brought.

The most widely traveled or at least the most climatically adaptable of these South American Nicotianas is a species called *glauca*. This species is referred to as "yellow tree tobacco" in California where it has so long become naturalized along highways near the coast that present day Californians, who sometimes grow the plant in their gardens, consider it a part of the native vegetation. On the lower west coast of Mexico it prob-

ably arrived somewhat later; but at any rate it has found conditions so much to its liking that it has completely taken over
considerable tracts of land and is looked upon as a most undesirable visitor. In parts of Australia it has gained a substantial
foothold, and a reward is now offered for its destruction on the
ground that it is poisonous to stock. It has been collected on all
but the most tropical coasts of South America, in the Canary
and Cape Verde Islands, and in Egypt, and doubtless can be
found growing in other regions equally distant from its Argentine home. For, despite local claims upon it as a native plant
elsewhere, *Nicotiana glauca* for many centuries lived only in
the foothills of the Andes in northwestern Argentina; and it
was man who carried it with him to the sea and thence in his
ships to the wide world.

Looser and I followed a different route on our return journey. Along it we slowed down to watch an amusing affair which
doubtless is being continuously repeated wherever in Chile,
and Peru also, goats and the tall columnar cacti of the Cereus
group are living in the same region. Goats, by the way, came to
the west coast of South America with the conquistadors and
during the intervening four hundred years have destroyed a lot
of native vegetation. In places where they are pastured—and in
how few they are not—the plant hunter despairs of arriving
early enough in the spring or getting up early enough in the
morning to anticipate the goats which nibble every green thing
down to the very level of the soil. As a result, the end of the
summer season finds them with a very limited supply even of
dry forage. They then proceed to eat cacti and especially the
somewhat less well-armed Bromeliads, except those species
whose spines are long and tough enough to penetrate horny
hoofs and leathery mouths.

On the barren hillsides which we were crossing, thousands
of tall Cerii—slender, fluted, dark-green, spiny columns—were
coming into bloom. These majestic cacti, giant candelabra,
were often fifteen feet high and a foot in diameter at the base.
The long yellow-green buds and large white flowers were borne
at intervals up the leafless trunks and opened in sequence beginning a few feet up from the ground.

On a steep slope a small herd of goats wandered in seem-

ingly aimless fashion through this scattered forest of green
columns. After watching them for a while I realized that there
was a definite purpose behind this wandering, because whenever a goat passed one of the tall cacti he cocked an eye upward.
The goats were methodically examining every plant to determine whether there were any buds or flowers within the limit of
their maximum capacity to stretch upward. Finally an old ram
decided that he could reach the lowermost of a series of fine
fresh flowers high up on the side of a big cactus which, unfortunately for him, happened to be growing on one of the steepest parts of the hillside. From long practice he thoroughly understood the technique required. Stationing himself as near as
he could to the base of the plant he settled his hind hoofs into
the soil and sprang straight upward, to come down with forefeet
resting well up on the side of the spiny stem. Then, stretching
against the plant, he began to elongate himself. First his hind
legs visibly increased in length, then his thin body, finally his
neck and head. Again and again he alternately stretched and relaxed, stretched and relaxed, but always the flower was just out
of reach of the long nibbling lips. Without warning his hind
hoofs began to slip and he slid down rapidly, leaving tufts of
hair from his belly and the inner surfaces of his front legs along
the heavily spined ridges of the cactus stem. Without pause the
old gentleman returned to the attack, and as long as we had him
in view he continued his apparently hopeless effort to secure
that tempting bite of soft, succulent plant tissue.

Later on in the afternoon these great Cerii gave me something of a shock. After being so continually present all day they
no longer possessed individuality and had completely merged
into the general landscape. Looser and I had now left the hilly
country and were following roads that ran through broad valleys. On their rather distant hillsides my eyes picked up unfamiliar dots of color which I certainly did not associate with
the tall cacti I knew must be growing there. Soon our road began to wind up a ridge, and as I approached the cacti I realized
that something had happened to them. Always before they had
been shafts of continuous green from soil line to apex, but now
their tops and sometimes their sides were painted a brilliant
scarlet. On closer examination I saw that this added color was

provided by the flowers of a species of *Phrygilanthus,* a parasitic plant or nonpaying guest, most of whose body was within the cactus feeding upon the stores of food and moisture conserved therein by its unwilling host.

During the following months I saw this phenomenon again and again. It remained, however, for me one of the most startling and in many ways one of the most attractive elements in the landscape of the Andean foothills: tawny, barren hillsides forested with gigantic cactus candles each one burning with a steady scarlet flame, or ridges dark against the evening sky fretted with black columns whose pointed apices glowed in the sunset light with living fire.

To this Santiago Museum botanists come to study the collections of the
Chilean floras made by early plant hunters

Our favorite flower vendors stood next a busy Santiago street corner near the
Hotel Savoy

Concepción's Cathedral shattered in the January, 1939, earthquake; many hundreds of dead lay under the debris that filled the city's streets

Walls and cornices buried those who fled their homes and churches

Earthquakes constitute another hazard for the motorist in Concepción

Chapter X

ROBINSON CRUSOE'S ISLE

IN NORTH AMERICA most of the dwellers in outlying areas have long since adjusted themselves to the chance naturalist—botanist, zoologist, or geologist—who pokes about, apparently more or less aimlessly, in their mountains and forests. The mountainman or backwoodsman has learned that these are quite harmless individuals impelled solely by a consuming curiosity about the animate and inanimate elements of his environment. He does not share this curiosity but he recognizes it as something real and legitimate. In South America, on the other hand, native populations are not familiar with the collector and his somewhat bizarre equipment. Nor are they at all ready to accept his explanation of his presence in parts of their domains which they know contain little of interest for the ordinary tourist. The natural resources of their home lands have for centuries been vigorously exploited by the foreigner; and so, quite naturally, they suspect the scientist from overseas of searching for something of great intrinsic value, presumably gold. That a plant, and often an inconspicuous or undesirable one, can be sought because of its scientific importance is beyond their comprehension. Even the more intelligent interpreted our explanations as indicating that we were professional gatherers of medicinal herbs which would ultimately be exposed for sale somewhere in Norteamerica. This inability to understand what we were about and the certainty that a pot of gold was directly or indirectly buried under each plant we collected, inspired a news item which appeared in a Chilean newspaper, and in translation reads as follows:

"On the Juan Fernandez Islands grows a variety of the tobacco plant, the rarest plant in all the world. It is worth five thousand dollars and a scientific institution in the United States offers this sum to the man who will present to it a plant of this tobacco."

This statement, which doubtless surprised and interested its Chilean readers, approaches the truth only in one regard—

there *is* a wild relative of the cultivated tobacco plant on the Juan Fernandez Islands. Concerning its rarity we shall see later on in this chapter that it is a plant exceedingly difficult to find. The fact that I am the "scientific institution" referred to should automatically discourage anyone from attempting to collect the reward. Nevertheless I do want this plant very much, and after an explanation of why I want it I shall tell you some of the things that happen when one goes in search of it.

Well out in the Pacific, almost due west of Valparaiso, lie the Juan Fernandez Islands—Mas-a-Tierra and little Santa Clara side by side and three hundred and sixty-five miles from the mainland, and Mas-a-Fuera ninety-two miles farther west. Insular floras are likely to contain plant species peculiar to the islands in question and the Juan Fernandez group is remarkable for the large number of such endemics which grow upon them.

In 1854, Filiberto Germain, then Assistant Director of the Museo de Historia Natural in Santiago, made one of the first important collections on the outermost island, Mas-a-Fuera. Among many new plant species discovered by this pioneer naturalist was a tobacco relative later named *Nicotiana cordifolia* by Dr. Philippi. It was a rather scraggly shrub growing to six feet in height, with large, velvety-white, more or less heart-shaped leaves, and bearing masses of inch-long, reddish violet, tubular flowers. Although other botanists visited Mas-a-Fuera in the interim it was not until 1891 that this remarkable plant was rediscovered by Dr. Federico Johow, who later wrote a comprehensive account of the botany of the islands.

In 1908, and also in 1916-1917 the eminent authority on insular floras in the South Pacific, Dr. Carl Skottsberg, Director of the Botanical Garden in Gothenburg, Sweden, visited Mas-a-Fuera and found *N. cordifolia* again. He collected its seed and, recollecting my interest in growing all the Nicotianas I could lay my hands on, was good enough to share the seed with me. In the Botanical Garden in Berkeley we succeeded, twenty years ago, in growing a few plants from this seed, which represented an important addition to our increasing collection of *Nicotiana* species. Through some mischance the remainder of the original seed was lost and in addition we failed to save any seed from the plants we grew. Since *N. cordifolia* is now almost the only important known species of *Nicotiana* which we are not growing and experimenting with in California, I was extremely anxious to secure the seed again.

When Florence and I were in Chile in 1935-1936, we were forced to sail for home before it was possible to arrange a trip to the Juan Fernandez Islands to collect it; and so I asked the General to arrange, if possible, with one of his botanically inclined associates to make the voyage for us. As will appear later on, this voyage can be a highly unpleasant adventure. Perhaps for this reason the General could not find anyone in Valparaiso willing to volunteer his services. The best that he could do was to send a man who was permanently established on Mas-a-Tierra, "Robinson Crusoe's Island," across the ninety and more miles of open ocean in a small fishing boat to Mas-a-Fuera in search of *Nicotiana cordifolia*. During the seasons of 1936-1937 this friend of the General's went to Mas-a-Fuera twice, but on neither trip was he able to find evidence of the existence of this plant. After the first trip he reported that the wild goats had exterminated it. After the second trip he declared that it must have been the humming birds that had destroyed it. I knew that like most Nicotianas this species possesses a rather nasty odor and decidedly unpleasant taste, so that even the undiscriminating goats of Mas-a-Fuera after one attempt to graze upon it would turn up their noses at it. Even if they learned to appreciate its foliage I doubted very much whether they could have exterminated the species, because it is a considerable shrub and probably lives over a period of years; and anyway, it would undoubtedly sprout from the base even if pretty heavily grazed. As to humming birds no one has been able to explain how the collector could have imagined that they had played an important part in the supposed extermination of the species. In addition to the attempt made in 1939 to find *Nicotiana* on Mas-a-Fuera which I am going to describe, I sent a Chilean collector there in 1940. The combination of so many efforts, some of which received certain publicity in Chilean newspapers, to find a particular plant on a remote Pacific island was too much for a Valparaiso reporter in search of a story, as witness the statement translated at the beginning of this chapter.

I was so certain that *Nicotiana cordifolia* still grew on Mas-a-Fuera that I determined, during the expedition of 1938-1939, to go myself or arrange that one of our party get there. Early in February our collecting in northern and central Chile was progressing so successfully that John could be spared for two weeks. He was glad to make the trip because the opportunity for a young botanist to see and collect the famous and, even today, relatively little-known vegetation of the Juan Fernandez Islands was alluring.

A lobster-fishing company with headquarters in Valparaiso owns two small schooners, the *Iris* and the *Gaviota,* which ply back and forth from the islands during the lobster season from December to March. We made a reservation for John on a Feb-ruary sailing of the *Iris*. This, we thought, would give him a week or ten days on Mas-a-Fuera to find the much-desired *Nico-tiana* and to increase knowledge of other elements of the flora of this rarely visited island by intensive collecting on its lofty mountainsides and in its deep gorges. I knew that in late De-cember and early January the vegetation on the Juan Fernan-dez Islands is at its best and that John would be a little late for the wave of flowering there which passes rapidly. Nevertheless there would be many plants in good condition, and if *Nicotiana cordifolia* were in seed and not in flower so much the better, be-cause it was primarily seed I wanted.

How many times, clinging to ocean cliffs, half hidden under rocky outcroppings on foothill slopes, glowing on high scree or talus slopes, or dyeing shady walls of deep Andean valleys with warm color, we discovered new or little-known plants of potential scientific or ornamental importance, and how often they gave us only flowers and leaves and stems and colored pho-tographs to take back to California. How many long, backbreak-ing and knee-wearying hours we spent going over every plant of these prizes in the hope of finding a little seed, so that as liv-ing things and not alone as dead, dried specimens they could be seen at home. And how far too many times we robbed the re-serve budget so that we could retrace our steps at a later season in the hope that seed could be found.

For anything but a sizable vessel the ocean between Val-paraiso and the Juan Fernandez Islands constitutes always a trial and often a menace. The little *Iris* on the homeward voyage before John's scheduled outbound one was badly buffeted by a storm, and sails were torn, masts loosened, and running gear damaged. Quick repairs were promised but day after day went by, each one filled with renewed promises. Finally sailing day arrived. By this time, however, it was so late in February that only favorable weather and a quick voyage, plus a short stop at Mas-a-Tierra on the way to Mas-a-Fuera, could bring John to his destination in time to accomplish much in the way of collecting.

After agreeing on the inevitable last-minute decisions concerning what should be discarded from the assembled collecting equipment, John and I went down to the quay with the still large accumulation of plant presses, duffel bags, and cameras. The uncertain light of an early Valparaiso evening made our descent of the barnacle-incrusted stone steps to the waiting skiff a dangerous operation, but at last we and the luggage were loaded. Since the *Iris* was supposed to sail that night she had been anchored well out in the stream, and the oarsman had a long pull through the crowded harbor where, from almost water level, the ships and lighters, larger and smaller, loomed enormous in the half light. We were, therefore, the more unprepared for the diminutive size of the *Iris,* and when our skiff approached her we felt certain that our oarsman had made a mistake. It was by all odds the smallest of the sea-going vessels in the harbor, and my heart sank when I realized that John was going to entrust himself to her on a voyage so relatively long and dangerous. Could I have foreseen all that was in store for him I would have ordered the oarsman to return us both *pronto* to the safety of the Valparaiso quay.

Covered with luggage we struggled up the side and tumbled onto the deck just at a point where steel water barrels were being hauled aboard. A glance around the deck made it immediately apparent that the *Iris* was not going to sail for a considerable number of hours. Carpenters were still at work, but not too busily, and a half-hearted effort was being made to complete the repair of one of the sails that had been blown away in the storm. The aft deckhouse which housed both officers and passengers was in a state of extraordinary but quite

typical confusion. In addition to John the passengers consisted
of two families, one a mother with three small children and the
second a mother and grown son. The total space available for
the captain, the engineer and his assistant, and these six passengers was hardly equal to that of a good-sized cabin and a
half on a transatlantic liner.

The deckhouse was divided into small cabins for the officers
and three cubbyholes for the passengers. Of the latter, one was
apparently for John since it had a single bunk. A second was
filled with ship's stores—dried meat, barrels of flour, dried vegetables, and so on. A third, about as wide as an ordinary writing
table with narrow upper and lower bunks was to be occupied
above by the mother and son and below by the mother and the
three small children. In the dim light of a little oil lamp we
tentatively examined the cotton mattress in John's recess, os-
tensibly to determine something of its physical characteristics
but actually to know the worst concerning its possible inhabitants. Of these the mattress gave no evidence, but it was extremely hard and its heavily ridged surface filled us both with
secret foreboding.

Escaping the turmoil of the deckhouse, John and I stood
for a few moments on deck watching the scene of confusion
there. Finally, I went over the side to the waiting skiff and received from John a far more cheerful farewell than I could have
given had I been in his situation.

The *Iris* finally pulled out of the harbor at about 1:30 in
the morning propelled toward the open sea by her all-too-small
Diesel engine. Immediately she ran into a severe headwind and
a high sea that had been lying in wait for the one hundred ton
schooner. John does not talk about what happened to the
vessel and to him during the next sixty hours, but his diary contains the story.

"The little schooner had a most amazing spiral, gyrating
motion which was absolutely devastating to one who had been
to sea only on sizable craft and usually in fair weather. On an
approximately even keel, the ship would rise like an elevator
on the long steep slope of a great wave and when the crest was
reached would lunge downward with the deck listing sharply
to starboard. When the next crest was attained we took a corre-

spondingly abrupt list to port. Soon I lost track of the seconds
of comparative calm, and the sequence of listings, first to one
side and then to the other, seemed to merge into a continuity of
horrible, jolting lurches. I lay flat on my back without even a
pillow to break the horizontal line of contact with the bunk.
Probably I dozed a little. Gradually a vague grayness penetrated the dirty little porthole above my head and I began to
hope that the dawn would bring some respite; but as the morning hours dragged along I realized that the sea was still rising.
The pitching and tossing of the schooner became so incredible
and unbearable that I rose a little on my elbows to turn over
and attempt to find a more comfortable position, one which
would protect me somewhat more from being thrown out of my
bunk. Even as little movement as this was disastrous and immediately I was disgustingly sick. From that time on my noisy, rack-
ing regurgitation was almost continuous and the more disagreeable because there seemed to be nothing to regurgitate. I tried
to read, I tried to think, I tried to sleep, but it was all useless.

"With the dawn of the second day I gathered a little courage, attempted to sit up, drink a glass of water, and eat a few
raisins. The result was immediately forthcoming and doubly
painful, but at least I had the doubtful satisfaction of knowing
that I had made a noble experiment. Late in the afternoon,
after forty hours almost continuously in my bunk, the dirty and
inefficient but quite sympathetic steward brought a mug of tea.
It was unexpectedly hot and gave me the momentary strength
to climb out of my bunk and try to stand erect. At that very
instant the poor *Iris* began to take aboard even heavier seas and
the decks no sooner achieved the greatest possible slant to
starboard than the vessel gyrated wildly and plunged to port.
My bunk was the only comfortable place, really the only rea-
sonably safe place, and once in it I could cover my head and
shut out, in part at least, the horrible sounds emanating from
the other seasick passengers.

"During the succeeding night the sea became a little
calmer. By morning I gathered the necessary strength and fortitude to go out into the cabin for breakfast. The table was so
small that only three chairs could simultaneously be drawn up
to it, but I had no competition from the other passengers who

apparently proposed to stay in their bunks until we reached land. After eating something I decided to lie down, but after a few hours I roused up and went on deck. The storm was blowing itself out and the horizon was beginning to clear. To the west I saw a misty silhouette which one of the sailors told me was Mas-a-Tierra. All the rest of that day we had the island in view but our few knots per hour made this part of the voyage exasperatingly slow. Late in the afternoon I was able to make out some details of the geography of the island and could identify Cumberland Bay which was to be our anchorage, and the lofty hillsides behind it."

From a distance on the sea Mas-a-Tierra, the "Nearer Land," is an isolated, serrated mountain range rising clean and sharp from the Pacific whose giant rollers ever surround it with first higher and then lower ranks of foothills. In its lee the eye travels almost vertically upward to the cloudy, three-thousand-foot apex of El Yunque, "The Anvil," and from deep notches on either flank of this highest peak rise lesser eminences—to the one side El Pico Central and to the other La Damajuana, "The Demijohn." Mas-a-Tierra, although possessing a land surface of only about twenty-two square miles, consists of a complex mountain system that centers in El Yunque. From The Anvil two ranges branch out, one extending to the east and one to the north. At its extremity the latter is uplifted to form El Cerro Alto before it ends precipitously on the north flank of the island, while from one face of "The High Hill" a third range extends toward the southwest. Within this complex of ridges and peaks El Yunque dominates. A ponderous block of stone, a lofty sentinel facing alone the high-swirling, down-racing, gray-white cloud masses, the sight of it has for more than three hundred years cheered the heart of the mariner on his approach to that verdant isle, toward which his thoughts have been at full stretch since first he hazarded the dread passage of Cape Horn.

The Juan Fernandez Islands are volcanic in origin and no sedimentary rocks are found. The layering seen in the sea cliffs and steepest mountain slopes, which so strikingly simulates a series of sedimentary accumulations, represents the result of an alternation between compact lava residues and looser, lighter, volcanic materials. This horizontal layering is conspicuous from

the sea on the north side of Mas-a-Tierra where the bluffs that
rise straight up from the water show in addition innumerable
vertical dykes of lava, which cut across the layers and represent
intrusions of the former after the latter had been laid down.

Discovered in 1563 by the Spanish sea captain whose name
they bear, the Juan Fernandez Islands, and almost exclusively
Mas-a-Tierra, served the early merchantmen from the Old
World, but especially pirates, privateers, and the navies of the
great powers, as havens of refuge in the southeast Pacific or as
a base for nefarious or semilegitimate naval operations. Sufficiently far out to escape the coastwise prowl of Spanish men-of-
war Mas-a-Tierra offered temporary sanctuary in addition to a
well-established rendezvous for convoys on one route from
Europe to the "Isles of Spice." Moreover, from their isolation
the fast-sailing buccaneer might overhaul the treasure ships
hurrying toward Spain from Panama, Peru and the Philippines.
Possessing a relatively commodious and protected anchorage,
they also offered at all seasons abundant stores of fresh water
and supported a luxuriant vegetation for "wooding and water-
ing" and refreshment of scurvy-ravaged crews. Here, too, the
crews had a chance to replace "salt horse" with fish and lobsters
readily taken from its reefs and shores and, finally, with great
herds of wild goats to be killed and salted down over against
the months of voyage still ahead. It is small wonder that as long
as sailors sailed Mas-a-Tierra was much in their thoughts and
mouths.

On a morning in October of the year 1704 the *Cinque
Ports* galley, part of a small British squadron operating in the
South Seas, rode peacefully at anchor off Mas-a-Tierra. Aboard
the *Cinque Ports* all was not peaceful. For months the Scotch
sailing master, Alexander Selkirk, had been at odds with his
superior, Captain Stradling, and that morning an open quarrel
broke out between them. In the heat of it Selkirk demanded to
be set ashore on the then uninhabited island in the lee of which
they lay at anchor. His anger cooled and he bitterly regretted his
demand when he found that it was about to be complied with.
Nevertheless, he was put on the beach at a point which is today
called Cumberland Bay. Beside him on the sand lay only "his
clothes, bedding, a firelock, one pound of powder, a hatchet,

cooking utensils, some tobacco and his books." Doubtless the
twenty-eight-year-old Scotsman, and certainly Captain Stradling,
who had taken such cruel advantage of a word spoken in the
heat of argument to rid the *Cinque Ports* of a shipmate he disliked, believed that before many weeks, or months at most, another British ship would chance to put in at the island and a
rescue would follow. Could either of them have foreseen that
four years and four months would pass before such a friendly
sail approached Mas-a-Tierra their quarrel might have been
temporarily mended and they might have sailed away together,
to quarrel again another day.

The story of Alexander Selkirk's difficult and lonely life on
the island comes partly from his own account of his experiences, but principally from Defoe's version of the story, *Robinson Crusoe.* He built two huts, thatched them with long grasses
and lined them with goat skins. One served him as living quarters and the other as cookhouse. From the beginning he hunted
the wild goats and when his meager supply of gunpowder was
exhausted he learned to catch them. Before his rescue he managed to dine on some five hundred and slit the ears of a like
number which had been caught in excess of his needs. When his
clothes became too ragged to wear he replaced them with goat
skins and hardened his feet until he could run barefoot over the
jagged volcanic rocks that composed the ridges and summits of
his island home. There were no dangerous land animals or
venomous reptiles to guard against, but Selkirk was much annoyed by rats. They, together with cats, had originally escaped
from ships and had considerably multiplied, especially the rats.
According to his account the cats were at first exceedingly wild
and shy, but he finally succeeded in redomesticating enough of
them to keep the rats away from his huts.

On January 31st, 1709, a British squadron again approached Mas-a-Tierra. Under command of Captain Woodes
Rogers and with Captain Dampier as pilot, the men-of-war
Duke and *Duchess* cruised off the island while they sent a yawl
ashore. Darkness came before a landing could be made and, a
fire being seen on the island, Captain Rogers suspected the presence of Spanish ships nearby and promptly recalled the boat.
It is easy to picture Selkirk's thanksgiving as he watched the ap-

proach of ships he recognized and which might carry him away from his prison island. How frantically he must have gathered and kindled the fire that should draw the boat to a safe landing place. What suffering he must have endured when he saw its bow turned back toward the ships.

His hope of rescue was renewed at dawn when his eager eyes again saw the sails which he feared had borne away the British ships during the night. Later in the morning Captain Rogers, finding no ships of Spain near Mas-a-Tierra, decided to send the yawl ashore again to scout a Spanish garrison that might have been established there. When the yawl failed to return he followed it with an armed pinnace, which scarcely reached the landing place before it hastened back to the ship. Aboard was Alexander Selkirk whose goatskin-clad figure, long hair and beard, and rusty voice combined to produce an impression both wild and pitiful.

Captain Dampier recommended Selkirk to the commander of the squadron, calling him the best man who had sailed in the *Cinque Ports,* with the result that Captain Rogers "immediately agreed with him to be the mate of our ship." With some hesitation and not until he had determined that the officer whose quarrel with him had ended so disastrously was not a member of the ship's company, Selkirk came aboard and "found all to his liking."

Thus, in the second month of 1709 was rescued and "restored to the society of his kind" the last and most celebrated of a long line of "Robinson Crusoes," who had lived, better or worse, for longer or shorter periods on Mas-a-Tierra. Today, two hundred and thirty-two years thereafter, it is still called Robinson Crusoe's Island. In competition with islands similarly designated, Mas-a-Tierra alone deserves the name because, however geographically hybridized and fancifully embroidered, it is Alexander Selkirk's account of his surroundings and activities on this lonely isle in the South Seas with which Daniel Defoe continues to thrill successive generations of boys and girls.

Tradition has it that Juan Fernandez himself landed the first goats on the islands, but whoever was actually responsible for their introduction could scarcely have anticipated how successfully they would adapt themselves to a somewhat remarkable environment. They multiplied exceedingly and from that day to this have represented a never-failing meat supply. For more than one hundred years the goat population on Mas-a-Tierra has been relatively scanty; but on minute, barren, nearby Santa Clara and on far-off Mas-a-Fuera it is apparently undiminished. In the seventeenth century it occurred to the Spaniards that the availability of fresh meat on Mas-a-Tierra might be a reason for the effectiveness of the forays on their South American shipping made by various categories of foreign naval vessels that used the island as a base. Therefore, they attempted to exterminate the goats first by intensive hunting and later by loosing dogs. The dogs promptly returned to a state of nature and, running in savage packs, soon killed a large proportion of the goats and drove the residue to the security of the highest mountainsides. The transient foreigners retorted by shooting dogs as well as goats. Constant hunting, particularly by the people of the village, which for two hundred years has intermittently existed on the shores of Cumberland Bay, has been responsible for such a reduction of the goat population that today the bagging of one is a sporting proposition.

At half-past eight in the evening of the third day out of Valparaiso, the *Iris* finally dropped anchor in Cumberland Bay. The voyage had been an unusually long and a peculiarly nasty one, although John has no basis for comparison except the homeward voyage he took some weeks later, which was bad enough. As the anchor splashed into the bay a boat came from the shore and there ensued a lengthy discussion of the voyage out, of the prospects for the lobster fishing, and of local happenings on Mas-a-Tierra. Finally some of the crew went ashore. During the long, stormy trip from the mainland no wine had been consumed on the *Iris*. Soon the sailors returned and brought with them bottles of the good Chilean red wine. Since John's was the only corkscrew available he felt justified in exacting tribute from each bottle. It was growing dark and he had no acquaintances on the island, only letters of introduction; he therefore decided to spend the night on the *Iris*. The anchorage was calm and the relief from the pitching and tossing of the

previous sixty hours and the great need for sleep enabled him
to spend a restful night, despite the corrugated mattress.

In the morning after a swim in water so clear that fish
could be seen far below the ship's hull and after the excuse for
a breakfast which the *Iris* offered, John went ashore for what,
according to schedule, would be a day's collecting before the
ship sailed for Mas-a-Fuera. Half a hundred houses, a radio
station, wharves and sheds filled with the lobster fishermen's
boats, huddle on the shores of Cumberland Bay between the
ocean and the almost vertically ascending mountainsides. This,
the village of San Juan Bautista, is the only permanent settlement on the Juan Fernandez Islands. Two streets parallel the
beach and two at right angles to it run up the steep hillsides.
Some built of wood and some of adobe, the houses that line
these streets are typically Chilean. Torrential rains falling on
the heights above descend as mountain torrents, plow the village streets with deep, rocky ruts, and flow swiftly on into the
ocean. Once past the houses the ascending streets rapidly
dwindle to rough mountain trails that lead to high, deep quebradas where the villagers cut their wood supply.

John had a letter of introduction to one of the oldest
fishermen on the island who was good enough to entertain him
during his stay ashore. For advice and assistance in plant hunting, he got into touch with a German who has lived on Mas-a-
Tierra off and on since 1915. This man was a sailor on the
German cruiser *Dresden,* which was sunk by the British near
Mas-a-Tierra that year. A part of the crew was drowned, but
he and the others who escaped landed on Mas-a-Tierra and for
a time were interned there by the Chilean government. With
the signing of the armistice in 1918 he went to Tierra del Fuego
where for many years he hunted sea otter. About ten years ago
he returned to Robinson Crusoe's Island and now appears to
be permanently established there. He and his wife, who came
out from Germany after a correspondence courtship, are happy
in the frontier atmosphere in which they live and have cleared
a bit of high hillside, have built a comfortable cabin, and maintain a flourishing vegetable garden. He has a typical German
flair for natural history and among other collections has accumulated a small one of the flora of Robinson Crusoe's Island.

During the first afternoon on the island John, accompanied by the German, two small boys, and two dachshunds, did his first botanizing. They started from the German's cabin where they had lunched and climbed a path carved along one of the steepest of the ridges. This trail was nothing more than a staircase in which rocks and the trunks of tree ferns constituted the steps. Quoting from John's 'diary:

"Tired and a little weak after my miserable days aboard the *Iris,* I made pretty heavy work of the staircase trail, but managed to do better than the dachshunds who were either underfoot or had to be assisted up a particularly long step or who succeeded in tumbling off into the brush on the trail side, requiring a rescue. Up a few hundred feet, I began to notice fallen flowers of a dark mulberry-violet tint. They looked extremely odd. Soon we came upon the plant which bore them. It was a tree belonging to the Verbena family and known by the islanders as *Juan bueno* and by the botanist as *Rhaphithamnus venustus.* This species, closely related to the *espino blanco* or "white thorn" of southern Chile, is the only tree native to the Juan Fernandez Islands which has spines.

"The trail rapidly increased in steepness and we began to haul ourselves up from step to step by grasping the trunks of tree ferns and the larger rocks which bordered the stony path. Out of breath and weary almost to the breaking point I dragged myself around a particularly perpendicular series of steps and without warning came suddenly out into the open on the knife-like edge of the island's main divide. Here the rough, rocky ridge was so narrow that I had to hunt for a space large enough to rest upon comfortably. Almost directly below me lay tiny Santa Clara, a low, barren islet set like a brown dot in the surface of the deep-blue ocean, less than a mile from the southwestern extremity of Mas-a-Tierra. As I looked out through the tree-fern branches down to the thundering surf breaking against the precipitous rocky cliffs and over the outjutting rocks in the channel between the two islands and then raised my eyes to the horizon, I tried to translate myself into Alexander Selkirk and to think some of his thoughts as he sat perhaps in exactly that same spot where I was sitting, or on what is called his lookout on the northwest shoulder of El Yunque, ever longing for the white gleam of the sail which was so long in appearing.

"I climbed a short distance up the incredibly steep slopes of La Damajuana and soon convinced myself that the report that this peak has rarely been achieved is undoubtedly correct. Everywhere there was evidence that it was too late in the season to find many plants in flower on the high ridges but I did succeed in collecting a few. There was an attractive Campanula-like plant (*Wahlenbergia fernandeziana*) quite abundant among the rocky outcroppings and, in looser, rocky soil just below, a single specimen of *Colletia spartioides*, a curious leaf-less plant with much-branched, yellow-green stems.

"From the village on the shore of Cumberland Bay, the two-mile-long trail which we had achieved and which had brought us to the notch between El Yunque and La Damajuana had seemed sufficiently steep in most places; but the approximately vertical drop on the other side of the narrow divide produced a shrinking feeling as I looked down the fifteen-hundred-foot mountainside to the sea, less than half a mile away. Finally, gathering courage, I worked my way down a few hundred feet to collect a plant of the endemic potato (*Solanum fernandezianum*), which had been described by Bertero as producing edible tubers. No other botanist since his time who has been fortunate enough to find this plant has confirmed Bertero's statement. This potato is a sprawling perennial growing in moist, shady woods, and the only specimens I saw were in fruit, the unripe capsules looking like miniature tomatoes."

It is said that Daniel Defoe when he wrote *Robinson Crusoe* had the impression that the Juan Fernandez group were desert islands. In order, therefore, to provide a more favorable background for his hero's activities and to furnish the surrounding area with a native population of cannibalistic tendencies, Defoe devised a West Indian locale for Robinson. Far from being desert islands Mas-a-Tierra and Mas-a-Fuera support a dense vegetation. Although geographically and climatically they are by no means tropical, the tangle of low forest trees and dense underbrush that fills the greater and lesser gorges on their mountainsides is definitely reminiscent of the equatorial jungle. During the winter season, from May to October, the rainfall is heavy, and lack of precipitation during the rest of the year is compensated for by a generally foggy climate.

We have already pointed out that the floras of oceanic islands tend to be rich in plant species that occur nowhere else, and that the vegetation of Mas-a-Tierra and Mas-a-Fuera is noteworthy because of the unusually large number of such endemics which it contains. John had his first glimpse of one of the most beautiful of them almost as soon as he landed on Robinson Crusoe's Isle. In a deserted garden where the trail to the highlands replaced the village street, grew a stately palm whose tall, slender, pale-green trunk was ringed at regular intervals with bands of darker green and bore at the very apex a dense flat crown of bright-green leaves. This attractive palm (*Juania australis*), the so-called *chonta* of the islanders, produces small, edible fruits which doubtless represented a share at least of Alexander Selkirk's food supply during his years on Mas-a-Tierra. These fruits and the soft, edible bases of the leaves furnished a fresh salad to many a scorbutic English mariner, and the plant was therefore known to him as the "cabbage tree." At one time this palm grew in quantity on the mountainsides above Cumberland Bay, but ships' crews have long since destroyed them all. The chonta is, fortunately, still quite abundant in less accessible portions of the island. To a limited degree it has been successfully introduced into gardens in parts of the world where climatic and other factors are congenial. Polished sections of the trunk made attractive souvenirs to sell to the ship load of English tourists which came once a year to Robinson Crusoe's Island; but recently the Chilean Government, anticipating its extinction, made unlawful the cutting of the chonta.

The most famous of the plants of Mas-a-Tierra was the sandalwood tree (*Santalum fernandezianum*) which undoubtedly grew there in abundance when Juan Fernandez landed on the island. Probably it was first cut for wood and ship repair, but soon the value of its beautiful and fragrant wood, previously available only in the Far East, was appreciated. During early Spanish colonial days on the west coast of South America it still grew in quantity on Robinson Crusoe's Isle, and a lucrative trade in sandalwood was carried on for many years. Gradually the trees became scarce and finally none could be found and long ago it was reported to be extinct. In 1906, however, a single specimen was discovered which, unfortunately, died in 1916. The General thoughtfully shared with us a piece of the wood that had been cut for him from this last remnant of a botanically and commercially valuable member of Mas-a-Tierra's remarkable flora.

The geographically nearest relative of the Juan Fernandez sandalwood is *Santalum freycinetianum* of the Hawaiian Islands. There are a number of other species of Santalum, all Eastern, of which the most important is *S. album*. This grows in dry regions of southern India and on the Indian Archipelago, whence for centuries it has been exported, chiefly to China where its wood is used for incense, perfume, and carving.

For the lay naturalist, as well as for the professional botanist, the most lively interest always attaches to the discovery anywhere of a plant that grows nowhere else. But on those two relatively insignificant uplifts of volcanic earth in the South Seas, Mas-a-Tierra and Mas-a-Fuera, not one species but actually eleven genera of plants are endemic; there and only there throughout the length and breadth of the world may they be seen growing on their native heath. Among the ten endemic genera of flowering plants and one endemic genus of ferns are some of the most ancient of all the living plants known to man. One of them, *Lactoris,* is the only genus of its family. Another, the chonta, is only distantly related to other genera of palms.

Of the eleven endemic genera seven are monotypic, that is to say they have only one species each. Four genera—*Robinsonia, Rhetinodendron, Centaurodendron,* and *Dendroseris*—are members of the Compositae, the Sunflower family. The four Juan Fernandez Compositae, as the names of two of them point out by the suffix "dendron," are trees or treelike, a growth form one never associates with the plant family to which they belong.

Don Carlos Bertero, whose name has already been mentioned in describing the wild potato John found, was an Italian physician who in 1830 made one of the best of the earlier collections of the plants of Mas-a-Tierra. It was from the dried specimens which he sent back to Europe that botanists first

learned of the existence of these tree Composites, which immediately were recognized to be among the rarest, most ancient,
and most interesting members of their plant family.

Among the ferns two species stand out prominently in the
remembrance of those who have climbed the steep ridges or
torn their way through the dense, matted forests of Mas-a-Tierra
and Mas-a-Fuera. Both are tree ferns and warrant that designation. One of them, named *Dicksonia berteriana* in honor of
Bertero, grew abundantly along the route of John's first botanizing on Robinson Crusoe's Isle. In deep quebradas it luxuriated and where low-lying fogs maintained high atmospheric
humidity it formed extensive and charming groves. On Mas-a-
Fuera the ascent of high mountainsides is made almost impossible by compact stands of this tree fern.

The other outstanding tree fern, *Blechnum cycadifolium*,
might be called the "cycas fern" because it resembles so closely
the sago palm of conservatories or, in California, of front lawns,
that the uninitiated refuse to believe that it can actually belong
to an entirely different subdivision of the plant kingdom. It
shuns the moist shade of leafy gorges and forested slopes, and
prefers to populate the dry, barren ridges, called "cordons" by
the islanders. There in the rocky waste land, silhouetted against
the burnished blue of the sky or framing a glimpse of the
darker blue ocean far below, it stands out as one of the most
characteristic elements of the somewhat bizarre and even sometimes a little other-worldly vegetation of the Juan Fernandez
Islands.

We expected John to be away a week or at the most ten
days and as I have said we hoped that he could spend most of
his time not on Robinson Crusoe's Island, but on Mas-a-Fuera
where alone grows the *Nicotiana* I was determined to have. We
knew that there would be practically no possibility of hearing
from him unless he had an urgent message to send us and
the radio station on Robinson Crusoe's Island was functioning.
The fourth morning after John's arrival in Mas-a-Tierra the
chambermaid was just bringing in our continental breakfast
when the telephone rang. It was the General on the other end
of the line and his first words were: "Have you seen the morning newspapers?" He then went on to explain that a radio

message had been published to the effect that the *Iris* had been wrecked on the Juan Fernandez Islands, but with absolutely no further details. The General kindly agreed to keep in touch with the owners of the *Iris* and with the newspapers and to pass on to us any later news. When noon came without any we tried to radio John on Mas-a-Tierra asking for a report on his personal safety. The radio company would not give us much satisfaction, however, because the abbreviated condition of the original announcement had been due to breakdown of the radio station on Mas-a-Tierra, something usually followed by a day or two of silence. We received no answer to our first radiogram, and sent two more during the next twenty-four hours. Finally, on the second morning, the newspaper announced that the *Iris* had been refloated. Since the account again gave no details we were forced, with lingering doubts, to assume that everyone was safe and that no particular damage had been done; but we had to wait until John's return two weeks later to get any account at all of what had happened.

The *Iris* was to sail for Mas-a-Fuera on the second evening of his stay on Robinson Crusoe's Island. Departure was set for 6:30, and although no one expected the schooner actually to get under way until about 10:00 John went aboard at the scheduled hour. After the officers had finished their supper there was every evidence that the *Iris* was going to sail only about an hour late. The red-headed German-Chilean engineer and his dark-haired Chilean assistant retired below to the engine room, the bosun took his crew of four forward to the winch, the steward left his galley and climbed into the chain locker to coil the anchor chain, the cook took over the wheel, and John, the only passenger, remained the sole inhabitant of the ship who did not have a task assigned. When everyone had reached his proper station the captain shouted to the bosun to take in the anchor. At the same time he signaled the engine room "Full speed astern." The bosun and his crew threw themselves against the winch and slowly the anchor freed itself from the rocky floor of Cumberland Bay. Steadily, now that some momentum had been gained, the winch went round and round and the anchor rose higher and higher. Without warning a strong on-shore wind began to blow and immediately the little schooner started to drift toward the rocky shore. Again and again the captain furiously signaled the engine room, when suddenly he and everyone else realized that the Diesel engine was not running. Any doubt on this subject was dissipated by the engineer who popped up on deck screaming in his mixed German-Spanish that the Diesel wouldn't start. With windmill arms the cursing Captain scampered about and repeatedly commanded the bosun to drop the anchor. Before anything could be done the bow of the *Iris* began to grate on the rocks fifty feet from shore.

Most of the population had gathered to watch the departure and had, of course, observed the whole operation. Sailing had been scheduled for high tide and the ship went on the rocks just after its crest had begun to recede. If anything was to be done to save the schooner obviously that something had to happen before high tide entirely passed. Immediately fishermen began to launch their large boats which were provided with outboard motors. The captain ordered his one lifeboat to be swung out and two members of the crew entered it with a collection of heavy hawsers. Soon the fishing boats were attached one to the other and to the *Iris* and, strung out in a long line, began a strong pull on the heavy lines. The captain, who was so obviously responsible for the disaster because he had not assured himself that the engine was running before he ordered the anchor up, had lost control over the crew and the cook assumed command. As the tide rapidly lowered it was quite clear that the *Iris* was not going to be pulled off the rocks that night.

Only the bow of the schooner was on the reef but it was firmly wedged between great, upjutting rock masses. All night long she pitched and heaved in dangerous fashion but the motion did not suggest that the bow was being driven farther up on the reef. By the greatest good fortune the on-shore breeze did not increase in severity and it was only the long Pacific swells that were rolling the ship from side to side. At daybreak the crew made another unsuccessful attempt to refloat the *Iris* and then planned for a final try during high tide that evening. This was to be the last good tide for a number of days, which meant that unless the ship could be refloated with its aid a week might pass before any passage from the island would be possible. Meanwhile, if even a moderate blow developed, the ship would go to pieces on the reef.

There were spare anchors in the warehouse ashore and during the day the sailors managed to get four of them aboard the *Iris*. By half-past five as the tide began to come in the anchors had been lowered behind the ship, two on each side, and these, by gently pulling on their hawsers, had been tightened on the rocky bottom. One by one, the twenty or more fishing launches were pushed off the shore and again slowly arranged themselves in a long line. Hawsers passed out from the ship were strung through the procession of launches until they formed a continuous strand. As the tide began to approach its crest the launches pulled full speed ahead, and the crew at the winches on the *Iris* began to put pressure on the anchors. The little schooner trembled, rocked, and finally lurched violently to port—only to settle into a new berth on the reef. The combined force of launches and anchors was repeatedly applied but with no effect, and the *Iris* continued to swing slowly from side to side as the long rollers flowed under her.

On the nearby shore everyone not allowed a seat in the launches had assembled to watch what was for them the show of the generation. A German schoolteacher from the mainland, spending his holiday on Robinson Crusoe's Island, was taking pictures in all directions and predicting in a loud voice that the *Iris* would never be moved from the rocks. Little boys weaved in and out among the crowd and dashed back and forth along the beach to work off by exercise the nervous tension they shared with the older spectators. Suddenly, as the tide surged to its final height and the small waves broke just a little closer to the feet of the company assembled on shore, a final pull was given and the schooner slowly, quietly, slid clear of the rocks and in a moment was towed to safe anchorage.

The launches then gathered around the *Iris* and people began to come out from shore in rowboats. Soon there was a considerable group on and near the ship to begin a discussion that lasted for a long time. First of all, responsibility for the wreck had to be assigned. The captain and the engineer were both considered to be at fault, a decision against which they violently protested. In a moment everyone began to shout his opinion. Epithets were hurled, the lie was passed, fists were doubled, and the quiet anchorage reverberated to a din which the surrounding hillsides echoed. In the end, they arrived at the conclusion that the tank containing compressed air essential to the functioning of the Diesel engine, had been entirely exhausted during the voyage out from the mainland. Although either the captain or the engineer was obviously in duty bound to examine the condition of this tank before sailing for Mas-a-Fuera, the fact that both had forgotten to do so pointed to the final conclusion, with which all were in agreement, that the wreck of the *Iris* was an act of God.

The original altercation subsided suddenly but was at once replaced by an acrimonious discussion as to how much damage the hull of the ship had suffered during its period on the reef. One group contended that severe damage must certainly have been done, while another group took the reverse point of view. After extended argument it dawned on both groups that an examination of the hull should answer the question. A deputation thereupon descended to the hold and after a time came on deck to report that there was no sign of water being taken in. This satisfied all but the diehards who still insisted that only a severe storm would reveal the extent to which seams had been opened and masts sprung. However, the captain concluded that the *Iris* was in condition to proceed to Mas-a-Fuera and was about to designate the time of sailing when it occurred to him that without a tank of compressed air the engine could not be started; in other words, the ship was as securely tied to Robinson Crusoe's Island as it had been when it was on the reef.

It had taken the assembled company more than an hour to arrive at these various conclusions, and now that everyone was thoroughly talked out the crowd dispersed to the mainland or to their bunks aboard ship. During the following morning, radio communication was established for a few moments with Valparaiso and the *Iris* learned that the other lobster schooner had left the mainland on its regular trip to the island and was carrying an extra cylinder of compressed air. With good weather, and better equipped as to sails and engine than the *Iris,* late that afternoon the *Gaviota* appeared. Now that the

extra tank of compressed air was aboard the *Iris* and its Diesel
behaving properly, there appeared to be no reason why a start
for Mas-a-Fuera could not be made by the next morning at
least.

Immediately, however, a vital problem presented itself:
Should the *Iris* or the *Gaviota* go to Mas-a-Fuera? The island
radio station had broken down again so that it was impossible
to receive orders from the company owning the two ships. The
population of the island and the two crews, therefore, were left
to decide the important question themselves. To this discussion
they addressed themselves with enthusiasm and succeeded in
dragging it out for two whole days.

Because of wasteful methods of fishing, storage, and transportation, the lobster grounds about Robinson Crusoe's Island
were considerably depleted some years ago. Mas-a-Fuera then
became the more active fishing ground, and the company now
assigns a small fleet of launches to that island during the lobster
season. These launches and their crews, consisting of two or
three fishermen each, are carried from Mas-a-Tierra to Mas-a-
Fuera by one of the schooners, along with half a dozen people
who manage to land on the island and establish a temporary
colony there. An attempt to land is often risky and sometimes
days and even weeks are spent cruising on and off the only
possible landing place before the shore party can leave the ship.
Except in case of accident or other emergency the fishermen
never go ashore, but live for twenty to forty days in their
launches. The shore party prepares bread and other food and
transfers it to the cruising fishermen via a little boat which is
pulled back and forth on a rope attached to a barrel anchored
a short distance off shore. The reader will see later on what may
happen during the trip from barrel to shore and back again.

The lobsters caught by the Mas-a-Fuera fishermen are
stored in large, floating live-boxes from which they are removed
to the schooners on their regularly scheduled trips back and
forth from Valparaiso. The stores for the sea and land parties are
pretty closely calculated to last only until the next arrival of a
schooner, and any interruption in the schedule may work a real
hardship on fishermen and shore crew. Although this was a
well-known fact both to the crews of the two schooners in

Cumberland Bay, and to the Mas-a-Tierra fishermen, it did not in the least deter them from prolonging indefinitely the altercation concerning which ship should go to Mas-a-Fuera. For no apparent reason it was finally decreed that the *Iris,* and not the far better equipped *Gaviota,* was to make the trip.

This time the engine was started before the anchors were raised and kept running for an hour. Many forgotten articles remained to be loaded at the last moment but finally everything was aboard. Then the bosun and his crew of four barefoot, ragged sailors began the immensely difficult task of hauling in four anchors with the small, hand-powered winches. The steward again stowed the chain and the cook was at the wheel. At last the *Iris* pulled out of Cumberland Bay and headed west around Point Salinas on its way to Mas-a-Fuera.

A brisk breeze had by this time sprung up and the cumbersome sail was hoisted in an effort to supplement the efforts of the Diesel engine. When the last of the running gear was finally stowed one of the deck crew took over the wheel from the cook, who then undertook the preparation of some doubtful tripe and ill-cooked chick peas which together constituted the evening meal aboard the *Iris.*

Shortly after daybreak Mas-a-Fuera, the "Farther Land," appeared on the horizon. It is a much more compact, much smaller island than Mas-a-Tierra, yet the crest of Los Inocentes, its highest peak, rises to almost twice the altitude of the loftiest spot on Mas-a-Tierra. The surfaces of this volcanic extrusion in the South Pacific are scarred with deep, eroded canyons. From twenty miles away one can make out only the general outline of Mas-a-Fuera, but as the *Iris* slowly came closer, two V-shaped gorges stood out prominently on the mountainside near the middle of the island. In the mouth of the larger of these two, the Quebrada de las Casas, a number of tumble-down adobe houses gradually took shape. The other, almost as large and deeper, the Quebrada de las Vacas, showed incredibly steep walls that reached up into the wreath of fog hanging about the top of Los Inocentes and spilling down to cover the summits of these great quebradas.

At a snail's pace, the *Iris* pitched and tossed through heavy seas to within a mile or two of the shore. One of the fishing launches appeared around a promontory and rapidly approached. Almost before their shouted words were distinguishable above the roar of wind and waves the fishermen aboard the launch began vehemently to call for an explanation of why they had for many days been left without sufficient food. When they learned of the wreck on Mas-a-Tierra their attitude grew belligerent. Who, they demanded, had been responsible; why had not the culprit been punished? Since question and answer called for great lung power to carry the words from boat to launch and back again the discussion gradually died for lack of breath. The heavy seas made it impossible to load into the *Iris* the lobsters in the floating tanks or to send ashore any of the much-needed stores; so the schooner swung sharp to starboard and proceeded to the extreme northern end of the island, where in the lee of sheer volcanic cliffs she found some respite from the storm.

The so-called Juan Fernandez lobster, *Palinuris frontalis*, is actually a large salt-water crayfish, which lives only around the islands west of the Chilean mainland. The lobster pots, made of wire and cord, shaped like huge rat traps, and baited with dead fish, decaying cheese, and other malodorous materials are placed in shallow water and attract the attention of the lobster. Once inside he finds that the cone-shaped channel through which he has passed prevents his escape. The fishermen take up their traps periodically, remove the lobsters, and store them in the live-boxes to await the arrival of the schooner that will transport them to the mainland. The sides of the schooners are pierced midships with ports that permit fresh sea water to wash into a large hold. These holds consist of a series of shelves made of two-by-fours so spaced that the lobsters cannot fall through the cracks, yet which permit the sea water to wash freely back and forth. The constant washing in and washing out of the water is an effective method of aeration, and if the sea is sufficiently rough a large part of each cargo of lobsters reaches Valparaiso alive.

The fishermen receive about six cents U. S. for each lobster, irrespective of its size, that they bring to the live-boxes. In Valparaiso the lobsters, which average between three and four pounds, are sold for about fifteen cents a pound. A certain

proportion of each cargo is rushed from Valparaiso to Santiago
and there put aboard a Panagra plane; which means that a live
lobster landed in Valparaiso early in the morning can be served
in a Buenos Aires cafe at dinner that same evening. Although
six cents per lobster may seem a small reward the fishermen
appear to have a rather favorable arrangement with their em-
ployers, and many of them earn as much as one hundred dollars
a month during the lobster-fishing season.

From the moment of sailing from Valparaiso it had been
impressed upon the captain that the principal objective of
John's voyage was collecting on Mas-a-Fuera. During the trip
between the islands John once more pointed out this fact to
the captain. When, however, the *Iris* came to lie off Mas-a-
Fuera the captain denied any knowledge of John's desire to
land there. After a long and stormy argument John succeeded
in convincing the captain that he proposed to go ashore with
the first launch carrying supplies to the landing place.

The seas were now running a little lower and in the lee of
the cliffs the ocean was fairly calm. An hour or more was spent
in leisurely loading a fishing launch with fruit, meal, flour,
vegetables, the mail, and other things required by the shore
party and the fishermen. John's plant presses and cameras went
in last and then he swung over the side, clad in oilskins bor-
rowed from the crew.

The powerful Swedish motor drove the launch smoothly
through the quiet water, but soon the protection of the cliffs
was lost and they swung southwest into the teeth of the wind.
Waves crashed against the bow sending spray over the entire
boat. Now the full force of the storm caught them and began
to toss the launch violently about. As they approached the landing place, off the mouth of Quebrada de las Casas, the waves
appeared mountainous as they broke over the great lobster-
filled live-boxes moored near the shore. The drone of the motor
died to a whisper as the fishermen maneuvered up to the floating steel drum anchored two hundred yards off shore. From the
beach a narrow mole has been built by driving two parallel
lines of piling about thirty feet out into the ocean. On each side
of these pilings massive rocks have been piled as an added
bulwark against the crashing seas. Between the rows of pilings

each breaker roared far up on the sandy shore and then drained away rapidly to expose great ragged boulders at the mouth of the mole.

From high on the shore three men pushed down a small boat toward the bit of beach between the pilings. As they launched it in the swirling surf curling halfway up the narrow mole, the fishermen in the launch pulled on the rope, one end of which was fastened to the boat and the other to the steel drum. The little boat took one bad lunge that just escaped the pilings and then, buoyed up by the next roller and dancing like a cork on the water, it was quickly pulled out to the launch one-quarter full of water. First the precious cameras were placed in the center of the stern seat, then plant presses went in on either side, followed by mail, baskets of pears, fresh vegetables, and miscellaneous stores, and finally all was covered with a tarpaulin.

John was ready to jump into the boat and begin the obviously precarious trip to the shore; but the fishermen restrained him and as the launch and loaded boat pitched and rolled in the breakers each one in turn attempted to dissuade him. While the first man, a swarthy, stocky chap of twenty-five, shouted his advice the backwash of the heavy seas started to drag one of the live-boxes over the life line to the shore. The second man was a tall, slender Jew who spoke French in addition to fluent Castellano. He was certain that there was nothing on Mas-a-Fuera for John to collect, certainly nothing valuable enough to justify the risk of landing. The third was an old fisherman who had seen many seasons in the rough waters around the island. His only comment was that if John actually proposed to land he might just as well begin to do so. John tumbled in and seated himself amidships of the little skiff.

The two younger fishermen straightened the line along which the boat had been pulled out from shore. The old fisherman steadied the boat and shouted instructions to those on the beach who were to pull it toward them when he gave the signal. At last, when the waves seemed a little less wild and high, the old man waved his arm and the men on the beach pulled for all they were worth, running back with the rope up the beach as the boat came in. The three on the launch paid out their line slowly in order to hold the skiff as nearly on an even keel as possible. The taut line allowed them to check its forward movement the moment the boat seemed to be reaching the entrance to the mole too soon or too late to ride the crest of a breaker over the treacherous rocks. A hundred feet outside the mole they stopped the boat and it hung suspended with mountainous waves sloping in all directions; then, when a great swell surged beneath it and with a last strong pull from shore, it was dragged the length of the mole to touch the sand in the trickle of the expiring wave. John jumped out into six inches of water and helped to pull the skiff beyond the reach of the breakers.

We had agreed that, if possible, John should remain for a week or more on Mas-a-Fuera and return to Valparaiso on the succeeding trip of the *Iris* or *Gaviota*. But this was not to be. In the course of the arguments that he overheard during the long delay at Robinson Crusoe's Island, John gained the impression that because of the lateness of the season, the poorness of the lobster catch, and the disruption of the schedule caused by the wreck, it was probable that this would be the last of the season's voyages to Mas-a-Fuera. The captain of the *Iris* estimated that it would take him approximately twenty-four hours to load the available lobsters. This meant that John had only an afternoon and part of the next morning on the island in place of the many days there which he had looked forward to; and during which he had proposed an exploration of one of the most interesting and relatively little-known botanical treasure houses in the world. In the circumstances he decided to confine his efforts to collecting *Nicotiana cordifolia* and to mapping its distribution on those portions of the island that he had time to traverse. It never came into his mind that after all the discomforts, delays, and disappointments he had endured, the satisfaction of finding this plant that I so much desired would be denied him.

Upon landing John was cordially greeted by a remarkable individual. He was tall, bespectacled, gray-haired, academic looking, dressed in a worn but well-cut tweed suit, and in general appeared thoroughly out of place in his wild and rough surroundings. He proved to be the representative of the lobster-fishing company on Mas-a-Fuera and was in charge of the stores and all arrangements connected with the lobster fishing. He had set up headquarters in the less dilapidated half of an old adobe and wooden structure, which was one of a number built in the first years of this century when the Chilean Government maintained a penal colony on the island. With his señora and his young nephew he managed to exist on Mas-a-Fuera during the brief lobster-fishing season.

The three botanists who, beginning in 1854, had found the much desired *Nicotiana cordifolia* on Mas-a-Fuera gave the impression that this plant was fairly well distributed in the great canyon near the landing place and indeed was growing on the margin of the landing place itself. The manager claimed he had made a complete exploration of the island and had given some attention to its vegetation. When John described *Nicotiana cordifolia* to him and the places in which it had been collected, the manager shook his head and contended that he had never seen a plant of that description anywhere on Mas-a-Fuera. Together they made a rapid survey of the cliffs near the tumble-down encampment but found no sign of it. John then decided that since three of the previous botanists who had found *Nicotiana cordifolia* had all of them collected it in the Quebrada de las Vacas, he would devote every available moment that afternoon and the next day to a careful search there.

Unlike Mas-a-Tierra where steep cliffs rise sheer from the sea with practically no level coastline, on Mas-a-Fuera there is a bit of beach almost all the way around the island, so that it is possible to pass beside the sea from one of the deep gorges to another. From the landing place along this narrow beach John, accompanied by the manager and his nephew, hastened toward the "Canyon of the Cows." At one place the sea approached to within a few steps of the sheer cliffs, and when one has scrambled past this point he understands why it is called by the islanders El Paso Malo. The Quebrada de las Vacas is one of the steepest and deepest of those V-shaped depressions that raging torrents have cut in the sides of the great mountain which is Mas-a-Fuera. A low stone wall built many years ago across its mouth contrasts strikingly with the utterly wild and desolate appearance of the great gorge itself. A slender, cone-shaped hill fills its south side and forces the

rapid stream to run close along the vertical cliffs of the north
wall. Deep pools and sudden sharp curves mark the boulder-
strewn passage of the stream down from the heights above.

Climbing with difficulty up the treacherous, grassy slopes
they carefully explored the walls on either side of the mouth of
the quebrada. Nothing remotely approaching *Nicotiana cordifolia* was to be seen. Darkness came early here on the east side
of the island deep in the gorge, and they soon had to abandon
their search. Just as the last light was fading a great herd of
wild goats was silhouetted against the evening sky on one of the
lofty ridges and the manager took an unsuccessful shot at the
big-horned leader. In the half light with the rising tide and
breakers, the journey back along the narrow strip of beach and
across the Paso Malo was an experience John says he will long
remember.

John was glad to accept the manager's hospitality for dinner and the night, and at daybreak the next morning he set out
alone for a more thorough examination of the Canyon of the
Cows. The whole top of the mountain was covered with heavy
cloud masses and small tongues of fog drifted down into the
deep quebradas. The immensely rugged character of the island's
coast was more apparent in the morning light. At the edge
of the beach, ten to fifteen feet from the water's edge, cliffs rose
straight up five hundred to one thousand feet. Winter storms
that dashed high on these cliffs had pitted their flanks with
shallow caves and worn deep fern- and moss-lined hollows under
overhanging rocks. Where through the fast drifting clouds a
glimpse of the highlands above could be obtained they showed
a solid mantle of trees and underbrush. In the morning light
the Quebrada de las Vacas still maintained a grim and forbidding atmosphere. Just as on Mas-a-Tierra, so here also John
was too late for good collecting. The grasses and other herbaceous plants on the lower slopes of the Canyon of the Cows were
dry and brown. Only *Physalis peruviana,* the introduced ground
cherry from which the islanders make a delicious cider, was
still in bloom. Every moist and partially shady area on the walls
of the gorge was filled with ferns and mosses. Higher up the
walls of the canyon were straggling trees, outliers of the dense

forests that grow in the more humid atmosphere of the upper mountainsides.

Starting at the point where the explorations had left off the night before John made the best of his way up the almost vertical gorge. It closed in upon him immediately and he found it practically impossible to follow upward the course of the rapid-flowing stream. First along the more humid, mossy slopes and then climbing from ledge to ledge of the rough and precipitous canyon walls, he examined carefully every little grassy swale which perhaps might contain the plant he sought. Rounding a rocky outcropping he came upon a herd of wild goats peacefully grazing on a small stretch of grassy pasture land. A deep burnt umber, they made a startling picture against the bright-green forest background. Suddenly they all looked up and the leader, after intently studying the intruder for a moment, leaped up to the next ledge and in a flash all had disappeared.

A half-hour, an hour, two hours went by, but never a sign of *Nicotiana cordifolia*. More or less in desperation, John worked his way down again to the stream bed and then up onto the opposite slope of the gorge. On this south-facing slope there were practically no green plants to be seen. Nevertheless he made a thorough examination of the cliffs and ledges, slowly descending toward the base of the conical hill at the mouth of the quebrada. Having had considerable experience with the irresponsible attitude of the captain of the *Iris* and his crew, John knew that he must take no chance on being late at the landing place. Tired and sore from the hard, rough climb and utterly discouraged, he turned back about noon.

Although the waves rushed less violently against the mole than they had the previous afternoon, John discovered that the trip out to the launch that awaited him at the anchored barrel was psychologically a considerably worse ordeal than the passage to the shore had been. He seated himself in the little boat and, powerless to aid or direct its progress, watched the crests of the turbulent seas rush toward him, break on either side of the narrow mole, and, surging backward and forward, toss his helpless craft violently from side to side. Wave after wave dashed in and for a time the boat did not seem to gain an inch, but the fishermen in the launch pulled strongly and in a moment more the passage was over.

The deck of the *Iris* was piled high with half-dry, stinking carcasses of wild goats. Scores of equally stinking lobster traps were thrown everywhere. Slung on either rail were the launches of the fishermen who were returning to Mas-a-Tierra after their forty-five days' stretch of cruising the rough waters round Mas-a-Fuera. The heavy seas of the previous day had almost abated, and when the *Iris* pulled away from the island she ran into an almost dead calm so that for headway she had to rely upon her ineffective Diesel engine. As a result, the voyage back to Cumberland Bay was a slow and for the lobster-fishing company a costly one. Because on the calm sea the ship did not engage in its customary rolling and spiral wallowing, no fresh sea water with its life-sustaining oxygen was washed into the hold where the live lobsters were stored. The *Iris* was equipped with a motor-driven pump to force out water and thus to permit the intake of at least a certain amount of fresh sea water; but for some reason the captain never thought of using this pump. By the time the schooner reached Mas-a-Tierra, therefore, hundreds of lobsters were dead and floating on the surface of the lobster hold.

As the *Iris* entered Cumberland Bay boats filled with fishermen put off from shore, and no sooner was the ship anchored than they swarmed aboard, tore off the hatch covers, and began to count out the lobsters from the hold. The living ones were quickly put over the side into live-boxes and the dead were stacked on deck. The dried goat and the lobster pots went over the side into waiting boats. The fishing launches were unslung and their crews left immediately, doubtless anxious as soon as possible to feel land under their feet again.

Late in the afternoon the final loading of the lobsters in the hold of the *Iris* began. One full live-box after another was floated to the side of the ship and baskets of lobsters were passed up to the deck. Two by two, the lobsters were then handed down to men in the slatted hold below and layer after layer of lobsters were put into position. It seemed to be an absolutely endless task but about ten o'clock the complete load was aboard. A number of the islanders had meanwhile come out for a visit

Along this narrow ridge ran the precipitous staircase trail from El Yunque
to La Damajuana—"Robinson Crusoe's Isle" (Mas-a-Tierra)

The jagged crests of "Robinson Crusoe's Isle" from the *Iris,* at sea

Approaching Cumberland Bay, the only anchorage on Mas-a-Tierra

The final and successful attempt to pull the *Iris* off the reef

Checking Mas-a-Tierra lobsters from the *Iris* into floating live boxes

The rugged Quebrada de las Vacas on rarely visited Mas-a-Fuera Island
Looking down on Cumberland Bay and its plantation of Monterey Cypress

on the *Iris* and soon the captain and the crew started to persuade the visitors to go ashore. More than an hour was spent in seeing the last one over the side, but finally the last *hasta luegos* were shouted, the anchor was weighed, and the lights of the village slowly dimmed as the *Iris* moved out into the open sea.

Because the sea was somewhat calmer the return voyage to Valparaiso was more comfortable than the outbound as far as seasickness was concerned. This was fortunate because the *Iris*, which actually had accommodations for not more than five, was carrying fourteen passengers who had insisted upon being taken along on what would probably be the last chance for many months to reach the mainland. How and where they were all disposed John never discovered, and what the result would have been had the voyage been as stormy as the outgoing one he hesitated to imagine. Needless to say it was a decided relief to us when John finally arrived in Valparaiso, nineteen days after his departure.

There is plenty of room for speculation concerning the origin of the Juan Fernandez flora and the relationships of its species to those of other portions of the Pacific area. Apart from endemic genera, the flowering plants of Mas-a-Tierra and Mas-a-Fuera often are, as might be expected, related to some of those that today are growing on the mainland and perhaps more particularly on the central Chilean coast. Some that grow on the highlands of Mas-a-Fuera have their affinities in the Magellanic flora of South Chile. Among the flowering plants, but especially the ferns, some appear more nearly related to species of northern and others closer in relationship to those of southern Chile.

These mountainous islands appear to be wholly volcanic and it has been suggested that they arose at the close of the Tertiary, or during more or less the same period that the Andean backbone of the South American continent underwent its most recent extensive upheaval. On this assumption Mas-a-Tierra and Mas-a-Fuera may, geographically speaking, be thought of as quite young—something like two million years old. Presumably they would gradually have been populated by those mainland plants whose fruits or seeds or spores were capable of being transported to them by air or water, and which, once arrived, were able to maintain themselves. If we accept this theory then we must agree that two million years is a sufficient period for the evolution of the extraordinary series of distinctions between their floras and the plants not only of the Chilean mainland but also of Pacific floras in general, which are today exhibited to us on the two islands. Nowhere else in the world is there evidence of such rapid transformation, and certainly a comparison of the mainland flora of today with that of the Chilean Tertiary shows no evidence of abnormally rapid evolution.

An alternative and somewhat more attractive suggestion has been made to account for the origin of the islands and their peculiar plants. We are asked to assume that many millions of years ago the Chilean mainland was far more extensive than it is today and that on it and its volcanic mountains grew many ancient plants. Later, the larger part of this land subsided and only the Juan Fernandez group and a narrow coastal plain below the Andes remained above the surface of the sea to perpetuate at least a certain part of the ancient flora. On what is now the Chilean mainland this flora failed to survive, whereas on the Juan Fernandez Islands, due perhaps to lesser competition and a less altered climate, a few relics of that once extensive vegetation of the dim past have been preserved for our eyes.

Man, the universal despoiler, has been most largely responsible for those alterations in the composition of the Juan Fernandez flora that are known or are suspected to have occurred during the past four hundred years. He brought goats, rats, cats, and finally rabbits, each one undesirable and each having a larger or smaller share in destroying or restricting the perpetuation of a series of plant species. The crews of early buccaneers, naval craft, and merchantmen, cultivated vegetables grown from seeds that came from their ships' stores and planted the stones of fruit trees in the native forest. Along with cultivated plants man brought with him those ubiquitous weeds whose origin in the dim past is more obscure than his own. They flourish in the thoroughly friendly soil of Mas-a-Tierra and Mas-a-Fuera and help to rob the native vegetation of its rightful place in the sun. But despite the ravages of man and his plant and animal introductions these two islands remain a reservoir of curious and fascinating plants. A considerable number of them deserve cultivation in favorable climates throughout the world, and during a fifth attempt to collect *Nicotiana cordifolia* on Mas-a-Fuera, which is soon to be made, I hope that seeds of some at least will be obtained for distribution to those who live in areas where Juan Fernandez plants should thrive.

By giving the Juan Fernandez Islands somewhat the status of our National Parks the Chilean government has taken a first step in assuring the preservation of what man has not already destroyed there. Hopefully this gesture will be followed by appropriations adequate to maintain trained naturalists or at least interested and active caretakers on Mas-a-Tierra, or preferably on both of the larger islands.

In March, 1940, a fourth attempt to find *Nicotiana cordifolia* on the "Farther Land" was made by Rodolfo Wagenknecht, our former Chilean assistant. A set of complications, somewhat different from those that delayed John's arrival at Mas-a-Fuera, brought Rodolfo there so late in the lobster-fishing season that again there was doubt whether he could get away at all if he did not return with the schooner that had carried him to the Island.

With only an afternoon and the following morning for collecting he was forced, as John under like circumstances had been, to give all his attention to finding *Nicotiana cordifolia*. I had told Rodolfo to hunt for this much desired plant in some of the other gorges, the mouths of which could be reached from the landing place by following around the towering cliffs on the Playa Ancha or Broad Beach. He therefore started off along it to the south, and, passing the Quebrada de las Vacas which John had thoroughly and unsuccessfully explored, he came to the Quebrada del Varadero or Shipyard Canyon. It proved to be an even more wild and rugged gorge than the Canyon of the Cows and was formed by the union of two smaller, narrower ravines whose perpendicular walls limited exploration to the restricted stream beds between them and to a few ledges near their bases.

Failing to find any trace of the plant he wanted, Rodolfo began in a rather desultory fashion to scan the higher inaccessible ledges and cliffs. Suddenly he saw a low shrubby bit of vegetation which seemed to correspond to the description of *Nicotiana cordifolia*. The plant bore no flowers which would have helped to identify it, but the shape and color of its leaves and its growth form were exactly right. In considerable excitement Rodolfo cast about for some means of reaching the plant. Thorough examination of the precipitous canyon walls revealed no route by which even a goat could have found his way to the cliffs above. At last he had the bright idea of trying to lasso the plant and drag it down to a point to which he could climb. He found some heavy string in his pocket and some bits of rope on the beach. Piecing them all together he made a strand with a terminal loop long enough to reach the plant. Then began a long and tiresome series of casts one of which was finally successful, and at his feet there fell a branch or two and a few leaves. Examination of the specimens in California a month later left no doubt that Rodolfo had proved that *Nicotiana cordifolia* still grows on Mas-a-Fuera.

The next morning he had a few hours for collecting before the schooner sailed and was in high hope of finding the plant in flower and seed now that he had "gotten his eye on it." This, by the way, is an important psychological aspect of plant collecting because, unless you are unusually observant, you are quite likely to overlook an unfamiliar or inconspicuous species that may actually be growing in some quantity in the area you are traversing. But once you have seen it and collected it then it is definitely a part of the floral landscape, and if you want more specimens there is usually little difficulty in finding them. Thus Rodolfo, feeling assured that he would recognize *Nicotiana cordifolia* if he saw it, began an exploration of the Quebradas del Mono, del Ovalo, and del Pasto, all three of them deep ravines that run up into the forested mountainside north of the landing place. He saw no sign of the much-sought-after tobacco relative, but his time was so limited and he was so fearful of being left behind that he was unable to make a really careful search.

Now assured that *Nicotiana cordifolia* can be found on the Juan Fernandez Islands I am going to make another attempt, the fifth one, to obtain seed of it. Beside a perhaps too-obstinate unwillingness to be beaten in such a quest, there is a reason for growing this plant in Berkeley; a reason even more important than being able thereby to make one of the final additions to our otherwise practically complete living collection of the known species and varieties of *Nicotiana*. The external appearance of *Nicotiana cordifolia* suggests that it is closely related to two other *Nicotiana* species which today are found only near the desert coasts of northern Chile and southern Peru. Of these two species of the mainland far above the latitude of the Juan Fernandez Islands, we collected seeds, and from them we have grown plants and have studied their cell and tissue anatomy. If now we can make equivalent studies of living plants of *Nicotiana cordifolia* we shall be able to compare the results with those obtained from research on the two, apparently related, northern mainland species. Then there will be available for students fundamental evidence concerning the relationship of a characteristic member of the Juan Fernandez flora with plants now growing on the continent of South America.

Since this chapter was written the last hunt for *Nicotiana cordifolia* has been successful. With the General's help Pablo Aravena, a Chilean amateur botanist, was outfitted with proper rope ladders and grappling hooks and shipped off to Mas-a-Fuera in January of this year. He had days rather than hours to spend on the island and made a careful survey of the seaside cliffs up which, with the aid of his rope ladder, he climbed to the plateaus above. There he found the long-sought *Nicotiana* and collected an abundance of flowering specimens and enough ripe seed to plant a dozen acres. Late this summer I shall see mature plants grown from this seed blooming in the Botanical Garden. Beside them will be the *Nicotiana* species of the Chilean mainland.

Chapter XI

TOP OF THE WORLD

MEMBERS OF both expeditions did a good deal of collecting in the central Chilean Andes. This magnificent mountain barrier, separating Chile from Argentina, is the top of the world as far as the two Americas are concerned because it contains Mt. Aconcagua, the apex of both continents. Its summit rises to an altitude of a little more, or a little less, than twenty-three thousand feet. For neighbors it has Tupungato, Juncal, and the Mercedario, thrusting toward the sky to altitudes above twenty thousand feet, and many lesser eminences, all of them ten thousand and some fifteen thousand feet above the sea.

Among the unforgettable days in our lives is the one when first we stood at the foot of Aconcagua. It was early in January, which means the beginning of the short alpine summer at eight thousand feet and above in the highlands of central Chile. We had spent the night at Puente del Inca, where the cold, blustery wind off the snowy peaks was continually threatening to shake the little wooden hotel to pieces.

Puente del Inca has been headquarters for most of those who have attempted an ascent of Mt. Aconcagua, and from it a number of less arduous excursions can be made. The most popular of these takes you to the "Christ of the Andes," the famous statue that stands on the lofty border between Chile and Argentina. During the almost sleepless night in our creaking, rattling hotel room, Florence and I discussed plans for the following day and, with considerable reluctance, finally agreed that we really should be able to say that we had seen the Christus. In the morning, however, we found that the Argentine trippers at the hotel had already booked all seats in the available automobiles. I am afraid that we were not so disappointed as perhaps we should have been. Someday we must see the Christ of the Andes, but not with a crowd of tourists; see it standing alone on the bleak, rough mountainside, and read, but not over the shoulders of other travelers, the words that are inscribed in Spanish on its pedestal: "Sooner shall these mountains crumble into dust than the peoples of Argentina and Chile break the peace which at the feet of Christ, the Redeemer, they have sworn to maintain." There are those who like to scoff at this inscription. They insist that no one, either in Chile or Argentina, ever looked upon this pledge as representing more than a typically Latin gesture, something for the world to watch. I like to think otherwise, and to believe that such an affirmation reflects at least a little of the spirit of the two republics whose territories are joined beneath the figure of the Prince of Peace.

From Puente del Inca we tramped up the highway in the wake of the tourist-filled automobiles. At first we thought that we might manage the ten miles or so to the pass that leads to Chile and the nearby statue, and then hitchhike back to the hotel. Puente del Inca lies at almost nine thousand feet and the road eastward begins to climb rather rapidly on its way to the 12,800-foot pass. The wind that had blown through the night was still strong and, as the road swept in wide curves up the mountain slopes, it blew alternately in our faces and on our backs, and was equally disagreeable either way. The combination of wind, grade, and altitude made progress slow, and after a mile or two we realized that we would not reach the frontier or see the Christus that day.

Collecting in the wind was difficult, but we managed to put a few plants in the presses. Except on the steeper ridges, where it was thin, the soil was moist. Along little valleys and in most of the lesser depressions, it was boggy, sometimes exceedingly so. In such spots the yellow and red flowers of a delicate *Mimulus* (monkey flower), shone brilliantly against the dark background of the bog. Thin, brittle stems, only a few inches long, appeared to be highly insecure supports for the flaring, gaudy trumpets nodding at their tips. Behind ridges or in the lee of boulders on drier ground, small groups of shrubs were flourishing. Most conspicuous, and the only one in flower that we recognized, was an excessively spiny species of *Adesmia*, which sometimes grew to five or six feet.

Farther on, the valley of the Rio de las Cuevas became broader, and we began to traverse increasingly barren plains that ended abruptly in steep mountain walls. At first glance these sandy, rocky expanses appeared destitute of vegetation. Actually, however, they supported a variety of rather remarkable plants. Many of them were composites, members of the Sunflower family. All were dwarf, and hugged the ground to escape the wind and enjoy such warmth as the soil retained, especially at night. Most of them seemed to be species of *Senecio*, and all suggested the common dandelion gone a bit crazy. Some of their flat rosettes were massive, and most were either woolly or provided with a coating of wool plus glandular hairs, the latter making the plant exceedingly, and sometimes unpleasantly, sticky. These true alpines were usually perennial species and grew from partly woody and partly fleshy roots, deep-seated in the soil. Beneath the heavy winter snows such underground organs retain vitality, and each year, with the melting of the white blanket and the first warming of the soil that comes with the highland spring, they send up new leaves and short thick stems. Abundant food, with its contained energy, flows from the storehouses in the roots, to make successful the competition of these perennials with the rigors of their environment. Growth has to be very rapid so that maturity, with its flowers and seed, can be attained before the short summer season is at an end.

These prostrate composites were devilish things to bring to press because the ruffled margins of the strong, stiff leaves were set with short, sharp bristles. To dig up even part of the root system without injuring the leaves meant that one side of the broad, prickly rosette had to be held up with the left hand while the digging tool was manipulated with the right. On such occasions Florence retired upwind where only faint echoes of the imprecations, in which my anguish culminated, might reach her ears. Once, I failed to recognize the dangerous character of a charming plant whose big white, bell-like flowers were half hidden in masses of much divided foliage. It grew on the margin of the only moist spot we passed while traversing the wide plains and was so much in contrast to the monstrous "dandelions" we had been collecting that I turned to it with interest and pleasure. Too late I realized that I was handling a species of *Cajophora*, a near relative of the Loasas, whose violently

stinging hairs had taught us many a sharp lesson in the foothills of the Peruvian and Chilean Andes. At the start the pain
seemed to be almost unbearable, but it decreased fast, only to
rise again and again, but with diminishing intensity.

As we walked up the highway, with short excursions, first
to one side and then to the other for plant collecting, the character of the terrain began to change. The curves became steeper
and narrower as the road followed along one side of deep
gulches and then turned back along the opposite one. There
was again evidence of moisture in the soil. With it shrubs appeared and, in their protection, a few herbs. On open hillsides
we saw our first alpine nasturtiums. They grew from tubers,
or, perhaps better, from corms, which I discovered were securely
hidden below massive boulders or at the bottom of deep, rough
scree. From this security they trailed for two feet or more over
the rocky soil like dark but shining, flat, green feather boas.
Each was tipped with a tight nosegay of cream to reddish orange,
nasturtium-like flowers. This was the plant that we had been
waiting to see, and I had been afraid that we were too early for
its blooming. On somewhat shaded slopes it was still in bud,
but, in more exposed areas where the hot alpine sun had full
sway, the flowers were open. With their deeply divided margins,
reminiscent of the foliage of the California poppy, the leaves
are quite different in appearance from those of our garden nasturtiums. Of course, there was no ripe seed and so I began to
dig the tubers. My digging tools consisted of a light, short-
handled, double-headed pick, and two scratched hands that,
alternately, glowed red and then paled to a white-pustuled
surface, as the venom of *Cajophora* reduced or increased its
authority.

The succulent stem of the nasturtium was often three-
fourths of an inch in diameter where the leaves grew densest,
but further back it suddenly decreased in diameter and, slender
as a thread, disappeared between the rocks. This meant that
only with the utmost care could the layers of rock be removed
without breaking the delicate, leafless lifeline to the underlying
soil. Once broken, it was almost impossible to find the point
where the white thread extended through the tightly packed
scree. After a number of tedious and unsuccessful attempts to

burrow through the rocks, each of which involved considerable excavation, I began to work on the plants that grew, in what appeared to be sandy soil, beside the big boulders. It seemed to me that the tubers could not be very far back under the boulders and that a minimum of delving should uncover them. At any rate there would be no rocks to contend with. I was entirely mistaken. The sandy soil-surface was a sham, nothing more than six inches of covering above closely set, small boulders. The sand proved to be the light, almost dustlike, product of decomposition of granite and sandstone. At the slightest disturbance it rose in the wind and filled eyes and nose with an irritating mist. Keenly disappointed I finally had to give up the attempt to bring home alive one of the finest alpines of the Andes.

From time to time we had been turning our eyes northward up the increasingly large valleys that crossed the highway. Somewhere behind the high ridges in which each of these valleys ended, was Mt. Aconcagua. Then, around a turn of the road, we looked up again, and there she was—a tremendous, glistening-white truncated cone, rising in majesty above a jumble of lesser peaks. On an air line we must have been about fifteen miles away from the crown, which rose only eleven thousand feet above us, so that Aconcagua's height and breadth were not as impressive as they would have been had our view been a closer or much more distant one. Nevertheless, there was some mysterious, some detached quality about that mass of snow and ice which glowed and shimmered against the intensely blue sky. It made this sky and all familiar things seem a little unreal, and the very air took on a new, more heady quality. Close together, hand in hand, we stood, as if to share physically every individual reaction and emotion; a word would have broken the spell.

Growing thick and strong on a wide, gentle slope the alpine nasturtiums made an almost completely green foreground for the surpassingly beautiful picture that we were trying to absorb. Beyond, a long, broad, barren, boulder-strewn valley led directly to the dark ridges from which Aconcagua sprang. Near us the valley walls were very high and almost vertical, and the morning sun was strongly reflected from their tan, orange, and rosy rock surfaces. It made a brilliant frame for the vista of the great white peak.

As we stood there attempting to appreciate and evaluate all that we had before our eyes something new began to be added to our consciousness. At first it was a very distant, almost imperceptible hum. Rapidly this faint breath of sound came nearer and increased in intensity. We looked at each other and then, with the same thought, simultaneously directed our eyes to the ground and searched it for the bumble bee that, with noisy flight, should be visiting the golden nasturtium flowers. There was no bumble bee. Again simultaneously we put back our heads and stared straight up into the bright sky. I saw it first, and in an instant felt the answering pressure of Florence's fingers. Directly overhead a shining, silver insect raced across the zenith, halfway between us and Aconcagua's white shoulder. Hands tightly clasped we slowly turned our heads to watch it disappear eastward, behind a distant ridge. A gradually diminishing hum floated in the air long after it was lost to view. It was only one of the airplanes that in good weather fly daily, both east and west, over the pass and beside Aconcagua. But, for the moment or two during which that silver thing was in the sky, it became part, almost a natural and appropriate element, of the very top of the world, and not a familiar man-made and man-directed machine.

To escape the wind we walked up the valley and gained the shelter of its precipitous walls. For an hour we rested and watched the mountain. It seemed to take on new aspects as the sun came to lie more directly overhead. We felt the magnetic quality of great eminences; the urge to pit feeble human strength against the immensity of the forces that hinder their ascent, to demonstrate again that high courage and the driving power of the human will can successfully transport the body beyond its normal sphere, and that resourcefulness of mind can circumvent the limitless powers of nature. All this the Fitzgerald party demonstrated when they made the first ascent of Aconcagua in 1897. We tried to identify the nineteen-thousand-foot saddle, beneath the summit, where they established their highest camp and from which a number of attempts were made to climb the remaining four thousand feet. On both of the two successful ascents Fitzgerald was forced to give up at about twenty-two thousand feet. One of the Swiss guides who accompanied him was the first man to stand on the top of Aconcagua. Later on, Stuart Vines, an expedition member, with another guide also reached it. On this second ascent almost eight and a half hours were required to complete the climb from the nineteen-thousand-foot camp.

The summit itself proved to be a square plateau, measuring seventy-five paces each way, sloping at an angle of seven degrees toward the southeast and entirely free from snow. In Fitzgerald's book, *The Highest Andes,* Vines thus describes the unparalleled panorama lying at his feet: "Northward over the cloudless expanse my eye wandered down the great slopes of the mountain, over glaciers and snow fields . . . to where the great snow mass of the Mercedario, towering above all the surrounding heights, barred the way. . . . In the enormous distance to which I could see beyond, numerous giants reared their mighty heads, many of them in the shape of perfect pyramids. . . . Over Argentine territory, range beyond range stretched away; colored slopes of red, brown, and yellow, and peaks and crags capped with freshly fallen snow.

"Away over the surging mass of white cloud that lay on the glacier at my feet, rose the southern frontier chain, Torlosa and the Twins, on either side of the Cumbre Pass, like colossal sentinels guarding the great highway between the two republics . . . the lofty glaciers lying between the rugged crags of Juncal . . . and some sixty miles farther on, the magnificent white summit of Tupungato.

"No lens or pen can depict the view on the Chilean side . . . I looked down the great arête, past the western peak of Aconcagua . . . over ranges that dwindled in height . . . to where, one hundred miles away, the blue expanse of the Pacific glittered in the evening sun. . . . The sun lay low on the horizon and the whole surface of the ocean . . . was suffused with a blood-red glow." Such is the soul-stirring reward of the alpinist.

We stayed on and on, saying little and constantly watching the mountain. As we gazed at it a faint, delicate, milky halo seemed to form above the peak, and soon wisps of cloud sailed over and around it. They appeared intent upon accumulating to hide the summit from us. But they were never successful and always trailed away in thin streamers, to be lost in the blue background. Again and again they returned, to relieve a little the grimness of the great block of snow that was dominating our eyes and consciousness. At last we were satisfied and started down the valley to the highway, but constantly stopping to look back toward Aconcagua. It was as though we were still convinced that it was unreal and that, with the breaking of the spell of our absorption in its wonders, nothing would remain. Our progress was slow, until a turn of the valley walls hid the mountain.

In 1935 we had come by automobile to Puente del Inca and the Uspallata Pass, from Mendoza. In 1938, at about the same season, we again made the journey from Argentina to Chile, this time by automobile and train. The alternative was to fly over the Andes, but we wanted to be on the ground to study the vegetation, and to stop for a time in places where it looked promising.

The railway journey has long been familiar to South American travelers. Until January floods in 1934 washed out a section of the track above Mendoza on the Argentine side one could travel all the way by train from Buenos Aires, on the Atlantic, to Valparaiso, on the Pacific. There is, at present, a joint Argentine-Chilean proposal to reconstruct that portion of the right of way which was washed out. Meanwhile, travelers are carried in automobiles from Mendoza to Punta de Vacas, where the Argentine section of the railway begins again. In 1939, a new, or at least much-improved, highway made the automobile journey comfortable and easy.

The old road which we traversed in 1935 had seemed, with our then limited knowledge of Andean roads, to be a trifle on the dangerous side. There was, for example, one spot where the rough, one-way roadbed wound around the walls of a deep valley. The almost sheer drop over the unprotected edge must have been more than a thousand feet. A mountain stream, tumbling down from the heights above, crossed the road at the point where it made a sharp turn before running back along the opposite valley wall. Below the road this stream became transformed into a long waterfall. A strong upward current of

air lifted the spray from this waterfall and carried it, as a
dense mist, over the road. The narrow track at the head of the
valley was swallowed up in this thick mist and the chófer had to
run dead slow, with horn at full blast, as we splashed and rolled
through the ford and made a narrow hairpin turn against rocky
walls. For an hour a succession of fast-moving trucks had been
meeting us at highly inconvenient spots along the narrow highway, and one couldn't help imagining what would happen if
another one chanced to come roaring into the mist as we were
moving slowly out of it.

From Punta de Vacas, at over seven thousand five hundred
feet, the train began a rapid climb which ends at ten thousand
five hundred feet in the two-mile tunnel under the thirteen-
thousand-foot pass on the Chilean-Argentine border. The first
stop is Puente del Inca. The guide book calls it "one of Argentina's most romantic spots." The *puente,* or bridge, of multicolored rock, that spans the seventy-foot gorge over the Rio
Cuevas, is spoken of as "one of the natural marvels of South
America." When we saw it so many tourists were wandering
about this "natural marvel" that it had anything but a natural
appearance.

A week or so before our arrival a young compatriot had
appeared at the hotel with the announcement that he proposed
to climb Aconcagua. According to the hotel proprietor, who
took me aside as soon as we had registered and emphatically
disavowed any responsibility for what had happened, this youth
confessed to practically no mountaineering experience. Nevertheless, he was absolutely determined immediately to begin the
Aconcagua ascent, which is one of the most difficult in the
world, at least so far as physical strain is concerned. He had left
a ship in Valparaiso only a few days earlier, and certainly needed
a week or two to become adjusted to high altitudes and to
harden himself by preliminary climbing, before attempting an
assault on the highest American peak. The proprietor said that
he had been able to put him off for two or three days by claim-
ing that trained guides were not available. Finally, however, the
young man became so demanding and generally obstreperous
that the guides were forthcoming and the ascent was begun.
After reaching about eighteen thousand feet, the poor chap

collapsed, and died before he could be brought down to a lower altitude.

Once through the long tunnel and out on the Chilean side the railway runs along natural and artificial ledges that hang on gigantic mountain slopes. The rock scenery just below the tunnel is said to be the grandest in the world. It certainly is stupendous, and considerably more impressive than anything we have seen in Europe, or the Rockies, American or Canadian. Florence and I twice watched it pass the windows of the observation car on the Transandine train and, later on, I spent two days in an automobile and on foot in the midst of it.

I could never decide whether a near view of the incredibly rugged, broken complex of two- to four-thousand-foot rock walls, toothed ridges seamed with tightly packed snow, steep, ruddy scree slopes pimpled with immense boulders and, finally, a group of white peaks, was more impressive than the view at a lower altitude, upward toward this complex. From below one sees a superb panorama of rough plains between confining mountain slopes that rise in unbroken four-, five-, and six-thousand-foot sweeps to a black ridge against which presses a semicircle of snowy peaks. These white pyramids carry the eye still another five thousand feet up into the intensely blue sky of the Chilean highlands. The almost impossibly steep angles of repose of mile-long scree slopes, the piling of one rock mass upon another and then upon another, the snowy crown almost directly overhead, combine to create a panorama that cannot anywhere be surpassed. It is as though a steep little gorge high in the Rockies or Sierra Nevadas had been expanded a hundred times, preserving all geological features and relationships, but enlarging each of them to a monstrous degree.

For a number of reasons the spring and summer vegetation on the Chilean side of the pass was an object of special interest. Since altitudinal changes are abrupt in this broad, rapidly ascending, vertical valley that the Transandine Railway skirts, the zonation of plant species is as striking as it had proved to be in the deep canyons of Inca Land, in southeastern Peru. I was particularly concerned with the reaction of *Nicotiana* species under the influence of altitude. On both sides of the pass *Nicotiana corymbosa,* a previously little-known, low-growing

tobacco relative, was here and there abundant, and particularly
so near corrals and along the trails used for cattle on their way
to market in Chile. On the Argentine side these plants began to
appear at about seven thousand feet and continued to occur
until the altitude reached a little over nine thousand feet. As
we descended the Chilean side they reappeared at nine thousand five hundred feet and disappeared at six thousand five
hundred feet. After an additional drop of two thousand feet
an entirely different species, *Nicotiana acuminata,* took up the
westward distribution of this genus, which can be followed almost down to the shores of the Pacific in central Chile.

A singular thing about the distribution of *Nicotiana corymbosa* is that one also finds it rather commonly at much lower
altitudes, on the southern edge of the Chilean coastal deserts,
and in the Cordillera de la Costa that rims the Vale of Paradise.
Still more interesting is the fact that, in addition to the two
localities just referred to, *Nicotiana corymbosa* is found only
in arid Patagonia, five hundred miles and more south of the
pass. Doubtless it was once, and still may be, more or less continuous in distribution from the far south on the Atlantic side
of the continent, along the eastern flanks of the Andes, over the
Uspallata Pass, and down into Chile. Next year Florence and
I hope to search for it in the Argentine Andes from Mendoza
southward to the Patagonian pampas. The vegetation of that
portion of its probable range of distribution has never been
adequately explored by the plant hunter and so may uncover
many things of interest.

Not only to examine at first hand the *Nicotiana* situation
on the Chilean side of the pass, but also to collect seeds of the
fine ornamentals that we had seen in bloom, toward the end of
the alpine summer, I started up into the highlands. The General went with me. From Valparaiso we took a train to Los
Andes, more properly called Santa Rosa de los Andes, and
there engaged a car with driver. I never discovered just what
kind of a dicker the General made with the chófer. Certainly
he proved to be most obliging, and throughout the trip there
was none of that arcrimonious bickering about where and how
often the botanists should stop along the roadside, that I anticipated on the basis of past experience.

From Los Andes the automobile road over the pass into Argentina has its official beginning. I was told that it represents a section of the Pan-American Highway. Although on the Chilean side there were spots along this Pacific-Atlantic highway which would give the average touring North American considerable pause, it is, in general, a remarkable accomplishment, and on it, for years past, a steady procession of automobiles, most of them from Argentina, has successfully crossed the Andes and back again. Since we were botanizing and not in a hurry to get somewhere, the chófer, where he could, turned off the road whenever there was a honking from the rear or he saw a car approaching. We were quite content to let the hurrying world go by.

Until we had passed Rio Blanco and risen above five thousand feet there was not much that was new or exciting in the way of plants. Thereafter the first of the vegetation that attracted attention were scattered growths of something resembling tall, loosely-growing, single-flowered garden stocks, except that the color was wrong. They proved to be a species of *Malesherbia,* belonging to a strictly South American plant family. It was quite a charming plant with long flower spikes covered with flat, inch-and-a-half across, navy-blue disks. Elsewhere in the Chilean Andes we saw this same *Malesherbia,* and often in shades of paler blue. Sometimes the petals of the dark-blue flowers showed an intricate design of faint white lines that added considerably to their attractiveness. Whether it was a normal condition, or resulted from the activities of insects of the "leaf miner" clan, is not as yet determined.

Wherever we found them the *Malesherbia* preferred rocky, well-drained soil, and made most of their growth under decidedly dry conditions. When they first appeared on the way to the pass there was no seed, but higher up, where the season was later, we collected it in abundance. For some reason this seed did not germinate, and so we must secure new collections before this apparently desirable ornamental can be given a trial under garden conditions.

Along with the unfamiliar *Malesherbia* was *Schizanthus,* a well-known garden plant. I was glad to see it on its native heath and in its original, unimproved condition. It is commonly grown in California, but usually as a pot plant, and is called butterfly flower or, sometimes, poor man's orchid. We collected the seed of a number of *Schizanthus* species in Chile, and have grown them in Berkeley. Two are proving to be of some interest, one perhaps a real novelty. The one which the General and I came across is the familiar *Schizanthus* that bears bluish magenta flowers marked with orange stripes at the base of the petals. The particular virtue of the plants from our seed is their robust habit, either field or pot grown, and the size of their flowers, almost that of the hybrids offered by the seedsmen. These hybrids tend to become weak-stemmed and usually need support when full grown, while our plants put up a number of three-foot-long flowering stems that are strong and stiff and stand considerable abuse without breaking.

The other *Schizanthus* we brought back is also a robust plant, but its importance comes from the delicious, if faint, fragrance of its pure-white flowers and their unusual shape and form. In place of the rather flat-faced blossom we expect in *Schizanthus* the flower of this species has become a tube. At the end of the two-inch flower the tube broadens to form wide upper and lower lips from which hang delicate, deeply cut, white fringes. In this unfamiliar species we apparently have something that should be valuable, at least as a parent for hybridization to produce new garden races.

The Malesherbias and Schizanthus occupied a definite altitudinal zone, and when we got above it the vegetation became more sparse. Still higher, the scattered plants were largely confined to sandy, gravelly spots between the large boulders that had fallen from high cliffsides into the narrowing valley and come to rest on its floor. In a few of these protected areas I saw silky, brown, foot-long stems rising in twos, threes, or fours directly from the sandy surface of the soil. Each was topped by three dark-brown balls that popped open at a touch, to shed neatly packed rows of flat, black seeds. It was obviously some sort of an amaryllid, and I gathered a lot of seeds in the expectation of having to wait until flowering-sized plants had been grown in Berkeley before seeing its bloom. It appeared probable that if the plant was in fruit at lower altitudes it would be even more mature at higher ones. The reverse, however, was true, for soon I saw the smooth, brown stems crowned with flowers instead of seed capsules. These flowers showed that it was a species of *Placea*. They were large, shell-pink trumpets held so strongly in horizontal position that they jerked stiffly back and forth when the quick-thrusting breezes from the snow fields overhead slipped around the protecting boulders, to blow across their delicately colored surfaces. From time to time during our stay in the pass I tried to dig *Placea* "bulbs," but was not too well rewarded for a lot of hard work.

Over a considerable distance the highway ran in wide curves across a broad, up-tilted plain. Above, in the rapidly narrowing valley, the foreground ended abruptly in a solid, two-thousand-foot wall. This barrier was so steep that the full course of the snakelike track on which the highway climbed to an upper plateau could only be seen from above. As we began the ascent the automobile entered a rubble-filled trough, on the sides of which the wheels began to spin and continued to do so until they reached a firm, rocky bottom. In other words, the highway was nothing more than a boulder-free depression in the gray, powdery, decomposed rock. In some places it had been worn down to a depth of six feet. I presume that as the traffic exposes underlying boulders and outcroppings of rock these menaces are supposed to be periodically removed. We must have negotiated that part of the road between such repair periods, because there were a good many rough spots that contrasted sharply with the cushiony quality of most of the road trough. Neither on the up nor on the down trip did we meet another car, and so I still have no idea how the apparently impossible business of passing is accomplished.

In a westward direction the beginning of the descent over this piece of the trans-Andean highway is spectacular. The upper plateau is large and not too steep. As you motor down and rapidly approach the wide cliff edge the road ahead suddenly disappears. Beyond it there is absolutely nothing for miles, until the high mountains far down the valley rise against the sky. The combination of this distant background and the tremendous height of the vertical rock walls around the upper plateau make it seem certain that a glider, rather than an automobile, is the proper conveyance from that point onward. In another moment you dive over the knife edge and catch one quick glimpse of the road spiral below and of the far-off valley floor at your feet, before the car settles down, almost out of sight, in the trough.

Later on, I walked toward the edge to determine the impression that this first descent over the cliff would make on a foot passenger, and also to take a longer look at what lay below. The margin of the steep drop proved to be a strategic point at which to obtain the sum of all the impressions of grandeur and immensity that crowd upon the traveler who passes over this portion of the Andes by train or automobile. I realized that those partial, fleeting views that we had previously obtained were far more unsatisfactory than they had seemed at the time to be. From this, in a sense, halfway point, the rock masses to the east were almost overpowering in their sheer bulk, in the crudity of their silhouette, and in their total lack of natural arrangement or symmetry. Directly above them the peaks of Aconcagua's neighbors showed only as white apices, but the fact that they were able to appear at all above the nearby, vertical foreground left no doubt that the summits were supreme in altitude. To the west, down the valley, a more distant background of softer horizons made the view easier to understand, even though it was on a far grander scale. From my vantage point on the cliff edge I could form some accurate estimate of the steepness of the mountainsides. Seen in profile, it was almost impossible to believe that their rock surfaces could long remain in position, and it was easy to understand why in that region no hour of the day goes by without the distant rumble of rock slides. However, as many times as I stopped to scan the surfaces of those almost vertical slopes, I never detected rock movements until I was in the midst of one myself.

We put up in the small hotel near the station at El Portillo. This is the first railway stop below the tunnel on the Chilean side. From it an easy climb leads to Laguna del Inca which all passengers from east to west on the Transandine know, because the train pauses to give them a short look at what can be one of the most beautiful alpine lakes in the world. It lies at about ten thousand feet, spread narrowly in the bottom of a deep cleft between immensely steep mountain slopes, with the snow-mantled peaks of the Aconcagua Range in the background. At high noon the sun briefly illuminates its deep, still waters on whose surface the gray, brown, and red rock walls and the white peaks are reflected. At other hours of the day, and especially once when I saw it in the half-light of early evening, Laguna del Inca is a forbidding place of giant shadows thrown across black depths, with inhospitable walls of dark rock everywhere about.

Below the Laguna, the General and I walked down the track until we found a spot where the long scree slopes could be entered. This was not easy, because on the mountainsides the railway ran along shelves and through cuts, the inner sides of which were in most places too steep to climb. The General, armed with his big butterfly net, was out for certain rare, fast-flying insects peculiar to higher altitudes in the great valleys below the Andean crests. At one moment we were walking slowly, picking our way over the surface of the rough scree; at the next, the General was thundering away as fast as the footing would permit and with net extended toward something that was either so small or so fast as to be invisible to any but the trained eye of the entomologist. Thereafter he came into view only now and then, in the nearer or farther background, and rarely were we in hailing distance. His enthusiasm as a naturalist and his unbounded physical energy were never better demonstrated than on those almost vertical mountainsides. To me it was a mystery how he could so continually be dashing up hill and down, at an altitude that began to constrict my breathing apparatus soon after I started to engage in moderate physical exertion.

My notes, made after two sets of observations from the train, had located a series of areas in which the alpine nasturtiums grew abundantly. Following our first sight of them near Puente del Inca three years before, and appreciating their unique character and ornamental value, I was determined to obtain their seed so that they might be grown in California. Although detailed study of the Nicotianas and their distribution up the pass on the Chilean side was the primary objective of our journey into the highlands, its season had been selected partly in favor of finding, in fruiting condition, such alpine ornamentals as the nasturtium.

The General and I entered the scree and boulder slopes about a mile from one of the nasturtium areas and I worked over to it as fast as I could. At a distance, the surface of the mountainside appeared to be flat and rather uniform in composition and in angle of repose. Actually, however, it was a sea of smaller and larger blocks of stone and an undulating one, with broader or narrower depressions, steeper in one part than in another. In the depressions large boulders, dozens of tons in weight, stood at crazy angles, either alone or in a loose arrangement. On the low ridges between the depressions the rocks were smaller, mostly from fist- to head-size, tightly crowded together, and sometimes covered with a thin skin of coarse-grained gravel. Now and then this rough, but comparatively even, scree surface had shifted and loosened, to exhibit layer after layer of rock and rubble extending down toward the bedrock. That, in a few spots at least, this solid bed beneath the rocks could be near the surface was soon demonstrated to me. It was a thoroughly convincing demonstration.

Forward progress over the mountainside involved climbing obliquely upward and then downward. At rare intervals, where the slope was not too extreme, I could walk straight ahead. The powerful autumn sun poured upon my back and was strongly reflected from the rock surfaces. I often stopped to wipe dust from my black goggles and perspiration from the spectacles underneath them. During these halts a sense of insignificance as a physical element of that stupendous mountain panorama began to oppress me. Even my immediate surroundings were on such a formidable scale that I felt out of place. Above my head the mountainside rose many thousands of feet, even though the angle of its inclination was too steep to disclose more than a third of its upward extent. At my feet the rocky slope fell away abruptly for three thousand feet to the broad secondary terrace of the great valley. In the light of succeeding events it now seems strange that I was impressed only with the incongruity of my presence as a part of the gigantic mountainside and not at all with what might happen if all, or my portion, of its surface should begin one of those downward shifts in position that I knew periodically occurred.

During my slow progress I began to see on the rock in the foreground more and more greenish yellow splashes. When I came up to them they proved to be the much desired nasturtium. In most cases the plants were long past flowering. Their masses of drying stems and foliage made a faint rustling, scraping sound as the rising afternoon wind, blowing fitfully down the mountainside, tossed them lightly back and forth across the scree. The first group of plants I handled bore only one or two ripe seeds—light-brown spheres, a half-inch in diameter. They were attached, insecurely, to the dried ruins of the flowers and apparently the remainder of the seed had already fallen. Once the little balls rolled down into the scree it was impossible to find them. This I soon learned when I hunted for them on the rough surface beneath the plants. It was, however, with a pleasurable sense of achievement that I heard those first few nasturtium seeds rattle down into my paper seed envelope.

Intent on nothing but collecting as many seeds as possible I moved slowly from one group of plants to another. They were disappointing. Often a dozen plants yielded only a single seed, sometimes none. Finally I realized that the majority were almost completely sterile, with shrunken, undeveloped seed-bearing parts at the base of the dried petals. During the next hour I must have handled a thousand plants, and still the seed envelope was only two-thirds full. Oblivious of my surroundings I moved up and down and across this first low ridge on which I had found the nasturtiums. As I gradually descended into the depression beyond the plants became more scattered and decreased in number.

I straightened my aching back and surveyed the possibility of finding more nasturtiums. On the next rise there seemed to be a few spots of color, and so I clambered between and over the big boulders in the hollow, and started out across the smaller rocks beyond. Working slowly out toward the next low ridge I noticed that the rocky surface seemed looser, and I found it necessary to climb more carefully than before. If I had been less intent upon seed collecting, or had possessed more mountaineering experience, I might have realized that when rough scree lies loosely on a steep slope it is dangerous. At any rate I was entirely unprepared for a slow but definite shifting downward of the surface under my feet and did not appreciate what it signified. Indeed, I merely tried to settle my boots more firmly into the increasingly insecure footing while I continued to pick seeds from the more fertile plants that I was beginning to come across.

In the next instant the rock surface went out from under my feet. Struggling to stand erect I was dimly conscious of a deep, grinding note that rose from the churning rocks about me. To this undercurrent of sound was added the dull, smacking, sharp crashing of larger boulders that were beginning to leap from one impact to another, faster and faster, higher and higher, longer and longer, down the almost vertical mountainside. Stumbling and falling I tried to ride the rapidly developing rock slide. I can remember seeing the bedrock through the moving rock cover and realizing what this meant—that I had been climbing over a rock surface, not many feet deep as it elsewhere had been, but very shallow and most insecurely held on smooth outcroppings of the solid rock foundation.

Fortunately I had not crossed much of the loose surface before it had begun to move, so that I was near the edge of the slide. Of even more importance was the sudden division of the moving rock mass, one part of which carried me into the lower end of the hollow filled with big boulders which I had just left, while the rest went crashing down the slope for a thousand feet or more. How much of the time I was on my feet and how much of it I spent on my hands and knees, I cannot say. After it was all over my knees and hands were pretty raw. I must have fallen a number of times.

My friend, Dr. Joseph Rock, the famous plant hunter, who directed the University of California's 1931-1932 expedition in western China and Tibet, once told me that when, without warning, you find yourself falling forward on a rocky surface, it is important partially to close the fists. Then you will receive the impact of the fall upon them rather than upon the palm of the hand. He said that, in falling, a person unconsciously thrusts his arms outward and flattens the palms of the hands, as though to ward off the equivalent of a blow. With the fists loosely closed the impact of the fall is cushioned a little and, of greater importance, the more delicate tissues of the palms of the hands will be protected. Dr. Rock did not refer to what happens to the skin over the knuckles and to the rest of the epidermis on the closed fist, but, as soon as I was out of the rock slide, there was definite evidence on this point. In other words, I must have remembered his advice at least part of the time. Unfortunately, however, there must have been other times when I neglected to close my fists, for when I got around to looking myself over the palms as well as the backs of my hands were bloody. More deep-seated and apparently permanent injuries developed later. Strange and unpleasant things also happened to my back and hips. After two years I am still aware of them. An entirely unexpected aftermath of my experience on the rock slide was the discovery, in a hip pocket, of the paper packet of nasturtium seeds. How it got there, I have not the slightest idea. It should have been in my hands when the slide began and should therefore have been dropped and ground to bits or carried down the mountainside.

Now, the proper, the happy ending of this nasturtium story would be the report that from those seeds, collected at the expense of considerable effort, pain, and blood, we now have a fine stand of interesting and beautiful plants. Actually, however, not a single seed has germinated. They have been in the ground and out of it, kept in the cold room for months, alternately dried and wetted, but nothing happens. Nevertheless they still give evidence of being alive.*

That night at the El Portillo hotel I had a light attack of siroche or mountain sickness. It must have been the result of unusual exertion, plus the late unpleasantness, because the altitude was only about ten thousand feet. From a previous attack in the Peruvian Andes, but at a much higher altitude, I knew the symptoms. This time the gradual onset of a severe headache was followed only by a remarkably slow heart action; something that was, however, singularly distressing. Half awake for hours, I listened to one heart beat and then seemed to wait an eternity for the next one. The General, who was sleeping nearby, came

---

* A month after this was written and two and a half years after it was collected in Chile this seed began to germinate!

in at least once during the night. What he said or did, I do not remember. Probably I slept a reasonable amount. At any rate in the morning everything was normal.

The General and I, along with a few other guests not headed for Argentina, were waiting outside the hotel until the diminutive dining room was free of early morning automobilists. Fogs draped the great peaks that guard the pass, but a few slanting shafts of light penetrated the mountain crests and their misty coverings to dapple the boulder-dotted plain with flecks of golden light. Otherwise the morning was gray and gloomy between the steep, rocky hillsides and high, outjutting shoulders of granite, and its chill was penetrating enough to keep us on the move with stamping feet.

At a corner of the hotel stood a gasoline pump, at which a stream of cars had been filling up. I was absorbed in watching their loading when the General suddenly grabbed my arm and, just in time, pulled me back into the doorway of the hotel. With only a light, rattling, creaking sound from their gear and occasionally a crackling noise when hoofs scattered sharp gravel, a string of laden mules and horses swung rapidly past the doorstep and out of sight around the corner of the hotel. A huaso, his poncho worn high to ward off the chilly mists, rode slowly behind. As the travel-stained animals, drooping under relatively insignificant loads, picked their way between the cars and wandered past the gasoline pump, they created a picture that epitomized the contrasts between primitive and modern transportation over the mountain wall of the continent.

A number of automobile parties had arrived at the hotel during the previous evening. Some of them arose, noisily, at an early hour, to begin the difficult grade that led over the pass into Argentina. The hotel stood on the edge of a level plateau through which the highway made a wide curve before rising toward two zigzags, which, from the hotel doorstep, was all that we could see of the road into the thirteen-thousand-foot pass. From below it was difficult to appreciate the steepness of the grade above the first turn. The behavior of the automobiles told the story, however. This first turn, a few hundred feet directly above the hotel, was really not a curve at all, but, rather, an acute angle. Unless the driver had a relatively short car and was willing to skid it around the turn at high speed he had little chance of successfully making the grade above, at the first trial at least.

A succession of modest automobiles just managed to disappear up into the misty peaks or slid back, time after time, before overcoming the ascent above the first sharp turn. Then, a long, sleek Mercedes was driven up to the door and began to load. There were five considerably overdressed passengers, the family chauffeur, and a lot of gaudy baggage. This party had spent the night at the hotel. After going out of their way to comment unfavorably on the food, accommodations, and personnel they promptly retired to their rooms. Instead of sleeping they engaged in a family altercation, which for more than an hour echoed along the hotel corridors. Under the circumstances the staff and other guests, who were watching the hill-climbing contest, were distinctly hopeful that misfortune would attend the efforts of the big Mercedes to make the hairpin turn and the grade above it. However, those who claimed to know, regretfully pointed out that many foreign cars were provided with a special gear for heavy going on bad grades.

With spouts of gravel from their wheels, as though metaphorically brushing off the dust of their distasteful association with the hotel and its inmates, they sailed away and started up the first gentle rise. Gathering speed rapidly the long black car approached the difficult turn. With farther and farther back-tilting of heads we breathlessly followed its upward course. It seemed to be moving far too rapidly to permit a quick sharp turn with safety. This proved to be the case, and with a crash the car stopped dead, just as it was halfway around. Immediately the doors opened and the family poured out, to gather around the chauffeur, with waving arms. Their angry shouts were taken up by the cliffsides and thrown back and forth in diminishing volume up and down the valley.

We gazed at one another with ill-concealed gratification. The cook and his assistants had been cutting up a side of beef on a table outside the kitchen door. Simultaneously one raised a cleaver and the other a long, bloody butcher knife, as if in salute to the highway that had revenged the kitchen for the guests' uncomplimentary remarks about its product.

Some of us climbed up through the rocks to survey the situation. The Mercedes had almost made the turn but a last shoulder of rock on the inside caught and crumpled the right front fender, and the heavy car had skidded across the road, partially blocking it. At a respectful distance we waited until the passengers had exhausted themselves in heaping abuse upon the chauffeur, and then we advanced to the rescue. It required a dozen hands and backs—not, however, including those of any of the passengers—to help the chauffeur pull the fender off the tire and straighten out the machine on the road. Without a word of thanks the still disdainful passengers re-embarked. After two unsuccessful attempts, a great deal of shouting, and some blocking of the rear wheels our delightful friends finally passed out of sight. I am happy to report that they were neither North nor South Americans.

Descending from our rescue work we came across an extremely fine plant. It was obviously an *Alstroemeria,* but so altered in size and general appearance as a result of its alpine habitat, that, at first glance, it appeared to be something quite unknown. It grew on thin, light scree, so that the rather stout stem had to push up only six or eight inches to expose the plant to the light. Often its rosette of small, fleshy, light-green leaves, four to five inches across and heavily powdered with white wax, lay flat on the finely divided rock surface. Sometimes the plant was raised a few inches above it. From the center of the geometrically disposed mosaic of leaves there arose a compact knot of wine-red flowers. Each of the three to four in the knot was an inch-and-a-half-long tube that broadened toward the top and ended in a shallowly lobed margin.

Later on we found many of these same unusual and attractive, dwarf, succulent-leaved Alstroemerias, both under the pass and on Andean hillsides farther to the north. In no case, however, was their seed ripe. The General and I took the hotel proprietor at El Portillo out on the scree slopes, made him gaze intently at the Alstroemerias, and then extracted from him a solemn promise that he would periodically examine them and collect the seeds when ripe. We made it abundantly clear that ripeness would not be attained in less than a month. A week later, in Valparaiso, I received a small box containing nothing

but withered *Alstroemeria* flowers, accompanied by a letter
from the proprietor expressing gratification that he had been
able to co-operate so successfully in our most important botanical investigations!

During both expeditions we worked along the higher slopes
of the central Chilean cordillera; over a north-and-south distance of three hundred miles—approximately one hundred
miles south of Mt. Aconcagua and two hundred miles north of
it. In addition to the more intensive botanizing on both sides of
the pass under the brow of the great mountain, a part of which
has just been described, we collected in the Andes east of Ran-
cagua, Santiago, Petorca, Illapel, Ovalle, and Rivadavia. Sometimes the luck of the seasons was with us, sometimes it was not,
but altogether we took abundant loot from the Chilean highlands.

The grandeur of the Andean crest near the twenty-two-
thousand-foot peak of the Mercedario is perhaps more impressive than in the Aconcagua area, because the Mercedario massif
is very extensive and involves a large number of snowy peaks,
between and below which, on the Chilean side, vast snow fields
and glaciers are exposed to view.

Within the shadow of the Mercedario the Chilean frontier
swings sharply to the east for a number of miles, and then out
again to form a small dimple on the Argentina side. In the
depths of this dimple members of both expeditions collected,
and with considerable success. Carl, John, and Rodolfo rode
into it one December morning.

Their tough, little Chilean horses carried typical huaso
saddles, with no horn and built of heavy sheepskins strapped
over a wood and iron base. The botánicos' style of mounting
made a distinct impression on a crowd of peons that had assembled to see them off near the corrals of the hacienda which was
supplying the horses. Carl, disregarding technique of any sort,
quickly inserted a foot in the stirrup, grabbed the saddle with
both hands and climbed in, just as he would climb a ladder. At
this the Chileans shook their heads in amazement. Rodolfo,
having spent a year in military service, knew exactly how to
mount in Chilean style. He conveyed this information to the
crowd, unfortunately forgetting, however, that he had gained

twenty pounds since his army days. The result was highly undignified. Meanwhile the slender *vaqueano,* who was to accompany them, slipped effortlessly into his saddle. John watched
him and carefully noted his entirely unorthodox technique.
Loaded with a thirty-pound pack, which his horse eyed sus-
piciously, John attempted to modify his accustomed mounting
procedure to include some of the vaqueano's. The result was
unsatisfactory to a degree and was proportionately enjoyed by
the onlookers. They had been brought up on horseback and
could not understand why anyone, even a gringo, should have
difficulty in mounting a horse.

When the vaqueano saw that they were all safely in the
saddle he led the way up a hill behind the hacienda. The rough
trail ran beside the rushing torrent in an irrigation ditch that
followed along a contour on the lip of the hill. When the party
tried to cross, the horses, fresh and a bit skittish after their
night's rest and feed, shied badly at the foaming water, and so
they had to go downstream to a quieter ford. They skirted the
base of high hills, crossing and recrossing small ditches that led
the precious water from the melting snow fields of the Mercedario over the rocky slopes to small plots of arable land. The
buildings of the hacienda and most of its extensive areas of farmland lay in the valley below, at an elevation of twenty-five hundred feet. At three thousand feet they were in the midst of the
small farms of the laborers, rarely more than an acre or two in
extent, and oftentimes much less.

The trail began to follow a river. At a sharp bend it had
been piling up aluvium for centuries. A progressive farmer was
laboriously clearing away the larger boulders and his incredibly
slow oxen were scratching the soil with a primitive wooden
plow. Later on they saw a little boy driving a small mule which
dragged a sizable pile of brush back and forth across this
"plowed" land. The primitive harrow was supposed to break up
the cloddy soil, so that potatoes, a little wheat, and a few vegetables could be planted. These crops, together with eggs from a
motley collection of multicolored hens around the little farm-
house, milk from a small herd of goats pastured above, and meat
from kids and lambs, represented practically all the food that
this family unit required.

For a time the trail followed one of the numerous, small streams that flowed together to form a larger river. Then it started to weave in and out of quebradas, as they followed up each little tributary until a suitable ford could be found. The vaqueano began to look at the sun, something he continued to do all day long, as though to estimate the number of hours that still remained for their journey. He continued to lead the caval-cade and soon opened a gap of several hundred yards between his horse and Rodolfo's. John followed close behind Rodolfo and Carl brought up the rear. Realizing that the animals were accustomed to spurs and that only he was provided with them the vaqueano stopped and cut sharp switches from the shrubby mesquite beside the trail. He insisted that the other horsemen use them constantly and maintain his pace, else the party would never reach the high country in time to do any serious collect-ing.

At an elevation of thirty-five hundred feet they passed the last farmstead. All the country above and beyond, so vast an area that one can ride for days without seeing a single person or any sign of human life, was devoted solely to pasturage. With a scanty rainfall and raw, rugged mountainsides there was little level ground and certainly no soil, in the farmer's sense of that word, above four thousand feet. They had entered a rocky wil-derness. It stretched away to the Argentine border, and far be-yond it.

After another hour's ride the path began a long, slow climb across rough hills, toward the highlands. Near the streams they had been riding through tangles of that curious, leafless vine or straggler, *Muehlenbeckia,* with its inconspicuous flowers. Here also were thickets of *Escallonia* and an occasional tree of *Quil-laja saponaria.* Soon after beginning the climb the vaqueano paused for a brief descanso in a clump of small Quillajas. They cast a thin shade into which the horses crowded close. Ahead, the rock-bound foothills of the Andes rolled higher and higher toward the snow, like brown waves piling up to be shattered into foaming white as they broke against the highest snowclad mountainsides.

The wet mountain meadow for which they were bound, La Vega Escondida, lay at an elevation of 9,250 feet, which meant that there were still five thousand feet to climb. Ahead was nothing but the stony, zigzag trail which here and there cut gashes through the low, gray-green chaparral, or monte. The rock formations were, in general, sedimentary, of sandstone-like quality, and occasionally shale ledges and outcroppings of quartzite occurred. The vaqueano, like all of his breed in Chile, fancied himself a prospector, and insisted upon carefully inspecting all these outcroppings. The sparse, low chaparral consisted of *Baccharis,* a tough, resinous-leaved species with pale, greenish white flowers, *Acacia cavenia, Adesmia,* and other of the more common shrubs or diminutive trees of the Andean foothills. They competed with the highly specialized Puyas and Cerii for the scanty moisture held in the rocky, sandy soil. Among these woody or succulent plants, in exposed bits of thin soil, they found a red-flowered *Stachys,* or mint, with woolly, gray leaves. There was, also, an occasional pink-flowered *Alstroemeria ligtu.*

At sixty-five hundred feet they approached a high black crest. Over it a stream tumbled in a fine little waterfall. There they called a halt in order to collect flowering specimens of the dry, shrubby flora through which they had been riding. In addition they tried to persuade the vaqueano to stop for lunch. He, however, insisted upon continuing to the *vega.* Although pressed he refused to give any estimate of how much longer luncheon would be postponed, and, as if to close the subject, he began to climb to the plateau above the falls. Ahead was a wide scarp, hiding the vega. Its situation was reflected in its name, *escondida,* or hidden. To the northeast rose a great conical peak, on whose southern flank lay a large, circular, dish-like depression filled with snow. The trail soon began to climb steeply again, and the terrain became even rougher, if that were possible, and the monte ever more scattered and poor. At one o'clock they finally reached the vega and immediately fell to preparing the midday meal.

A vega is a boggy meadow. This one owed its origin to a quantity of small springs and many seepages of water in the bottom and on the walls of a wide valley. Over the deep, green, wet, cushiony surfaces, grasses and sedges were common and among them grew many showy plants—delicate orange-red

A storm gathering over the crests of the highest Chilean Andes

After the storm—new-fallen snow on the continental divide

Gleaming Mt. Aconcagua, the highest peak in the Western Hemisphere
The Transandine railroad has tunneled under snowy summits to enter Chile

Mimulus, Epilobium, Trifolium, Gentians, Calceolarias, and many other less familiar genera. All grew in some abundance. Around the margins of the vega there were other ornamentals and among them they saw their first Andean violet, a dwarf *Malesherbia,* and a number of brilliant Argylias.

After lunch Carl decided to climb the scree slope above the vega, and John and Rodolfo collected furiously on the marshy surface and over the nearby slopes. In two hours they had put almost sixty species in press. Later Carl returned and told of finding the snow-line at ten thousand feet. This meant that they were too early in the season for any collecting on the upper Andean slopes in the Mercedario region, but they consoled themselves by recalling that this was only a scouting trip. Besides, the vegetation in and near the vega had been more than up to expectation.

The afternoon was well advanced and they finally heeded the urgent requests of the vaqueano that the homeward journey be started. Rodolfo explained that their guide had just been married and wanted to get back to his village before dark, because encamped nearby were some *"muy molas, muy molestos"* miners. For Rodolfo the Andes held certain terrors. Whenever we were out of doors after dark, he informed us that the mountains were liberally infested with miners who butchered and robbed everyone they came across. Doubtless there were a certain number of professional prospectors about, but no one of us ever saw one.

Later in the Andean summer the highlands below the Mercadario ought to show a rather remarkable vegetation, at altitudes between twelve thousand and thirteen thousand five hundred feet. However, when John and Rodolfo explored them at that season, the plant hunter's curse, a dry season, pursued the botánicos even to those altitudes. In a foothill village they had secured the services of a vaqueano and his string of mules. It was their plan to spend three or four days above ten thousand feet.

They had first to cross the dry, lower slopes of the foothills, a tan to brown landscape except for scattered, gray-green *Acacia* and *Prosopis.* These uninteresting, wasteland plants had been transformed by the parasitic *Phrygilanthus* into masses of broad, thick, dark-green leaves, set with rich red flowers. Because of a late start, seven hours in the saddle brought them only to an altitude of six thousand five hundred feet. They camped on the edge of an extensive vega, covered with grass. Scores of fat cattle were pastured there. They grazed with a vicious thoroughness that was killing the thick turf in many places. After the grass is dead the hoofs of animals break up the dry vegetation, and soon a circular spot of black, crumbly soil is exposed.

The next morning they set the vaqueano to rustling dried dung and the resinous "vegetable sheep," so that there might be plenty of fuel for the cooking fire. After some collecting on the vega that yielded much the same species they had previously found at La Vega Escondida, John and Rodolfo rode out toward higher altitudes.

It was to be a quick sizing up of the vegetation and a determination of the best route to follow on their way to the snow line. Ahead of them was a high ridge that later proved to be a series of ridges, each one rising higher toward the Andean summits. As they drew nearer the distant panorama of peaks and snow fields disappeared behind these ridges. Over the first of them lay a large depression. In a normal year it would have been a sizable lake; now they could ride across its bed—a dry, rock-bound, cuplike field. The next ridge was steeper and the mules took the climb leisurely, as though saving themselves for the still harder work that they seemed to know lay ahead of them.

For hours rapidly shifting, ever-darkening clouds had been sweeping down from the crest of the continent toward which they were proceeding. Without warning these clouds closed in upon them and brought a rapidly rising wind. First it carried a few drops of rain; then a downpour. The rain was cold, sharp, stinging, and held a threat of something more severe to come. The mules did not seem to mind, but plodded slowly up the ever-increasing gradient. Soon the sky became still darker, and the rain gradually changed into a cutting sleet. Their faces burned as it lashed them with icy whips. Then came a hailstorm, and in an instant the muddy trail was full of big, white marbles. The pounding of the hard pellets and the uncertain footing annoyed the mules, and they struggled hard to turn their rumps to the storm. But John and Rodolfo relentlessly forced them onward and upward, and finally the twelve-thousand-five-hundred-foot ridge was topped.

No sooner had they crossed it than a thick snowstorm developed. It walled them in so completely that, for a few moments, they had to halt. The snow had come so rapidly that they had had no time to take stock of the foreground or the background, and for a time they lost all sense of direction. Then, as suddenly as it had come, the storm was at an end. The wind fell to a gentle breeze, the clouds burst open to permit the passage of shafts of sunlight and then dissolved to clear the blue sky. In a few moments the snow began to melt, steam arose from the backs of the mules, and their riders felt warmth flowing back into clammy, shaking limbs.

They dismounted to wring some of the water from their soaking coats and sweaters and to stretch cold, cramped muscles. Rodolfo examined the mules, found that their softened hoofs were showing signs of soreness, and insisted upon starting for the camp. John decided to go forward on foot, while Rodolfo led the animals back. On the return journey he was to stop and dig as many tubers as possible of an alpine nasturtium they had come across on the slopes of the first ridge. The plants had begun to wither before they were old enough to flower, but the leaves suggested that it might be something different from the Tropaeolums previously collected.

John climbed higher and higher through the slush, until he stood upon the last and highest of the foothill ranges. There, at thirteen thousand feet, he looked across a deep, glaciated valley to the magnificent Andean peaks. Around him the hail and snow were fast disappearing, but, on the farther wall of the valley, a wide belt of whiteness swept up from ten thousand feet to the permanent snow fields that began at sixteen thousand feet. Through his binoculars the soft, brilliantly white, new-fallen snow, which looked to be half a foot deep, contrasted strangely with the glazed, bluish white surface of the almost limitless fields of perpetual snow. From them rose one glittering white eminence after another. He identified Cerro las Lanas (fifteen thousand seven hundred feet), Cerro la Mesa (nineteen thousand nine hundred feet), and, dominating them and

many lesser summits, twenty-two-thousand-foot Cerro Mercedario. Great, white cumulus clouds began to float up behind
these giant mountains and made shifting patterns of light and
shade on their white expanses.

He unshipped the cameras and recorded, in black and
white and in color, the unsurpassed panorama that stretched
away, north and south, only fifteen miles from his lofty coin of
vantage. Hardly was the picture-taking at an end before the sky
became heavily overcast once more and another snowstorm
threatened. In addition there were no plants to collect; the
unusually early drought had seen to that; in short, a rapid retreat to the camp three thousand feet below was indicated.
Cutting across the zigzags of the trail John slid and floundered
straight down the mountain and across the loose, rough talus
slopes.

At the camp it had rained much more heavily and for a
longer time, and the poor vaqueano was lying prone in order,
periodically, to blow into flame the damp chunks of dung and
llareta (*Laretia compacta*) over which the *cazuela,* or stew pot,
was suspended. Mountain menus, although they never varied,
did not pall. For breakfast there was tea, some sort of bread-
stuff, and charqui (jerked meat, sometimes suspected of being
horse) that had been toasted crisp over the coals of the camp
fire. For lunch there was a big stew of charqui—to which had
been added any wild game that came to bag—tea, and a few
pieces of dried fruit. Dinner always proved to correspond exactly to luncheon, except that another two hours' cooking had
reduced the contents of the cazuela to delicious shreds and a rich
gravy, which went into the mouth via slabs of bread. After the
stew was gone serious tea drinking began and oftentimes two
big tea kettles full of a rich brown brew would no more than
satisfy the demand. If the day's work had been unusually tax-
ing a little cocktail of raw aguardiente was necessary to increase
interest in the evening meal.

When the last cup of tea had been consumed the bedrolls
were opened and spread on the least rocky areas that the fading
light revealed. A large, waterproof ground cloth was found
essential, because, however rapidly the burning alpine sun dried
the rocks or surface soil wetted by a mountain shower, there

always seemed to be a residue of moisture ready to dampen the bottom of a sleeping bag. During our experience in the Chilean highlands, no matter how rainy the daylight hours might be, the stars were sure to shine unclouded all night long. Thus, a tent or other protection was superfluous for us who proposed to make only one night stands in each collecting ground. After a night or two of watching those glowing constellations that, in the pellucid Andean atmosphere, seem to have gained scores of brilliant stars, no one of us could have borne to substitute a close, canvas sky.

To try for pictures of the unclouded morning Andean crest John arose early and rode up to another portion of the thirteen-thousand-foot ridge he had climbed the day before. Under the clear sky and brilliant morning light the Mercedario and its satellites seemed to have decreased the distance that before had separated him from their glaring white slopes, now sparkling and glittering like living things. Just below the peaks, and some ten miles across the deep, U-shaped valley at his feet, a higher ridge marked the Argentine frontier and hid the Aconcagua massif. John determined to cross the valley and climb until he could see and photograph the highest American summit.

Returned to camp Rodolfo and the vaqueano were horrified to hear that he proposed to go back again toward the continental divide and, therefore, remain another day so far from civilization. They pointed to the depleted commissary and called attention to the sore hoofs of the mules. Both reasons for starting the return journey, that would require at least a day and a half, were thoroughly valid, and, without argument but with reluctance, John agreed to an immediate departure.

The collecting on the high ranges had been pitifully meager. They found a number of hardy grasses, one of which was probably *Stipa chrysophylla,* and a few prostrate editions of some of the shrubs that sparsely populate the lower foothills. Frequent above twelve thousand five hundred feet were the "vegetable sheep" already mentioned. One soon begins to take them for granted, despite the fact that these umbellifers are strictly top-of-the-world plants with interesting adaptations, permitting them to withstand the most rigorous environmental conditions that plants attempt to meet. On the return trip the party crossed a half-dozen dry lakes, each one of which, in a normal season, would have contained some water and accompanying vegetation.

For the camp that night they found a vega still moist enough to support a little vegetation on which the mules could be scantily pastured. The evening meal was a decided disappointment and consisted principally of the crumbs at the bottom of the charqui bag, washed down with tea. John routed out his companions at daybreak and they discovered that the only food remaining was a five-day-old roll apiece, and no tea. During the first of the eight-hour ride, all three were hungry, restive, and cross; but, as the altitude decreased and the heat correspondingly increased, they lost interest in one another, in their surroundings, and even in the prospect of what the grubby little pension at their destination would supply in the way of food.

Plant hunting in the Chilean highlands has an enduring fascination. Where the vegetation is right, new or little-known species lead the collector across the vegas and over the ridges from one excitement to another. Even when the plants are few and far between there are sure to be some of them so charming or so scientifically impressive that their presence in the press excuses the fact that it is not as full as one could wish.

There are other compensations for all the long, hard, sometimes hazardous, climbing, the midday heat of the alpine sun, the struggle against cold storms that arise so rapidly on the barren plains below the highest Chilean Andes. At the close of day all this is forgotten when, in the hush that comes at nightfall in high altitudes, the sunset transforms the horizon. A long, deep shadow rapidly unfolds to creep across and above the tan foothills, to touch the snow line, then on to spread its gray cloak over the snow fields and glaciers, and finally to fall across the peaks that glitter against the pale sky of early night. Hardly is shadow's work accomplished before the ruddy sunset glow, for all too brief a season, brings a new and colorful existence to the rugged Andean crests. Their lofty, white expanses become transformed into clouds of rosy light, which shades to deep magenta in the broad depressions on the gray-hued snow fields.

Gradually the roseate panorama fades into the deepening violet of the evening sky, as though the final curtain were being drawn across the brilliant alpine stage. Then, suddenly, the highest peaks are touched with rich, warm light and begin to glow like beacons invisibly hung against a darkening background. Their light is so long sustained that the forward progress of time seems suspended, while one strains fully to comprehend the glory of the alpine afterglow and fix indelibly in remembrance a picture of the top of the world aflame.

Chapter XII

EARTHQUAKE

WE HAD a big room in the Hotel Lebell, a modest hostelry far enough removed from Valparaiso's center of business activity to be relatively quiet. Our room was on the ground floor of the two-story hotel. There was one large, heavily barred window that opened directly on the sidewalk. When we were ready for bed this latter feature necessitated an elaborate ritual of curtain arrangement. Our desire was that sufficient air should be free to enter the room while, at the same time, the vagrant eye of the early morning pedestrian would find as little as possible to reward it. In order that he should not be unduly tempted, we also removed the odds and ends that during the day had accumulated on our broad windowsill. Without thinking we deposited our day clothes, as we exchanged them for night ones, on any convenient chair, and often on one near the window. The General called our attention to the unwisdom of this procedure and then demonstrated the success that a sidewalk fisherman would have with a long stick passed quietly through the bars of our open window. Thereafter we made a greater nightly use of the garde-robe.

Past our window the traffic on foot and on horse- and burroback was a constant source of entertainment. In South America people do such human things in public. Only rarely, in the cities, are these things embarrassing, even to the foreigner whose conventional inhibitions are most acute, because the municipal authorities have wisely provided numerous public conveniences. They are arranged and designed according to the classical European tradition, except that even more conspicuous positions have been discovered for them, and, structurally, the absolutely irreducible minimum of convenience and privacy has been achieved.

The wide avenue outside our big window was constructed with two narrow lanes for traffic and a broad, grassy promenade between them. It was one of the principal thoroughfares paralleling the shore of Valparaiso Bay, and along it early in the

morning and late in the afternoon the country people came
and went. Their journey had begun hours before on some outlying farm and was approaching its weary end. The soft padding
of tired feet had a deliberate quality as, with low-voiced commands, the farmers slowly guided their laden animals in and
out of the wheeled traffic toward the city markets. But late in
the afternoon the street sounds had a different tempo. The soft
footfalls were quicker and lighter. On the cobbles the hard
little hoofs of the burros provided a staccato accompaniment
for the steady creaking of empty leather panniers and the soft,
gossipy laughter of the country people homeward bound.

There was an endless fascination in these parades that
flowed past our window. Just opposite, in the promenade, a
municipal water faucet had developed a leak. It was just sufficient to give a continuous trickle that had dug a little moist
basin and spread beyond it to make a miniature marsh. Clearly
a plumbing defect of long standing, at first we wondered why
somebody did not do something about it. Soon our question
was answered. A hot, dusty muleteer would leave his line of
loaded animals for a moment, paddle his bare feet in the little
pool, and stand for a brief, delicious instant in the soft, cool,
wet grass before he stepped out again onto the hard, hot roadway. And the tired lines in his face would be a little smoothed,
as with a handful of water he would wash a part of the gray dust
from them. What a simple explanation of a leaking faucet. How
often in South America we saw such unobtrusive evidences of
appreciation for the problems of the poor and underprivileged
—regulations relaxed, their infringement overlooked, or some
helping hand coming from an unexpected source. For us these
proofs of an underlying social consciousness and generosity in
South American life did much to counteract the unfavorable
impressions which small natures in high places sometimes insisted upon making.

Before our window the organ-grinders of Valparaiso
learned to congregate. As substitute for the bonnet-tipping
monkey the Chilean organ-grinder carries a parrot. After the
concert is over this bird, usually somewhat bedraggled, claws
open a little drawer on the organ case. With his beak he ex-
tracts from it a colored slip of paper which he is willing to ex-

change with you for a few centavos. On it you read your fortune. Before long Florence had acquired a large and varied
acquaintance among organ-grinders; through constant repeti-
tion of a considerable repertoire of hand-organ music my meager musical education had been unwillingly enhanced; and between us we had accumulated a large collection of encouraging
or ominous reminders that what the future holds in store is not
revealed.

Our room, one of two on the ground floor of the hotel, was
situated midway between the dining room and the bar. This
location was convenient, but provided us with an entirely un-
deserved reputation for alcoholism in the eyes of transient
guests. At each meal they watched us enter the dining room
from the direction of the bar and later leave it in the same direction. To judge by the lifting of expressive South American
eyebrows we must have given the impression of living in the
bar.

Can we ever forget the dining room in the Hotel Lebell?
The big table near our little one was reserved for the French
proprietor, his plump but chic madame, their grown-up sons,
the French consul in Valparaiso, and always a guest or two.
Their brisk French, pouring out in an unending stream, formed
a continuous undercurrent of sound in the noisy dining room.
Sometimes in the evening they sat late at their wine. Then we,
in the next room, fell asleep with subdued fragments of old
songs of the French countryside in our ears. Ernesto, our devoted waiter, having the benefit of advance information, guided
us successfully, when sober, through each luncheon and dinner
menu. I can still feel his rich breath on my neck as he solicit-
ously bent over me to point out his suggestions on the printed
card. He early discovered that I was not an experimentalist
where food was concerned, whereas Florence would welcome
enthusiastically any addition to her gustatory experience.

We looked forward eagerly to the infrequent appearance
of the ferret through his special role in the dining room wall.
Without him none of the smaller Chilean hotels would be complete, nor relatively free from rats. Often of nights we heard
him rushing along within the walls of our room, and now and
then the grisly deed was done in our hearing and another rat

had learned the folly of choosing our hotel as a place of residence in preference to the nearby harbor shipping. Our ferret
was old and gray, and built like a miniature and extremely
elongated edition of a dachshund. A dignified fellow, he slipped
between the tables with a preoccupied air and a sinuous movement, disdaining the food that Florence always tried to persuade
him to accept.

Of course, we were objects of extreme interest to the other
guests in the dining room. For some of them we represented the
only authenticated, by the proprietor, representatives of our
country they had come across. They examined with frank and
unabashed interest our clothes, table manners, choice of food,
and our general deportment, and lent a long ear to as much of
our English as they could catch. When we entered the dining
room all heads were turned in our direction and then put together for whispered comment. But friendly smiles and bows
were always ready when, upon reaching our table, ceremoniously and according to custom, we acknowledged the presence
of the other diners.

At about eleven o'clock in the evening of January 24th,
1939, we were in bed and almost asleep. On the street outside
our window only an occasional automobile rattled by. At last
quieted were the high, shrill whistles of the launches that all
the evening had been escorting coal barges across the bay of Valparaiso. The thin edge of consciousness was gradually wearing
away. Drifting visions of the day's exploits were merging into
dreams. Suddenly stark, rigid reality seized us. Without preliminary trembles or that distant rumbling in the earth which
to Californians is a preamble to its tremors, we were in the
vicious grip of a violent earthquake. It did not begin gradually,
as though tentatively feeling out the weakness of a fault line
before accelerating to maximum movement. Rather it engulfed
us, mature and at the height of its power. The immediate transition from peace to horror was totally beyond normal comprehension. Something was happening which so transcended experience that full consciousness was instantly suspended. For an
eternity of seconds we lived in another world. In company with
two hundred thousand others in Chile that night we were struck
dumb and rendered entirely incapable of action. Then con-

sciousness flowed back, and with the others about us we joined
our voices in agonized, frenzied protests and appeals that rang
out above the deep, grinding roar of the earthquake. It was the
first time that I had heard human voices reflect elemental terror in the high falsetto or deep bass of animal throats.

R.L.S. knew earthquakes. His frightened old buccaneer,
lying sick in the Admiral Benbow, told Jim how in distant lands
he had "seen the blessed land a-heaving like the sea." During
those eighty seconds of earthquake we unconsciously affirmed
the blessedness of a normal earth, an earth free from movement,
but not this earth that now, like the stormy sea, was heaving,
pitching, twisting without respite, and with obvious intent to
bring complete destruction upon us.

In remembrance nothing that I did or thought during that
overwhelming experience is clear. Almost from the beginning
I must have realized the menace, not only of the land, but also
of the sea, only a few hundred yards from our ground-floor
room. I knew that we must escape to higher ground over against
the coming of a tidal wave, that frequent follower of earthquakes which all too often has completed the destruction begun
by them in Chilean coastal cities. With this thought came despair because, so long as the earth movements continued with
their initial violence, escape was out of the question. Perhaps
we were still in a state of partially suspended animation produced by the sudden onset of the earthquake. Perhaps we were
suffering from a certain lack of muscular co-ordination induced
by it. At any rate, by the time we realized the desperate need of
action, we found ourselves so violently and so rapidly tossed
about in our beds that leaving them seemed impossible. In addition, the beds and other furniture were beginning to move
about the room in dangerous fashion. Finally, the ceiling plaster
began to fall and, like the ostrich, we thought only of protection for our heads, something that the pillows alone would
give. Each succeeding second seemed inevitably to be our last.
It was impossible to believe that the building could longer
withstand the continuous shaking, and certainly any increase
in its violence would bring it down.

Then, as suddenly as it began, the earthquake was over.
We lay there side by side, without a word, each gathering to-

gether the shattered remnants of faith and courage, in a now motionless, noiseless world—waiting for the earthquake to return. A long minute passed, and with it the strain was released. Immediately our world awoke, we heard running feet and shouts in the street, above our heads there were tentative movements and then quick steps and strained voices, a subdued hum of activity traveled about us through the city, and we too came back to life.

There was no tidal wave and no further perceptible earth movement on that night or during our remaining two months in Valparaiso. But earth adjustments were not complete for many weeks. Gutter pools would one moment show a calm surface and the next be covered with shivering ripples to indicate the quick passage of a minute temblor. The city gave little evidence of what it had endured. Chilean architects of the last generation had insisted upon adorning their larger buildings with many elaborate cornices and heavily decorated window frames. Most of these architectural excrescences fell in the destructive Valparaiso earthquake of 1906 and some of the remainder came down in 1939. A few buildings were structurally damaged, much plaster fell, many walls were superficially cracked, and plenty of crockery was smashed. Probably a number of persons were injured in Valparaiso and in Santiago, where the earthquake was felt almost as strongly. But their misfortunes were forgotten in the news that next morning began to filter in, and that told of heavy loss of life and terrible destruction of property in Concepción and Chillán, some two hundred miles to the south.

The first reports made it clear that a major disaster had occurred in one of the more densely populated portions of Chile. The city of Concepción, the third largest in the republic, with a population of seventy thousand, was near the epicenter of the earthquake. Chillán, a city of about forty thousand, was even more disastrously located. Telegraph and telephone lines were down over a long distance within the earthquake area. Because of damage to roadbed and rails, train service ended at its margin. With all normal means of communication interrupted, preliminary estimates of damage had to be made from the air. Early morning editions of the Valparaiso newspapers carried estimates that amounted to almost complete destruction of Chillán and very grave damage in Concepción. On the basis of this evidence claims of loss of life in the devastated area were naturally placed at a high figure. Later, when radio communication was re-established, and rescue parties by land, sea, and air reached the earthquake zone, these claims were somewhat reduced; but it was still believed that many thousands of persons had been killed or injured. An unfortunately long experience in Chile with the effects of serious earthquakes suggested to authorities that the injured rather than the dead would make up the larger proportion of this total. As a result all available physicians and nurses in the Valparaiso-Santiago region were mobilized, and coastwise shipping was requisitioned to carry them and medical supplies to Talcahuano, the port of Concepción.

The General, of course, volunteered to organize a medical unit, and went about it in his usual vigorous and effective fashion. Florence and I were anxious to be of whatever service we could. At the beginning I planned to go with the General and his party, in the expectation that there would be much that even medically untrained hands could accomplish. One of our first thoughts after the earthquake had been for the safety of the three members of the expedition who were collecting in Andean Patagonia. Although we knew that they were far removed from the reported area of damage exact information was unavailable. There was the possibility that serious seismic disturbances might have traveled down the volcanic Andes into the collectors' sphere of operations. In addition, what might have happened in Peru, and thus to the members of the expedition working there, was also prominently in our minds. There was no reliable news from the north upon which to base judgment. I hesitated to leave Florence, however, while the threat and unspoken dread of additional earth movements were still undercurrents in our thinking. All things considered I decided that my place was at the expedition's Valparaiso headquarters. There I would be in a favorable position to communicate with the scattered units of the group for which I was responsible, and also with their families at home. I suspected that they would be greatly disturbed by the undoubtedly exaggerated North American newspaper accounts of what had happened in Chile. This proved to be the case.

Both John and I had planned, for different reasons, to be in the center of the earthquake area at the most critical time. It was certainly fortunate for us that these plans had been altered just before the disaster. During the night of despair John also had been in Valparaiso. When I realized that I ought not to go south with the General, I asked him if he would be willing to take my place. We particularly wanted someone who would take money for us to distribute to those who, as always happens in such catastrophies, were not immediately able to obtain the assistance that the Red Cross and local relief organizations were sending to the earthquake victims. John at once agreed to go, and the General wangled an appointment for him as a male nurse in the medical unit he was organizing.

It was finally arranged that John should go to Concepción on the coastwise steamer *Teno,* along with the General and his son Alfredo. The *Teno* is not a large ship, and the sea was exceedingly rough. The only excitement during the thirty-six hours' run was the appearance of the cruiser *Ajax.* With the now equally famous *Exeter* she had been lying in the harbor of Valparaiso at the time of the earthquake, and was at once ordered to southern Chile to assist in rescue work. A year or so later, when John read about the remarkably rapid and clever maneuvers of these cruisers in the battle off Montevideo, he recollected how the fifteen-knot *Teno* seemed to be standing still as the *Ajax* sped by on the way to Talcahuano. The *Teno* arrived there too late in the evening to permit passengers to go ashore, and so they had to spend a second night on board. Early the next morning the party of doctors, nurses, and a few sightseers was landed.

They hurried up the landing steps on the quayside and then toward the port captain's offices. The port buildings showed little damage but what they saw around the corner was pretty bad. Everywhere the adobe- and brick-walled houses had toppled into the streets, most of which had become a shambles of broken plaster, cracked tile, and splintered wood. Twenty-seven victims of the disaster had already been buried in Talcahuano and there were still more bodies to be dug from the ruins. Later on they saw most of the population living out of doors in vacant lots and in the plaza.

John and the others stood about in the gloomy fog, trying not to look too often into the ruined town. Finally they were herded into a dilapidated bus to begin the ride to Concepción. The fog began to rise from the surface of the bay and slowly its dense, shroudlike mantle was lifted from the desolate streets of Talcahuano to the tops of the wooded hills behind the port. The day was dull and cheerless. The bus wandered from street to street to pick out those that were passable. Most of them were narrow and had been choked from curb to curb with knee-deep piles of bricks, tiles, blocks of cement, and loose rubble. Through a few of these streets crews of road workers had cleared tortuous paths. Because there were so many different kinds of things to be done during the first hours after the earthquake, these channels through the ruins had been hurriedly completed, and, in consequence, were rough and narrow. John and his companions were glad to get clear of what was left of Talca-huano.

The rolling, sandy countryside between the port and Con-cepción slipped past quickly, the chófer skillfully steering his bus over smoother parts of the considerably damaged highway. Farms and little settlements that they passed showed the effects of the earthquake—fences were broken or out of line and walls had fallen or had been badly cracked. Half the tile roof of one house had slipped away to become a high heap of debris before the front door. John wondered whether the occupants had stayed inside or had got clear before the tiles came crashing down. Perhaps their crushed bodies still lay beneath the ruins of their roof. How many times that day was he to ask himself similar questions, and only rarely were those questions to be answered.

The closer they came to the city of Concepción the greater was the degree of destruction. Whereas in Talcahuano two or three houses in a given block—or half the front walls of twice that number—had fallen, in Concepción they saw streets in which all the buildings were demolished. After many detours and a rough, jolting passage along the few partially cleared thor-oughfares, they reached the center of the city and disembarked

The rock scenery on the Chilean side of this railway line which pierces the highest Andes is said to be the finest in the world

Almost at the "top of the world"; near the pass from Argentina to Chile
Transportation, old and new, in the highest Andes at Chile's border

This composite lives in roughest screes on lofty Andean slopes

Lovely to look at, dangerous to touch, is this high Andean *Cajophora*

An attractive pink-flowered Amaryllid of Chilean coast and cordillera

A rock slide interfered with collecting this alpine Nasturtium

beside the great plaza where the twin-towered cathedral looked across at the Intendencia. Both structures gave evidence of the destructive power of the earthquake. The main plaza in any Latin-American city is normally the center of human activity. In Concepción it was headquarters for all the work of rescue and rehabilitation that was in progress.

John's diary tells the story of his brief stay in what, a few days before, had been one of the most attractive centers of population in Chile:

"At first glance, the great plaza appeared to contain only a milling mass of humanity. Actually, however, there was a good deal of organization. The largest crowd was assembled in the center around the bandstand, which had been occupied by the officers of government. They had moved what was left of their furniture and records from the ruined Intendencia. To the left of this government headquarters, there was a considerable area that had been roped off and filled with benches. Overhead, a large canvas sheltered part of this roped-off space. It gave to those who sat on the benches some protection from the rain that had been falling and threatened to come down again at any moment. A number of pretty Red Cross nurses were treating innumerable superficial injuries, and men and women kept coming in to have their wounds dressed. Small wonder that some of these wounds looked dirty and angry. They had not received attention since they had been acquired, forty hours before.

"On the other side of the bandstand, registration booths had been set up by the local political parties of the Left-Radical, Socialist, and Communist. To these booths party members came to sign for work in clearing the city, and to obtain tools and work assignments. Each of them had the insignia of his party on an arm brassard or in his hat. At regular intervals, groups of these workers marched out of the plaza toward their assigned areas. The remainder of the plaza was given over to refugees. Everywhere there were families who had been sleeping out of doors either through fear of recurrence of the *terremoto* or because their homes had been smashed beyond immediate repair. One family, a mother and six children, had placed two benches back to back about six feet apart, and in the space between had spread all the bedding they had salvaged. The mother and older children were cooking a light breakfast over a small fire, while the smaller children slept fitfully in the dim morning light. They all seemed dazed, oblivious of their physical surroundings and of the crowds around them.

"Everyone was talking about the extent of the disaster in terms of dead and injured. I spoke to an Englishman who said that three thousand had already been buried in Concepción and that the number in near-by Chillán must be as great. People were referring to thirty thousand dead in south Chile. It was obvious that under the stress of emotion accompanying such a terrible disaster, no one could be expected to be conservative in estimating anything connected with it." (The final record showed that a little over eight hundred people died in Concepción and not over ten thousand in the entire earthquake area. Compared to the Lisbon earthquake in 1755, which killed some forty thousand persons, the one at Messina in this century, when over seventy thousand died, this figure of ten thousand is not very large. On the other hand, the earthquake and fire that destroyed San Francisco in 1906 took a toll of less than two hundred lives.)

"Twelve of us crowded into the little truck that was to take our party to the hospital. Half the morning had gone, and still no one seemed to know whether we would be needed there. Apparently, we were to find out for ourselves. From the floor of the truck we got almost no view of the ruined city we were traversing. The hospital proved to be a rambling, one-story building, constructed of huge adobe blocks, whitewashed inside and out. It looked to be at least one hundred years old. The visiting doctors seemed disappointed that the terremoto had not damaged the building sufficiently to insure its demolition in the near future. But because it was so heavily built, it had not suffered much. On the inside, a good deal of thin plaster and whitewash had been loosened, especially near the corners of the rooms. Some of this rubbish had originally been swept into piles, long since scattered and ground to dust by hurrying feet. No one could take time to clean the floors.

"The local doctor in charge said that he had all the help he needed. Due to some peculiarity of the terremoto, perhaps its sudden onset or the late evening hour at which it occurred, people were killed outright or suffered only superficial injuries. Fractures were rare and, in general, the number of persons requiring hospitalization was quite small as compared with those who had died almost immediately or had been only slightly injured. Nevertheless, the facilities of this hospital had soon become overtaxed. As a result, several buildings at the University of Concepción had been pressed into service. The director suggested that we might care to inspect his hospital, and then report to the Santiago doctor who was in charge of the auxiliary hospital at the university.

"We looked into disordered surgeries and walked the length of huge wards where the plaster and whitewash hung in shreds and sheets over the crowded beds. The whole place had a depressing atmosphere, and as a hospital was a pretty terrible affair. Then, perhaps by accident, we were led out of the building through the mortuary. Those whose task it was to bury the dead in Concepción had been more than busy those past forty hours and the corpses in the hospital, being relatively small in number, had been neglected. The atmosphere in that small room where sheet-enshrouded figures lay on tables and floors held the faint, sickish-sweet unmistakable odor of neglected human cadavers. By comparison, even the heavy air outside under the low, black storm clouds seemed invigorating.

"A few blocks brought us to the modern buildings of the university. They were practically undamaged. We entered the first one, a large, white, reinforced-concrete structure, to find the whole foyer given over to beds for the sick and the injured. The marble floors and columns, and the smooth plastered wall surfaces showed no trace of the earthquake's fury." (With regard to their capacity to resist earth movements, Chilean buildings can be divided into three classes. Wooden structures, if properly constructed and kept in good repair, suffer only slightly. Reinforced-concrete buildings escape almost unscathed. But any combination of wood and adobe, adobe and cane, brick and stone, wood and stone, means ruin, often total ruin.)

"The Santiago doctor in charge of this temporary hospital told us that his group, sent from the capital to augment resident medical forces, had been busy during the first twenty-four hours after their arrival. Now, however, all emergency cases had been taken care of and the need for medical assistance was steadily decreasing. In other words, none of us was needed. We therefore decided to see something of the ruined city. It was ten o'clock, and the man in charge of our party told us to reassemble about noon in the plaza. A small group, including the General, Alfredo, and myself, decided to walk rather than return in the bus.

"The residential area had been hard hit. There were many streets where every house had lost its cornices or other brick or stone ornamentation the architects had seen fit to design. It was a curious sight to look down a street and see every building standing, while the sidewalks in front of them were covered to a depth of three feet with cornices, gargoyles, and the like, all apparently thrown down at the first shock. About three blocks from the university we came upon a dozen English sailors methodically clearing away the debris in front of a ruined house. The General, always happy when he could use his fine English, accosted them. Several straightened up and answered that they were from the cruiser *Ajax*. To tease them, he inquired whether this wasn't an Englishman's house that they were clearing. Not catching the joke, they quite seriously replied that they did not know whose house it was; that they had been sent out to clear away debris, and this, being a corner house, had seemed a good place to begin. The General, who likes to experiment with people's reactions, then asked one bright-faced English lad where he supposed God had been on the night of January 24, when churches and cathedrals were destroyed while banks, university buildings, and some houses were not seriously damaged. The young sailor was indignant and angrily retorted that all the churches hadn't fallen!

"When we arrived at the plaza about eleven o'clock, the General had some official business to transact. I agreed to accompany Alfredo, who had been asked to look up a number of relatives and friends. We walked down a narrow street past the skeleton of a large store that had been burned after the terremoto. Two blocks beyond this blackened ruin, we found the two-story apartment building where one family of relatives had lived. From a man standing disconsolately on the curb, Alfredo learned that none of them had been killed or injured, and that probably some of them were still in the building.

"From the street, this building looked unharmed. It had not been provided with cornices, so that even the sidewalk was relatively clear. We opened the door to find the stairway deep in broken plaster. Dust swirled about us as we slowly and carefully picked our way up the stairs that felt rather shaky under our feet. When we reached the second-floor landing, we discovered that outside appearances in Concepción were deceptive. Inside, this house was entirely ruined. Ceilings had come down, walls had fallen in or out of the rooms, everything was in a state of complete smash. We found one of Alfredo's cousins in a back room. In a dazed, hesitating way he was trying to gather together some of his belongings to take to his family. They were living with another relative whose home was less damaged. For Alfredo's benefit, he enumerated all the relatives then in Concepción. Many had lost their homes, some had suffered minor injuries, but none had been killed.

"We looked into the bedroom where this man and his wife had been asleep when the terremoto struck. How they had managed to get out alive, I could not imagine. All the rear wall, built of unsupported brick, had crashed into the room, and there were hundreds of bricks piled on the flattened bed and thrown about over the rest of the broken furniture. His explanation of how he escaped sounded simple enough: 'The instant we felt the house begin to move we jumped out of bed and ran for the stairs that led outdoors. Arrived at the front door, we stood under the casing for a moment until the plaster had stopped falling and there was no longer any danger that the surface of the building would fall into the street, and then we went out.'

"Alfredo and I walked slowly away from this ruined house toward the plaza. No longer were we interested in the ruins about us. That look behind the walls of an apparently undamaged home had given us a new conception of the extent of the terrible human catastrophe that had occurred. All damaged structures in this stricken city would have to be rebuilt from the ground up. Otherwise, the next earthquake, or the next, both of them certain to come, in one, or ten, or ninety years,

would be even more destructive. How could a poor country like
Chile afford to do that kind of rebuilding?

"In the plaza, we got our baggage from the Red Cross
tent, and I took tripod and movie camera to get views of
ruined Concepción before the black clouds reduced the light
still more or ruined my day completely by giving up their rain.
It was not easy to photograph such a disaster. One had to be a
little hard-hearted. To intrude upon the private affairs of grief-
stricken people is difficult. Old men and women sat dejectedly
on the curb in front of the remains of a home or little shop, and
they weren't much interested in a photographer. Under such
circumstances tact must be used, and that is not so easy when
one's Spanish is a little weak.

"As I started out, people began to stream from all directions into the plaza. There were well-dressed Chileans, English-
men in boots and riding breeches, and many *rotos* with bare
feet and ragged pants. As I stopped and looked about me to see
what could be the excitement, Alfredo came over and whispered, 'Look, there is the President.' I looked in this direction
and in that direction, expecting to see a platoon of soldiers or at
least a guard of carabiñeros conducting the official party. But
what I saw, almost directly in front of me, was Don Pedro
Aguirre Cerda, the President of Chile, walking slowly from a
sedan parked across the street and unprovided with any guard
or, so far as I could see, any official entourage. A man was
walking beside him, and the President's head was bent as he
listened to what this man was saying.

"The crowd opened a wide path as the President approached. He passed us and went on to the headquarters of the
government in the center of the plaza. I could hardly believe
my eyes. Here was a public figure of great importance walking,
unprotected, across a plaza crowded with people of all kinds of
political enthusiasms. Their nerves might well have been shattered by the experience they had lived through and some of
them might lose their heads and become dangerous, or at least
very abusive. How could the President take such a long chance,
even though everyone knew that he was in the earthquake area
on an errand of mercy. Alfredo must have seen the surprise in
my face, because he said, 'Oh, he doesn't need a bodyguard; he

is a Socialist!' Later on, we met Señora de Aguirre, the First
Lady of Chile. She was walking resolutely about in the midst of
the ruins, expressing interest and sympathy and asking for information about her friends and her friends' friends. She had
spent the day before in Chillán. To me she seemed a gracious
person, this tall, strong, well-dressed President's wife.

"At noon I returned again to the plaza, and joined my
group of *medicos*. It had been decided that two or three of
the doctors would be needed here and there in the smaller
hamlets of the terremoto area. The General and Alfredo were
going to Santiago in one of the automobiles accompanying the
presidential party. I was told to leave that afternoon on a
steamer bound from Talcahuano to Valparaiso. A young doctor, who practiced at the port, offered to take me in his automobile if I could be ready at one o'clock. Thereupon, I dashed
about to get more pictures. In particular, I wanted to record
with the movie camera the dynamiting of one or both of the
badly damaged towers of the cathedral, which had been set for
noon. After waiting around a bit, I discovered that the dynamiting had been postponed to permit more investigation of the
condition of the towers." (This further investigation showed
that they could be repaired. Later on, these repairs were made,
and probably the towers will stand at least until the next serious
earthquake.) "I got a picture of a 1938 Ford V-8 sedan that
had been thoroughly smashed by a huge block of concrete, and
took movies of the white-uniformed English sailors from the
Ajax, some of them with full beards, who were receiving a
bouquet of flowers from a little Chilean girl.

"Back in the plaza, the refugees were beginning to prepare
the noonday meal. One family, all grown people, sat in a circle
on a path bordered by flowering Hydrangeas. To judge by their
clothes, they had been people accustomed to comfort, perhaps
luxuries. With the corners weighted down by stones, a number
of newspapers had been spread on the pavement to serve as
tablecloth. As I walked along on an adjacent path, one of the
younger people in the family was staring intently at this im-
provisation. Suddenly, and as though remembering something
neglected, she turned and broke off a flower, fitted it rather
clumsily into the broken neck of a beer bottle, and then leaned

forward to place flower and incongruous container in the center of the newspapers. I lingered a moment to watch this panto-mime. No member of the family smiled or spoke or moved. With apparently no realization for the moment of their sur-roundings, they sat there like statues and gazed unseeingly at their pitiful table decoration. I had no right to be watching them and, with smarting eyes, turned away in search of my transportation to the port."

When John reached Talcahuano he began to see another distressing aftermath of the earthquake. From the port captain's office, where he presented the slip of paper that gave him return passage to Valparaiso, stretched a long line of refugees. For hours they had been waiting patiently to be assigned to one of the various rescue vessels lying in the harbor. Most of these sad people had lost practically everything they possessed, and the government was transporting them to Valparaiso and Santiago, where relatives or friends would take them in. They had piled the remnants of their possessions along a high fence separating the quay from the street. John, rather overwhelmed by this final evidence of human want and suffering, got away from the waterside as soon as he could. The hour or two before sailing was spent in taking pictures in Talcahuano.

He made the return voyage to Valparaiso on the steamer *Chiloé*. It was a small freighter with a few passenger accom-modations on an upper deck. At the bow and stern were large canvas-covered hatches, and on them and on all available deck space the refugees were sitting or lying down. John had gone aboard at eight o'clock in the evening, and the ship sailed soon after. His diary describes the experiences of the next fifteen hours:

"As soon as we got under way, I realized that later on it was going to be pretty chilly on the open deck and that I had nothing but a sweater to add to the thin suit I was wearing. I found a vacant spot on the afterhatch, worked my way to it, and lay down. Most of the tired refugees were already asleep. After a time I, also, slept. A little past midnight I awakened, cold, and stiff, to find the ship gliding along over a calm sea, its lights shining eerily through the thin, opalescent mist. All trace of the severe storm that forty-eight hours before had made the voyage from Valparaiso such a misery had now disappeared, but it was much too cold for more sleep on the hatch. I got up and paced up and down the deck through narrow aisles between sleeping refugees and their baggage. How slowly time passes out of doors on a cold night—it is impossible to sit still, yet walking seems to be the last thing one wants to do.

"As I walked steadily back and forth and up and down, I tried to imagine myself in the position of these poor people about me whose homes, whose hopes, whose very lives in such large measure lay behind them. Some men had buried wives and children before leaving for the north. There were many widows and some of the small children would never see their parents again. Materially, these people had never possessed many of the things we require for our comfort and happiness, and still, until the earthquake had in an instant changed the current of their lives, they had managed to be happy, outwardly at least. How would they react to this disaster which had overwhelmed them so suddenly?

"After a while the door of the deckhouse opened, and a dirty oiler from the engine room slipped quietly out on deck for a breath of air. We fell into talk, and finally he asked me if I did not want a warm place in which to sleep. I thanked him and he led me behind the hatch to a small, wooden grating over the engine room. It had escaped the notice of the refugees because heavy pipes ran above it. There was just enough clearance so that I could squeeze under the pipes and stretch out on the warm grating. I must have fallen asleep almost at once.

"Breakfast was the same for all—tin mugs of black coffee and huge hunks of fresh bread. I began to talk with a young chap whose English proved to be better than my Spanish. His name was René and he introduced me to his elder brother, Lucho. They had learned my language in the Valparaiso schools. I spent the day with them and Lucho's wife and baby daughter, Elena. The four had lived near Talcahuano where the two young men worked in a large textile mill. When Lucho felt the first shock of the earthquake he leaped out of bed, grabbed his wife, dragged Elena out of her crib, and yelled to René in the next room. They stood in the doorway between the rooms and watched the back wall of the adobe house crash down to bury their beds and the baby's crib. Only this and a part of another wall fell inward, so that they were unharmed, and soon managed to get outdoors.

"Later on, Lucho and René salvaged some clothes, bedding and a few other personal possessions. The next two nights and days they spent in the plaza at Talcahuano. When it was not raining the fog was dense and they could not keep warm. Swarms of mosquitoes added to their misery, and Elena's face was thickly sprinkled with bites that she had scratched until they were bloody. René and Lucho were badly worried about their future. The textile mill had been wrecked and much of the delicate machinery damaged. These machines had been imported, and could not be repaired in Chile. It would certainly be months before the mills would again be in operation. Meanwhile, with no home, no money, and no prospect of work, they must go to their father's home near Santiago.

"In the late afternoon, having had a calm sea and thus the full benefit of the Humboldt Current, we came into Valparaiso harbor several hours ahead of schedule. The quay and the streets bordering the port for blocks around were packed with people. They were expecting relatives and friends, or wanted to inquire about loved ones whose names had not appeared in the published lists of dead or injured. As we docked, a number of port officers boarded the ship and the gang planks were pushed ashore. The one from the upper deck was for refugees on their way to Santiago who were given passes for the train that was to take them there from Valpariso. On the main deck the officers asked to see your pass and wanted to know whether you had made satisfactory arrangements to remain in Valparaiso. My pass took the least time of all to verify and so, after I had said good-bye to René, Lucho, and their family, I was able to hurry ashore before the bulk of the refugees left the ship. To be one of the first off a refugee ship isn't a nice experience. Immediately everyone asks about his uncle or aunt or some friend, or *"por favor, señor,"* did I happen to see Señor So-and-So, who lived near the plaza in Talcahuano. Such questions spring from the pitifully earnest desire to be told only one thing

—that the friend or relative is alive and well. I could answer none of these questions and so felt useless and miserable."

Of all regions of the earth that have been subject to seismic disturbances, Chile has suffered most severely. Relative intensity is difficult to determine in comparing Chilean with Japanese or with Californian earth movements, but in total number of recorded earthquakes Chile has the misfortune to lead the field. It is said that for every one thousand earthquakes felt there, only slightly over four hundred occur in Japan and about eighty in California. Earthquakes have been recorded in Chile since 1570, at least. On February 8th of that year, less than eighty years after the discovery of the Americas, severe shocks destroyed Concepción. A Spanish historian describing this first terremoto endured by the conquistadors refers to an almost total destruction of the houses in the city, the appearance of cracks in the earth, and the occurrence of tidal waves that completed the ruin begun by the earth tremors.

Because of the long history of earth disturbances in Chile, many speculations and theories concerning the direct or associated causes of earthquakes are current and much discussed there. You hear that a series of slight movements relieves subterranean pressures with the result that nothing serious will happen for a long time to come. Others say that slight movements are going on all the time, and so can have no relation to the time or place of a disastrous one. There are people who try to convince you that weather, wind, volcanic disturbances, or the combined pull of Venus and the moon are causal agencies. Rain often appears to be a concomitant of Chilean terremotos. On that terrible night in January, 1939, rain began to fall in Concepción, Chillán, and near-by areas soon after the earth movement was at an end, although January normally represents the height of the dry season in south-central Chile. Chileans sometimes insist that any unseasonable rains, especially those that occur rarely on the excessively arid northern coasts of their country, are always related to earth movements. This, however, is not the case, as witness the torrential rains of 1940 that caused destruction on the nitrate coast but were not preceded by an earthquake. The predicting of earthquakes is, quite naturally, a popular indoor sport in Chile. Since a

large number of noticeable earth movements is practically certain to occur each year, the chances of picking the right day,
now and then, are pretty good. Of course, erroneous predictions are promptly forgotten, whereas correct ones receive local
publicity for years to come.

Charles Darwin visited Concepción several days after the
disastrous earthquake and tidal wave of 1835. He called attention to the fact that on the same night volcanoes became active
from southern Chile to Ecuador, even Mt. Aconcagua, long
quiescent. Whether this was merely coincidence, whether volcanic activity was responsible for the earthquake, or whether
the earth movements brought the volcanoes into action are all
questions for which there are apparently no final answers.
Darwin also pointed out that the "very heavy and evil odor of
brimstone," which was reported as early as 1570 to accompany
earthquakes in Concepción, was probably the result of a thorough agitation by the earth movements of the foul bottom of
the near-by harbor of Talcahuano. Certainly vile odors arise
when an anchor chain is dragged in that and in many other
harbors.

I have been permitted to copy a few excerpts from the
unpublished diary of a Forty-niner en route to California from
Boston on the brig *Rudolph*. They made the port of Talcahuano on May 29, 1849, one hundred and ten days out of
Boston, 'round the Horn. The diarist saw the town of Talcahuano and also the city of Concepción, with the evidences of
earlier terremotos in them. He includes some comment on the
flavor of Chilean life ninety years ago:

"*May 29, 1849* . . . The Captain of the Port came on
board, entered us at the customhouse, gave us the regulations
of the port and directed us where to anchor . . . We find it a
very fine harbor, protected on all sides except the north. The
anchorage is good and there is a fine chance to get wood, water
and provisions. The bay abounds in birds of all kinds but you
are not allowed to shoot them. The hills on either side rise
some five or six hundred feet above the level of the sea. They
are verdant and highly susceptible of cultivation. There are but
few trees on the hills but quite a number of huts, with a little

piece of cultivated land, from which the inhabitants get their living . . . Plenty of fish in the bay, which are very good eating.

"We found the following vessels in port, bound to California: ship 'Panama' of New York, 115 days' passage, and stopped 9 days at Rio, with 202 passengers on board and all well; ship 'Hopewell' from Warren, Rhode Island, 105 days' passage and made no stops, 150 passengers and all well except the Captain, who is not expected to live; ship 'Christoval Colon' of New York, 145 days' passage, stopped 35 days at Rio to repair (having sprung her main-mast in the Gulf Stream), 15 days off Cape Horn . . . ; brig 'John Pette' of Norfolk, Virginia, 130 days' passage, stopped 11 days at Rio, 14 passengers. Two old whalers are preparing to go to California as soon as possible. A large Chilean man-o'-war ship, two Chilean brigs and one American brig which has been seized by the Chilean Government. The town looks like a dirty mass of huts.

"After dinner it was 'Hurrah for the shore.' At two o'clock the first boatload left, and in the course of an hour nearly all were on shore. There is no wharf in this port; vessels are obliged to lay at anchor and land on the beach with their boats. The houses, with two or three exceptions, are one story high and generally built of brick and plastered outside and whitewashed. But some have a kind of frame plastered up with mud. They have no chimneys. They build their fires to warm their hours in earthen pans. They do their cooking out of doors. The roofs are made of bricks of the same material that the walls are made of, called tiles . . . There are three two-story houses, one of them the customhouse, one-half of which is occupied by a hotel kept by an American by the name of Canfield who, by the way, is one of the most obliging and kindest men you ever saw, and sets a fine table . . . He has a Spanish lady for a wife, who is a very fine woman. This is the only hotel in the place.

"This place is probably one of the most corrupt and licentious places in the world. There are four females to one male, and about two-thirds of these girls are prostitutes and are driven to it perforce of circumstances. There are no factories and the Gentry do not employ females for servants and in consequence they become bad and come to Talcahuano

because it is a place where a great many whalers put in for
supplies. These girls are healthy and robust, capable of enduring fatigue. They have generally black hair and eyes and round
oval features and are very pretty and many play the guitar
and sing very well. I wish they were in old New England where
they could find better employment. The Spanish people are
the most hospitable in the world, especially the Gentry, and the
government has done everything for their protection that they
could do. The streets are paved with small round stones and the
walks are stone and bricks but they are very uneven and it is
the muddiest place at this season that I ever saw. There are
six or seven Americans who trade in the place and do very
well. The principal amusements they have are billiards, ten-
pins, cock fights and Dame Houses. Wild game is plenty but
very shy; plenty of snipe, curlew, teal, partridges, and so forth.
We spent two days a-gunning and had a very pleasant time."
(He then mentions a hospital and certain Americans confined
there) "Mr. Hudson of Waterville, Maine . . . had his leg shot
off accidentally on board the 'Mary Wilder' from Boston . . . is
getting well fast and has engaged passage in the 'Globe' to
California.

"*June 3* . . . We made up a party and started to go to
Conception. The way is over a plain covered with low shrubby
trees and the roads run all around among them. One place we
stopped at they were roasting a hog, which seemed very novel
to us—I say 'roasting,' I suppose they were scorching off the
bristles. They do not scald them as we do in the States.

"Arrived at Conception at ten o'clock and took a stroal
over the city. Stopped in the American Hotel and got something to eat . . . then visited the ruins of the old Cathedral
and what they call 'Mother of Mercy' . . . we were invited into
several places and had a good time, especially at the Bishop's
. . . we sang several songs, which pleased him very much . . .
I thought the old fellow would get drunk, he drank so much
wine. We had a great time . . . at twelve o'clock found all beds
occupied at Mr. Brooks' hotel and I laid down somewhere on
the floor. I pulled one of the bricks out of the floor for a pillow
and tried to get to sleep.

"The next day we visited some more of the ruins caused

by the earthquake of 1751 which were very imposing and really worth one's while to visit them. There are some ruins of the earthquake of 1835 but that was slight to this one of 1751; then it was almost totally destroyed . . . the one of 1835 killed 7 men and threw down a few houses. We have all taken specimens of the ruins; we intend to carry them home. To the southwest of the city is a very high mountain, which we went up and had a fine view of the city and surrounding country." (They return to the city and rest in luxury with a Frenchman.) "They say he sets as good a table as anyone in Conception . . . we had the pleasure of picking oranges and lemons off the trees, besides having many given us. The trees about the city are principally orange, lemon and palm. The palm makes a very novel and pretty appearance. The houses are much better than those in Talcahuano but the same style. They have several cathedrals. They all have bells and when they are all ringing them they remind one of home and sound well.

"They are mostly gentlemen who live here and very fine people. The ladies are very pretty and very accomplished. They play the piano, guitar, sing and dance finely and they walk splendidly and I think I can spend a week here very well.

"The term by which the common people are called is *peon* and *choler*. If one of these trouble you on the road you are at liberty to shoot him, and the laws will justify you in it . . . there is a bay next up to Conception where it is fine sailing and fishing. Population, Conception 10,300, Talcahuano about 4,000 . . . Let me say one word in regard to the American Consul . . . in the language of another 'his wife is a fine man but he is a nobody.' He certainly is a very poor representative of our government and ought to be removed. He has been the means of reducing the value of American money 25 per cent, which is an outrageous thing and ought to be exposed. The British and French consuls are business men and perfect gentlemen.

"*June 11* . . . At four o'clock (P.M.) we are all on board and we are under way with a flattering prospect . . . have been here thirteen days and are glad to be on our passage again . . . we hope in fifty days to be in San Francisco." (It took them 96 days to reach their destination.)

The earthquake zone of 1939 lay south of the center of one of the most important agricultural areas in Chile. From the Rio Maule northward toward the plains that surround the city of Santiago, stretches a wide valley between the Andes and the coastal hills. Its deep, fertile soils have for many generations produced rich crops of wheat and barley, and fine stands of alfalfa. From its hillside vineyards come the wines that even the educated palate has difficulty in distinguishing from the better vintages of France. The annual rainfall of from fifteen to thirty inches, or sometimes more, is supplemented by irrigation water diverted from the coastward flow of rivers whose sources are in Andean snows. Thus optimum moisture conditions prevail during the long, sunny growing season. Many of Chile's great landowners are here the lords of little agricultural empires.

The total acreage of the approximately two hundred thousand farms scattered over the length and breadth of slender Chile is unequally apportioned. Well over half of it is contained within the boundaries of less than fifteen hundred of the two hundred thousand farms. In other words, if we think in terms of one family to a farm, it appears that more than one-half of all the cultivated land in Chile is owned by less than 1 per cent of the total number of families to whom farmlands belong. The collective value of the two hundred thousand farms has been set at approximately two hundred and fifty million dollars (U. S.). Of this total, the fifteen hundred large estates are worth seventy million. To put it differently, well over one-fourth of the farm values in Chile belong to less than 1 per cent of the farmers.

The economic and social implications of this extreme disproportion in the distribution of the land and its wealth in such a predominantly agricultural country as Chile appear vast and ominous in terms of our agriculture. Actually, however, social stratification and economic dependence are of long standing and therefore inherent in the life of Chile, as they are in that of other Latin-American republics. This makes her problem less immediately acute but proportionately more difficult of ultimate adjustment. Already, however, some of the larger estates

The monkey puzzle or Chilean pine (*Araucaria imbricata*) is found only in an isolated zone on the Andes of south Chile and Argentina

A party of poncho-clad Chilean cowboys and Araucanian Indians riding through the weird monkey puzzle forest; east of Temuco, southern Chile

are being subdivided, and the economic condition of the small farmer, and especially of the farm laborer, is being ameliorated.

The average small farm in Chile is worked by the farmer and all of his numerous family who are physically able to share in its labor. On the large estates the farm work is done by resident laborers called *inquilinos* who are under contract to serve the patron in return for board and lodging and a daily wage. For wages they receive from thirty cents to fifty cents a day, but it must be remembered that living costs in Chile are much lower than in the United States. For lodging they are given a rather dilapidated house, and for food a limited ration of meat and bread. In addition they have the right to work a small plot of ground for themselves and to pasture their animals on the patron's land. Of late years, especially on estates where the most valuable farm produce is grown, the inquilino is becoming better off as to living quarters. On the other hand, as in the United States, it will be a long time before adequate water, light, and plumbing come to the average Chilean farm.

In addition to the inquilinos there are itinerant farm laborers imported to lend a hand during the harvest and at other seasons when agricultural operations are temporarily heavy. These nonresident workers, called *asuerinos,* receive the same food rations as the resident peons, but a 30 to 40 per cent higher daily wage.

In our experience the Chilean farm laborer was a pretty healthy fellow and by no means down on his luck. He was not particularly industrious nor particularly lazy, but merely geared rather low to a monotonous round of simple duties. Man power usually appeared to be available in some excess, so that no one was forced for long periods to undergo severe physical strain. On the larger estates we knew, the patron and his family took a considerable, if somewhat offhand, interest in the spiritual as well as the material condition of their peons, and the whole situation had an atmosphere of the feudal at its best. Whether the ancient form of exploitation of agricultural labor practiced in Chile had its bad aspects when the contact was between the peon and the patron's overseers, we had no good opportunity to determine.

Naturally, many of the wealthy owners of large land hold-

ings spend only part of their time in the country. Most of their
time is spent in Santiago, the capital, or in travel. Formerly
they went to Europe, but today you find many of them in
other South American capitals or in New York City. The immediate administration of their estates has always been in the
hands of an agent or major-domo. Sometimes he is of foreign
extraction, usually German, but more often he has risen from
the ranks of Chilean farm labor by reason of having given some
evidence of administration ability rather than because he possessed superior technical knowledge. As a result the Chilean
farms show little appreciation of the importance of modern
methods and machines in agriculture. Only in the dairy industry, in the more valuable vineyards, and in a part at least
of the important sheep industry that flourishes in Chilean Patagonia, have advances in technique been introduced. Of recent
years considerable attention has been given to improvement
in the breeds of cattle and sheep, and some of the dairies and
most of the shearing pens and slaughterhouses are said to be
well equipped.

We spent some time on one of the great estates in the
lovely, fertile valley of the Rio Aconcagua, north of Valparaiso.
The proprietor and his family had been away for more than a
year, taking the cure at a European spa. We therefore found
ourselves in charge of the major-domo, who received us on
horseback. He was a Prussian gentleman who did the honors
of the establishment in what seemed to us a grudging and
perfunctory fashion, or perhaps he was simply made that way.
However, he warmed up a bit when we asked to see the dairy,
and condescended to dismount. This was quite a relief, because
his horse shared its rider's bad manners and had kept us, who
were afoot, at a distance by constantly bridling and rearing
when we attempted to approach near enough to make conversation easy.

As we walked together toward the dairy, about which we
had heard glowing accounts, we saw that it was the pride of the
estate. The other farm buildings had a neglected appearance.
Even the patron's house and garden could have received considerably more attention than had been given them in his
absence. But the dairy was in the best of repair and its surround-

ings were neat and clean. We arrived just as the milking was over. The milkmaids were exchanging the dairy's clean, starched, blue-and-white overalls and close-fitting white caps for their own, usually less attractive, costumes. The milking barn was in every way modern—large and well ventilated, with a good concrete floor seamed with many narrow channels through which water was circulating. At the close of our tour of the barns and corrals I inspected the building that housed the immaculate utensils and machinery for separating, pasteurizing, and refrigerating the milk. This part of the dairy was evidently the major-domo's special domain; at any rate, in exhibiting it to me he broke down completely and became altogether human in his enthusiasm. As a final gesture of hospitality he ceremoniously offered me a large glass of cold milk.

Florence, meanwhile, had seized the opportunity to spread good will and, incidentally, practice her Spanish by engaging in conversation with the shy but laughing and friendly dairymaids. I found her surrounded by a circle of them. She was putting on a rather remarkable performance and one that was decidedly mystifying, to judge by the expression on the faces of her audience. Apparently Florence's Spanish vocabulary had proved unequal to the accomplishment of some desired result and she had been forced to fall back upon sign language. As she afterwards explained it to me her technique sounded adequate and thoroughly logical. You first bend down to indicate the necessary preliminary to milking—that is, seating yourself on the milking stool. Second, you stretch out your hands and seize and manipulate a succession of imaginary nipples. Then you hold a make-believe container in the proper location, and finally you raise the equivalent of this container to your lips and finish off with a smile of satisfaction. I had to agree that this animated series of attitudes, motions, and facial expressions should lead anyone who was familiar with Florence's, to me incomprehensible, predilection for warm, steamy milk fresh from the udder, to the proper conclusion. On the other hand, I had to point out that undoubtedly the Chilean dairymaids disliked milk au naturel as much as I did and therefore could not imagine what result she was trying to accomplish by her entertaining performance.

I refused to join in Florence's elaborate sign language, and my limited Spanish completely failed to indicate that Florence wanted fresh, really fresh, milk. We had arrived at an impasse, and the young ladies were beginning to look a bit uncertain and worried, when the major-domo appeared. Thereupon we hybridized three or four languages, with the ultimate result that he sent a girl into the refrigerator room where some of the last milking was still untouched. When she returned with a glass of fresh milk smiles of understanding at once illuminated the faces of Florence's late audience. As we walked away I saw the dairymaids repeating to one another sections of her sign language and vigorously nodding their heads—as much as to say, "Why, of course, that explains it exactly; how stupid we were not to understand that the *muy sympatica señora norteamericana* wanted warm, fresh milk."

The great problem in maintaining large herds of dairy cattle in Chile is the difficulty of growing economically, or of importing at a reasonable price, the necessary amounts of proper feed. Natural pasturage in quantity is restricted to the more humid agricultural zones in southern Chile. Even there it is deficient in quality, and better species of foreign forage plants should be introduced and tested for their relative capacity to grow successfully.

In the Chilean farming districts we were constantly saddened by the picture of human machines in quantity laboriously accomplishing those elementary tasks that with us are assigned to agricultural machinery. There are less than fifty thousand plows in Chile, the total number of harvesting and threshing machines is under eight thousand, and the number of tractors is very small. Chilean horses are too light for anything but the easiest farm work, and the ox is the familiar animal in the fields. One man driving a yoke of oxen may have to put in two days or more to break an acre of soil. The sowing and harvesting of the large cereal crops is done almost entirely by hand. A small sickle is used in harvesting and often more than two days are required to cover an acre.

The broken topography of much of Chile's farmland combined with the dependence and rather low intellectual level of the rank and file of her peon labor makes anything approaching complete mechanization of Chilean agriculture neither feasible nor at present desirable. On the other hand, it should be possible to reduce, by at least one-third, the amount of hand labor now involved; and the average farmer would then become more prosperous, or rather, would for the first time know a little prosperity. This prosperity he would inevitably pass on, in some part at least, to his farm labor. With increased profits from his estates the larger proprietor could afford to improve the housing conditions and to raise the general standard of living of his contract labor, with a consequent improvement in its efficiency. In other words, even a limited increase in farm mechanization might usher in a new era in Chile. This means that, so far as Chile is concerned, we can effectively implement our efforts to increase hemispheric good will and solidarity by issuing credits earmarked for purchase of farm machinery.

In our time agricultural products from Chile are not likely to compete either in our own or in world markets with those grown in the United States. Chile now consumes practically all the wheat she harvests, and the wheat crop represents at least 40 per cent of the total value of her agriculture. Increased production, following increased agricultural mechanization, will not result in efforts to sell a portion of the cereal or potato crops in foreign markets. At present local consumption is by no means satisfied, and greater reserves must be built up to meet the often tremendous fluctuations in annual production of these staples that periodically occur because of unfavorable seasons. In addition, improvements in agricultural methods and facilities will for a long time do no more than compensate for recent decreases in productivity of Chile's best soils and for effects of erosion that are considerably reducing their acreage. During the North American winter a few Chilean crops come into our markets in limited quantities. Anyone who has tasted Chilean melons at a season when the best of ours are only a last summer's memory will be ready to demand an increase in their importation and can do so with a clear conscience.

Chapter XIII

LAND OF THE MONKEY PUZZLE

As the Andes flow south from the top of the world, in central Chile, the altitude of their peaks begins to decrease rapidly at about thirty-six degrees South, which represents Concepción's approximate distance from the Equator. Thence, southward, the mountains that make Chile a narrow coastal plain rarely rise more than ten or twelve thousand feet above sea level. After knowing intimately the immensity of the central Chilean Andes and the pass at Aconcagua's feet—where to accomplish a passage across them an altitude of over thirteen thousand feet must be attained—it was a surprise to find that only seven degrees to the south the extension of that high mountain range could be crossed at an altitude of less than three thousand five hundred feet. Either on the coast or in the Andean foothills a progression southward from central Chile is accompanied by a rapid increase of rainfall, which culminates when one enters a land of rivers and lakes where the annual precipitation is above one hundred inches. In localized areas it may reach two hundred inches.

For a number of reasons it was important for us to balance our collecting in arid northern Chile with a number of expeditions into its climatic antithesis, south Chile. In that rainy land we collected in areas along the coast from Constitution to below Valdivia, and also in the foothills and at high elevations in the Andes, especially in and north and south of the forests of *Araucaria imbricata* (monkey puzzle or Chilean pine).

Before the Spaniards came, considerable forests covered large portions of the central valley, the coastal mountain ranges, and the Andean slopes of South Central Chile. Much of this forest was long ago destroyed to provide the large areas that, for a century or two, have been devoted to crops and pastureland. Farther to the south the present-day forests of Chile are first seen. They are largely confined to the Andes and cover the mountainsides to an altitude somewhat above five thousand feet. Still farther south and then for over a thousand miles toward

Cape Horn the forests become denser and denser along the diminishing Andean crest.

The Araucarias, their name derived from the province of Arauco in Southern Chile, are among the most prized pot evergreens in cultivation. For one who is used to seeing stately trees of a number of *Araucaria* species growing out of doors in California, it is amusing to observe the enthusiasm evoked by a two-foot specimen decorating the center of an Eastern dining table. This pot plant is almost certain to be *Araucaria excelsa,* a symmetrical, light-green, little tree with two or three branch-stories, each of which is formed by four or five horizontal branches arising in a ring about the scaly stem. Its popular name, Norfolk Island pine, locates its native home. There are other Australasian species also.

The hardiest *Araucaria* is *A. imbricata,* monkey puzzle. It is probably the best known member of the genus, because most widely grown. It thrives in cultivation not only in California, Florida, and similar climates, but also in some gardens in Great Britain and Ireland. Like its dinner-table cousin it becomes a symmetrical tree, with branches occurring in whorls. These branches are not, however, horizontal but curve gracefully upward, and numerous branchlets, in pairs, stand out along them at regular intervals. This subdivision of the branching increases as the tree matures, and ultimately develops a complex that might well puzzle the monkey who attempts to find his way to the top of the pyramidal mass. On its native heath it grows to between seventy-five and one hundred feet. The trunk is bare for over one-half its height and supports a wide, flattened crown of long, somewhat scraggly, albeit symmetrically disposed, branches. Thus it often gives the effect of symmetry gone wrong, a weird, bizarre effect almost without parallel among sizable plants.

Like our Sequoias the monkey puzzles were, long ago, widespread in distribution, almost cosmopolitan, whereas today both genera occupy only minute fragments of the earth's surface. In South America the Brazilian *Araucaria* covers a quarter of a million square miles, with its best development in the State of Paraná—whence its local name, Paraná pine. The only other species in our sister continent, the monkey puzzle, is today limited to an isolated zone in the southern Chilean Andes, and across the border into Argentina. The Chileno calls this, his most famous conifer, *el piñon* or *pehuen.*

Tourists sometimes have the good fortune to see Volcan Villarica whose unbelievably perfect, snow-capped cone is reflected in the azure waters of one of Chile's loveliest mountain lakes. On and near the nine-thousand-foot volcano are some of the finest stands of el piñon. For fifty miles south of Villarica and thirty north of it, and nowhere else in the world, forests of this Disneyesque tree are scattered in larger and smaller groves. They like altitudes of two thousand five hundred to three thousand five hundred feet where they feel the pressure of cordilleran winds, which reduce the extreme humidity characteristic of lower altitudes in the southern Andes. I saw only an occasional monkey puzzle that had chanced to extend beyond the southern limits of its distribution, in the mountains northeast of Osorno. The Prince, however, spent some days in rainy December among the Araucarias east of Temuco, and Rodolfo, at a better season for collecting, made a big haul of fine plants on their northern margin.

In the Araucaria country the Prince met Padre Athanasius Hollermayer, who has spent forty-five of his eighty years as a missionary among the Indians of Southern Chile. First at one mission station and then at another he has labored to Christianize and to improve the material condition of the descendants of those hardy, warlike Araucanians, who for nearly half a century successfully defended south central Chile against the Spaniards. From boyhood he has pursued a love for natural history, and the opportunity to observe and collect the plants of one of the world's most remarkable vegetations has been a constant leaven in a life of toil and hardship, of unselfish devotion to the needs of those who live a primitive life far from the comforts and contacts of civilization. He writes to me often and sends seeds and pressed specimens of many of the fine south-Chilean plants he knows so well. With pardonable pride he has listed for me the numerous genera and species that have been named in his honor, previously unknown plants discovered by him in the Andean foothills and among the less lofty coastal ranges. Of special interest is the new genus and species of the

Cruciferae, or Mustard family, *Hollermayera silvatica,* which the padre found at the foot of ten-thousand-foot Volcan Llaima, that dominating landmark on the Andean horizon east of Temuco.

Our most intensive work in southern Chile was carried on somewhat below the area where the Araucarias are abundant, in the Switzerland of South America, often referred to as the Chilean Lakes. At one time or another seven members of the two expeditions collected in that glorious region, which recently has been advertised among, and increasingly visited by North American tourists. Florence and I, with the Prince, were there in December, 1935, John and Rodolfo in March, 1939, and Walter and Alan went through it a little earlier in 1939 on their way back from the Patagonian adventure.

There is, doubtless, a certain scenic analogy between the Chilean land of lakes and the Swiss Alps that may justify the tourist bureaus in trying to popularize the appellation "Switzerland of South America." For us, however, that marvelous country of dense forests, foaming rivers, sparkling lakes, and snowy volcanic peaks has a distinction all its own. It is sufficiently unique so that it need not, indeed cannot, be described in terms of any other geographic area.

The train we took for the south left Santiago in the evening and arrived at our destination, Osorno, in the late afternoon of the next day. It was a first-class train, with sleeping cars of modified wagon-lit design, and a good diner. Remarkable to relate, the windows in our coche dormitorio were not only clean but abnormally large and double-paned, so that the panorama of the Chilean countryside was clearly and conveniently displayed, while the dust and soot, which made many of our South American train rides uncomfortable, were excluded.

Most of the daylight portion of the journey showed a sequence of green and still greener landscapes. The actual and, even more, the potential abundance which its geologic and climatic features confer upon this extension of the great central valley of Chile was impressive. Everywhere we saw wide stretches of cultivated soil and wider sweeps of lush pastureland. Often the fields were set apart, one from the other, by rows of straight, slender Lombardy poplars, through the delicate tracery of whose narrow crowns the distant Andes hung like a vague, dull-green, white-capped tapestry let down from the pale-blue, cloud-flecked sky.

In midafternoon the character of the terrain was somewhat altered. More and more often the right of way crossed larger and smaller rivers. The land became more rolling, and its greenness acquired that depth and intensity of shade which tells of almost too abundant stores of moisture in the soil. River margins and all depressions became increasingly marshy. At the same time the areas of cultivated land were less extensive, and thin, scattered groves of *Nothofagus,* the southern beech, began to be a familiar element in the landscape.

On hilltops and slopes neat and attractive farm buildings appeared. They spelled prosperity and evidenced the pride that the hacendados took in the character and appearance of their establishments. Most farms elsewhere in Chile reflected a far different attitude, and had been characterized by an almost complete absence of paint and a considerable untidiness. They impressed us as decidedly dejected, even verging on the decrepit. But here we saw well-constructed and well-arranged collections of hip-roofed barns, low silos, fenced corrals, and hints of flower and vegetable gardens around the small but comfortable farmhouses. All the buildings were likely to be painted a dark red, and, like redded sheep on a Devon hillside, stood out in pleasant relief against their rich green background. It was all reminiscent of something quite distinct from the South America that we had known. Casting about in remembrance we realized that what we were seeing possessed a distinct flavor of the Danish countryside.

Actually we were traversing Chile's most important dairy district. It has been developed by German immigrants who began to arrive in south Chile nearly a hundred years ago. When we left the train at the spic-and-span little city of Osorno, the markedly Teutonic atmosphere of business and society in Chile's southland was immediately impressed upon us. There were German names on the shops, German faces in the streets, and the hotel porter understood my German better than my Spanish —not that the former could have been much more intelligible than the latter.

The middle of February is summer in the Chilean lakes, and December represents early spring. In 1935 it felt like winter after the balmy days in the Vale of Paradise, but we had been warned and were therefore provided with warm clothing. The Hotel Osorno, where we stopped at first, obeyed the calendar, not the thermometer, and the big radiators in all its rooms were icy cold. Otherwise our quarters were comfortable—a replica of the best chamber in the best inn of a small German town, a generation ago. It was full of overstuffed furniture with knitted doodads plastered over arms, backs, and seats of the chairs, sofas, and stools. The windows were decorated with elaborate lace curtains, double above and falling away to each side in fat curves. The double bed was a real bed, high with a two-foot-deep, near-feather mattress, wide with the biggest and hardest bolster that could be devised, and handsome with a heavily embroidered lace-trimmed spread. Everything was painfully immaculate.

The meals proved to be all that the character and quality of our room and its decorations suggested that they might be—clean, bountiful, and a little powerful. The first evening, when the succulent pot roast and brown gravy, flanked on one side with properly boiled potatoes and on the other with steaming sauerkraut, was placed before us, we looked at each other and said, "Heidelberg!" We always say "Heidelberg" when, in foreign lands, a period of semifasting on uncongenial viands unexpectedly ends in a proper pot roast. One of the winters we spent in Berlin threatened to become nothing but zwei Eier in Glas three times a day, because we could not eat the good meat rendered unpalatable by greasy gravy. At Easter we went to Heidelberg for a short holiday and were greeted by south German cooking in the form of pot roast properly garnished. Heidelberg may mean a lot of other things to you, but to us it means pot roast!

The tide of German immigration into south Chile began in 1852, probably as a result of the favorable reports of the half-hundred or so Germans who had arrived in the Osorno area some years earlier. In November, 1852, the three-hundred-ton schooner *Susanne,* four months out of Hamburg, landed about one hundred Saxons and Silesians. In six years the port

and town of Puerto Montt had increased in population from
fifty to six hundred, and of this total almost one-half were Germans. Thus in southern Chile as in the United States, a fair
share of the population which is of German origin has its roots
deep in the beginnings of the economic and cultural development of its foster fatherland. And, of course, the same is true of
other South American republics.

From Osorno as headquarters we made a number of collecting trips toward the coast, to the Andes, and into the heart
of the lake region. Our first took us some twenty miles east
of Osorno to the justly celebrated falls of the Rio Pilmaiquen,
just below the point where the river leaves Lago Puyehue—
most of the geographical names in south Chile have an Araucanian Indian origin and are more or less unpronounceable.
At the start the road through the gently rolling hill country
was good enough but later became rougher, and we were glad
to be packed rather tightly in the ancient Ford which, with
driver, we had hired for the day.

Just out of town we began to meet country people on their
way to market. Some were on horseback, sitting well forward
of large panniers containing fresh vegetables and other farm
produce. Others walked beside a yoke of big oxen that were
slowly but steadily pulling long, narrow wagons loaded with
forage or lumber. Their plodding steps were directed by a
touch of a long, slender goad. When we appeared in the offing
shouts were added to the authority of the goad and the team
swung off into a grassy track that paralleled the graded road.
A few huasos trotted by us, dressed in their going-to-town costumes—broad, low-crowned, stiff, felt hats, gaily colored ponchos, long, bright-buttoned, leather leggings, and big wheel-
spurs. Later we learned that in the south, as in the rest of Chile
to a lesser degree, only the townsman walks, and a fine horse is
the countryman's constant companion and most prized possession.

The vegetation near the falls was said to be of some special
interest for the botanist. So it proved, except that we were too
early for the blooming of many of the species that were the
most unfamiliar. After some persuasion the chófer brought the
car as close as possible to the falls. They had grooved a rounded

chasm into which the Rio Pilmaiquen dropped, first sheer and then in cascades, for a sufficient distance to create a dull, rumbling roar and a cloud of mist that rose in waves of moisture, as though the cauldron of white water below the falls was at the boiling point.

Florence has no special love for waterfalls. Therefore I was not surprised when she elected to stay by the car and chófer while the Prince and I went down to look over the dense vegetation at the foot of the falls and to collect downstream for a distance. This arrangement did not suit me very well. The chófer looked harmless, but I knew that as soon as we started down from the plateau the noise in the densely overgrown chasm would be so great that Florence could not communicate with us in case of emergency. It seemed to me that she needed some protection and so I took her aside and insisted that she secrete about her person a large, sheathed bowie knife I happened to be wearing on my belt. This was a poor move because, to make her take the knife, I had to refer to my anxiety. It ended by both of us becoming more perturbed than was necessary.

At the bottom of the chasm the Prince and I had our first contact with that remarkable south-Chilean vegetation that later we came to know so well. For hundreds of square miles the eastern surfaces of the southern Andes and parts of the nearby coastal mountain ranges are covered with a temperate rain forest. In general physical features such a forest, which occurs only in a few other areas in the world, corresponds to the tropical rain forest. In other words, the vegetational type and general plant complex near the falls of the Rio Pilmaiquen, at forty-two degrees south latitude, were singularly like those we encountered in east-central Peru, less than ten degrees from the Equator. Near the falls and on the walls of the chasm the forest floor was spongy and knee deep in green vegetation. The trees grew so thick that their crowns merged to form a lofty ceiling through which the sun penetrated only here and there, and then only in slender shafts of light. Rising from the ground among the tree roots climbing plants clasped the trunks and, on long bare stems, carried up their leaves and flowers to become a part of the green canopy above our heads. All this was on a smaller scale as contrasted with the Peruvian jungle, and the species of plants that constitute the two types of rain forest were utterly different. Nevertheless the quality and spatial relations of the two vegetations and the impressions that they made upon us were remarkably the same.

We were hopeful that the *copihue* (*Lapageria rosea*), Chile's national flower, would be growing near the falls, and already in bloom. We could find plenty of copihue plants, but they bore nothing but immature flower buds. Later in the season in a nurseryman's garden near Valparaiso I saw this beautiful, white-to-red-flowered climber in bloom. It is a typical south-Chilean plant, which recently has been discovered in the wild state in, or near, the Vale of Paradise. For many years grown successfully in gardens in Great Britain and Ireland it is little known in California, where, however, it should find a congenial home in favored locations around and north of San Francisco Bay, near the coast. At first glance its climbing habit and long, tubular flowers make it difficult to include it in the Lily family, but on closer examination it clearly belongs there. What appeals to one as most remarkable about the copihue flower is its substance. The petals are thick and firm, with a fine, shining granulation on their surfaces, which makes them appear to be made of frozen snow.

Many collections of *Lapageria* seed have been exported by plant hunters; we ourselves sent home a lot of carefully dried ones. For years it has been known that this seed gave no, or very scanty, germination when grown in cultivation. This was our experience in the Botanical Garden at Berkeley, even though we tried every recognized method of stimulating germination. Then I appealed to Father Hollermayer, who has lived for many years in regions where Lapagerias grow in abundance. He reported that in the forest the big, fleshy seed pods are shed before their contained seeds have escaped, and that as these pods gradually rot the seeds germinate in the decaying pod or in remnants of it that have become detached from the decomposing mass of tissue. In other words, under natural conditions the seed probably never dries before it has a chance to germinate. It should therefore be exported either in the pods or under artificially moist conditions. At my request the padre sent, by mail, a number of ripe seed pods. As I anticipated they began to rot and mold en route to California, and when the shipment arrived at Plant Quarantine in San Francisco it was a pretty nasty mess. Apprised in advance of what to expect and its explanation the inspectors did not immediately discard the apparently worthless shipment but sent on promptly, and in a moist condition, all the seeds that passed inspection. They were planted immediately in a water-retaining compost, whereupon germination soon began and continued until it reached over 80 per cent. Now we have more than two hundred six-months-old seedlings growing happily in the lathhouse.

Although there were no copihues in bloom, and in general we were too early for flowers in the rain forest, the vegetation in the humid chasm of the falls was important. The heavy mists floating across the down-pouring water and over the pools that it formed were continually blown downstream, as well as up the steep chasm walls. In this gentle bath, ferns, mosses, and other lowly plants luxuriated. On every overhanging rock they hung in festoons that waved in the currents of air blowing up and down the gorge. Even the almost vertical gravel slopes were carpeted with green. Where the spray itself splashed up into the forest near the falls, immense near-tree ferns formed an understory in the forest.

After two hours' hard, muddy collecting the Prince and I climbed wearily up the trail to the plateau above the falls, where we had left Florence, the chófer, and the automobile. To our amazement and consternation no one, and no automobile, was in sight. My worst fears had, apparently, been realized. I blamed myself bitterly for having left Florence to the mercies of the native driver, even though she was provided with a weapon of defense. In imagination I saw her protests, her struggles; then, suddenly, I caught sight of the automobile over to the right, partially hidden from view by a small grove of trees. We hurried over to it and were greeted by a most peaceful scene. One of the seat cushions had been extracted from the car and on it Florence sat, engaged in writing a letter. At a respectful distance, against the base of a large tree, the innocent chófer was peacefully sleeping, a local pulp magazine slipping from his relaxed fingers. With a twinkle in her eye and a finger

pointed toward her sleeping companion Florence made a ceremony of presenting to me the bowie knife that I had forced
upon her. She then explained that, at her request, the automobile had been moved to a greater distance from the roar of
the falls, and to a more sunny situation.

There was little sun and considerable rain during our days
in Osorno and the near-by collecting grounds. It therefore
seemed possible that the week we proposed to spend in the Chilean lake region might not yield enough sun for the natural
color movies we wanted, and also that collecting there might be
difficult as well as uncomfortable. Sometimes December, and
even January, tourists go through that aggregation of marvelous scenery without catching more than a glimpse of white
peaks, blue lakes, and green mountainsides through low, drifting rain clouds. However, on the morning we left Osorno for
Ensenada the early morning sun was shining bright and our
hopes were high for good weather.

For an hour or two the highway traversed the verdant, rolling, south-Chilean countryside to which we had now become
accustomed. Straggling groves of *Nothofagus* covered the upper
slopes of the higher hills and filled such stretches of level land
as had not been cleared for cultivation. A settled atmosphere of
comfortable prosperity was reflected by the substantial farms
and by the fat herds of dairy cattle slowly moving across the rich
grasslands. The warm sunlight began to dissipate the damp chill
with which southern Chile had so far afflicted us, and the mountains to the east and south slowly took definite shape and form
as the mists and rain clouds rolled away from the horizon.

The large, glass-enclosed autobus contained, in addition to
Florence, the Prince, and myself, a man and his wife and their
servants. Their speech indicated that they were of German extraction, presumably prosperous south-Chileans off for a holiday
in the lakes or heading across them to Argentina. Soon, however, our fellow passengers began to exhibit an unnecessary
hauteur and even some resentment at our presence, and so we
examined them a little more carefully. Their traveling clothes
cut in the English fashion, their motions and actions stiff and
punctilious, and their much-traveled and overlabeled baggage
suggested that they might be touring Germans—people of

In southern Chile from 150 to 200 inches of rain may fall annually which means rivers, waterfalls, and dense vegetation. Pilmaiquen Falls

Mount Osorno, the "Fujiyama of South America," gem of the Chilean Lakes

Chile's Switzerland—azure lakes, velvet forests, glistening peaks

Padre Athanasius Hollermayer, the missionary-botanist of southern Chile

The long trumpets of copihue, Chile's national flower, are white to maroon

Florence and the Prince in a flowery meadow, Lago Todos los Santos

In length, the leaves of *Gunnera* far exceed the author's 73 inches

means, perhaps of title. The latter identification later proved to
be the correct one.

From our windows we watched the pleasant panorama, and
now and then tried to photograph the increasingly diverse vegetation. On the hillsides there were larger and larger outcrops of
dark, soft rock. They reminded us that we were approaching a
more actively volcanic region than any we had yet seen. The
pasturelands decreased in extent until they became only small
interruptions of a more and more continuous forest. Cultivated
plots were few and brilliant with white daisies that sometimes
spread an unbroken carpet over them. In south Chile, as elsewhere in temperate climates, these imported daisies have become a trial to the farmers. On the margins of the forest and in
small clearings the European foxglove had gone native in a big
way. We saw thousands of purple, and some white-flowered,
foxgloves around and in the lake region. Their introduction,
also, has proved to be highly undesirable and difficult to control.
Even in remote portions of the rain forest we saw the big rosettes of leaves and tall, spiky flower stalks competing far too
effectively with native, ground-cover vegetation.

As the road topped a low ridge we had our first sight of
Lago Llanquihue (which, if necessary, can be pronounced
"Yankeé-way") and of some of the volcanic peaks whose pyramidal outlines add distinction to the mountain scenery throughout Chile's Switzerland. Soon we were running beside Llanquihue's blue surface and over the lower slopes of Volcan
Osorno, which at a distance seem to rise directly from the
water's edge. The greatest number and many of the most beautiful of the south Chilean lakes lie north of the familiar tourist
route into Argentina, and so the average traveler knows only
Llanquihue, Todos los Santos, and, across the border into Argentina, little Lago Frias and larger Lago Nahuel Huapi.

Ensenada, our destination, consisted of a hotel, its numerous outbuildings, and a few cottages. This little settlement
lay in a bay at the eastern extremity of Lago Llanquihue. In the
long-distant past the rushing river that flows westward from
Lago Todos los Santos must have entered Llanquihue at a point
where the hotel now stands. Doubtless in the days of Volcan
Osorno's activity its vomit filled the original river channel and

deflected southward the course of the river, which now enters
the Pacific via the estuary of Rellancavi.

From the road a long sidewalk led through gardens to the
porch of the low, spreading, two-story wooden hotel. With the
Germans and their entourage we descended from the autobus
and stood beside a mountain of baggage. Around it the Prince's
duffel bag, our battered suitcases, and the ragged plant presses
made a distinctly unimpressive fringe. The hotel proprietor and
a couple of servants approached us, but with eyes and hands
only for the Germans. In caste of countenance and language
mine host corresponded to them, and even without his obse-
quiousness in the presence of apparently distinguished guests
we had no difficulty in classifying him racially. Paying practically no attention to us he led the Germans along the sidewalk,
while their servants and the hotel porters attacked the pile of
German baggage.

We were tired and hungry. The last part of the ride had
been under cloudy skies and now chill mists began to pour off
the near-by lake. Rain appeared to be in the offing. We not only
wanted, but needed shelter. Under ordinary circumstances I
would willingly have carried the baggage into the hotel, and,
indeed, Florence and the Prince started to pick up some of it.
When I refused to move Florence took one look at my face and
asked me whether I proposed to make a scene. I had not exactly
decided what I was going to do but her question gave me an
idea.

At this moment the hotel porters returned and began to
load more German baggage. I told them to put it down and
pointed to ours. They quite naturally demurred, and we were
beginning to argue the point when the proprietor buzzed up.
Under the stress of emotion I became unexpectedly voluble in
German, and those deficiencies in grammatical construction
that my harangue exhibited were compensated for by its ve-
hemence. I produced my receipt for hotel accommodations,
purchased in Osorno. Smiting it with my fist I demanded to
know why to our rooms we had not immediately been shown.
Were we in the cold on his doorstep like dogs to remain standing while others within escorted were? These so important, so
honored guests, who were they? This last question loosed a

counterflood from the proprietor. Did we not know, had we not understood that during our journey from Osorno a veritable, thoroughly authenticated German Freiherr and his Freifrau were our fellow passengers? The hotel was exceedingly honored by their gracious presence and when his staff had made them comfortable he would gladly do the same for us.

During the course of these blasts and counterblasts Florence had walked away and now stood looking out across the lake with a decidedly indignant back turned in my direction. Meanwhile the diminutive Prince stood at my side, intently examining the ground at his feet. As already explained, he had long been known in California as James West, and his identity had been revealed to only a few friends. I wondered whether in this emergency he would permit me to reveal it to the Chilean lakes also. I turned to him and said, "Jim, may I shoot the works?" He looked up at me with a doubtful smile, hung his head for a moment, and then nodded assent.

By this time the porters had departed with another load of German baggage and the proprietor was bending over the last of it. With an authoritative finger in the small of his back I straightened him up. What had he said, I cried, concerning some German Freiherr? Who were we to be kept waiting on such a pretext? Did he not realize that he was in the presence of Egon Victor Moritz Karl Maria, Prinz von Ratibor und Corvey, Prinz zu Hohenlohe-Schillingsfürst! How could it happen that this Prince of the Holy Roman Empire had been practically turned away from the door of a small hotel, while a mere Freiherr was given every attention by its staff?

Wildly the poor proprietor looked first at me and then at the Prince. After a moment of hesitation Jim stepped forward and, much embarrassed, made suitable acknowledgment of repeated genuflections and waved aside the elaborate apologies that were instantly forthcoming. With a shout the porters were recalled and loaded with our baggage. A triumphal procession then formed—first the Prince, conversing amiably in German with our deflated host, then Florence and myself, and finally the laden porters. I caught the twinkle in Florence's eye and suddenly the humor of the situation took possession of both of us. The contrast between the elaborately outfitted six-foot

Freiherr and our little, bareheaded Prince, in faded sweater and ancient kahki pants, was too much. We were purple in the face by the time the proprietor had bowed us through the hotel entrance.

From that day on the Prince was a marked man in the Chilean lakes, and it did not suit him at all, particularly when touring North Americans caught up with us. The staffs of the hotels in which we stayed pointed him out with pride to their guests, and my compatriots sought his acquaintance in order to shine by reflected light. The word "Prince" was constantly floating from hotel transoms, and, to cap the climax, a wealthy Westerner, who was stopping at our hotel in San Carlos de Bariloche, made repeated efforts to introduce us to "my friend, the German Prince."

The hotel at Ensenada was a pleasant and comfortable place and the food proved to be excellent. During what was left of the afternoon following our arrival clouds lay thick on the heights above and mists filled the forests below, so that there were no views of nearby Mt. Osorno. As we went to sleep the rain began to rattle on the roof above our heads, and I had premonitions of leaving the shores of Lago Llanquihue without pictures of the famous "Fujiyama of South America."

Something awakened me very early. The first dawning was filling the room with uncertain light. Unconsciously I was drawn toward the open windows. In a moment I found myself gazing, almost without comprehension, upon one of the most beautiful things in the world. In the light of dawn, against a delicate, pale-pink sky, the mists were withdrawing from the white crown of the perfectly symmetrical, volcanic peak of Mt. Osorno. In the foreground scattered groves gradually became continuous with the green bulk of the rain forest which flowed without interruption up the smooth and rapidly increasing gradient until it seemed to end in the snow, three thousand feet below the gleaming apex of the mountain.

I called Florence and, enthralled, we hung upon the windowsill. While we were absorbing the wonder before us fiery lights began to play over the snowy summit, and the morning dawned fast. Suddenly I thought of pictures, and a few moments later the Prince and I were hurrying down the road with tripod and movie camera. We set up our apparatus and then prayed that the film was absorbing a little, at least, of the marvellous perfection, the unapproachable majesty of the glistening, white, pink-tipped cone above our heads. But it could not record the delicious, moist breath exhaled from the awakening forest, the shivering coolness of the gentle breezes that ruffled the blue-gray surface of Llanquihue and spent themselves among the rough, volcanic boulders over which we climbed; nor could it absorb the tiptoe-provoking stillness of earliest morning spread across all those miles of water and green canopy beneath our feet.

Soon Florence joined us, and together we watched a progression of lights and shadows fall across Osorno's summit. Clouds of pearl-gray mist swept in from the ever-deepening azure of the morning sky and then away again to permit broad shafts of sunlight to be reflected from the glittering snow. We alternately sighed as heavier clouds slowly crept all about the peak and gasped with wonder when they opened for an instant to reveal its entirety. Imperceptibly the broad expanse of water below us gathered blueness from the clearing skies. Beyond was the hotel and from its red roofs smoke drifted into the forest and slowly rose to create a broad stripe of blue-gray mist across the dark-green surface. On the far shore of the lake we could see the lower slopes of Volcan Calbuco, its shattered cone deep in heavy clouds. Now and again they blew apart to show the thin trail of smoke that floated up from the active fires, deep in the bowels of the crater.

By comparison with the supreme heights of the mountain summits in central Chile, the numerous volcanic peaks that add so much beauty to the Chilean lake region are altitudinally insignificant. For example, Osorno is a little less than nine thousand feet, Calbuco, about eight thousand, and Mt. Tronador, the Thunderer, something over eleven thousand feet. But the rains that fall almost daily upon them and the chill Antarctic winds that blow over them so much of the year combine to maintain a snowy cover on these and other, lower, mountain-tops. Long ago the glaciers scooped out deep depressions between spurs of the diminishing Andean ranges so that today the craggy or volcanic peaks seem to rise isolated above the surface of the forest, or abruptly from the margins of the blue lakes that once filled the glacial scars.

The temperate rain forest of southern Chile contains any number of remarkable and beautiful plants. Some of the best of the ornamental species have for years been grown in the famous gardens across the Atlantic. For example, *Embothrium coccineum*, the "fire bush," is not uncommon. It was never the flowering season when I visited the English and Irish gardens in which it was grown, but the size and general appearance of the introduced plants gave no promise of anything to approach the gorgeousness of its December blooming near Ensenada and along the western shores of Lago Nahuel Huapi. On a clear day the mountainsides above the blue lakes showed scattered dots of hard, brilliant, scarlet light that, at first glance, simulated the glow of a hundred little fires beginning to gain footholds in the green depths of the omnipresent forest. Where the density of this forest gave way to open glades or on the edges of cleared lands, *el ciruelillo*, as the natives call it, grew in small groves or as single specimens. They were rarely more than twenty feet in height, rather symmetrical but still somewhat loose and weak; really, treelike shrubs. At the height of the flowering period the extremity of every twig bore its corymb of threadlike, scarlet-crimson flowers against a background of dark-green foliage. A dozen Embothriums in a mass hurl back the sunlight as a burning red haze, so powerful and so rich that the onlooker prepares to shield himself from its expected heat. Sometimes plants are brought into gardens in its homeland, and prove to be adaptable and to respond to cultivation by an increase in their naturally rapid rate of growth and development. On the shores of Nahuel Huapi wealthy Argentinos have acquired large estates. Into some exotic species of trees and shrubs have been, mistakenly, introduced. Such foreigners look exceedingly out of place and compare unfavorably with the splendid and luxuriant native vegetation. On some estates *Embothrium* and other ornamental species of the encircling rain forest are employed in informal landscaping about the buildings. One designer, needing material for a long hedge, experimented successfully with the fire bush. Trimmed and clipped to a height of five and a width of three feet it made a tight and colorful protective edging.

Other genera of the ancient family *Proteaceae,* in addition to *Embothrium,* are interesting and decorative elements of the rain forest. First, the three species of *Lomatia* (*obliqua, ferruginea* and *dentata*) , none of them large trees and some with a tendency, like the fire bush, to be a bit on the loose side as far as branching and general habit are concerned. The second of these three species, called *el romerillo,* is the most important as an ornamental, and for the cabinetmaker provides a source of rich, close-grained wood that takes a high polish. Its large, shining, dark-green, fernlike leaves and racemes of yellow flowers attracted the attention of early plant hunters. Related to the Lomatias is *Guevina avellana,* again a small tree. At the beginning of the southern autumn it is covered both with the red balls of its maturing fruit and the white racemes of its late flowers. In common with *Embothrium coccineum* and the Lomatias, this *Guevina* should be grown widely, instead of rarely, about San Francisco Bay and farther north along our Pacific Coast. This is also true of the other plants from southern Chile that have been or will be referred to. Although they may not accurately preserve their native times of flowering, December to March, they are sure to add color to Pacific slope gardens at a season when color is at a premium.

Certain exotic ornamentals luxuriate in the cool, wet climate of southern Chile. Nowhere else in South America did we see Rhododendrons. In Osorno gardens there were magnificent plants of the hardier species and hybrids. I remember particularly the ponticums. Some of them had become trees, and under their wide-spreading branches Florence and the Prince walked about while I attempted to photograph the demonstration they were giving of the size of this ordinarily shrubby species. The surfaces of these giant Rhododendrons were decked with big, dark-lavender pompons, from some of which the flowers were being shed to cover the near-by garden paths with a heavy, colorful mantle on which we hated to walk.

Of annual garden material there was some, but none of it was flowering in December when we saw Osorno. Many of the larger gardens had collections of roses, and they were as remark-

PLANT HUNTERS IN THE ANDES

able as the Rhododendrons in size and luxuriance of bloom.
There must have been that same quality in the atmosphere
which, along the coast of the Vale of Paradise, gave flower
colors an amazing depth and intensity of shade. Most of the rose
varieties in Osorno gardens were the old European favorites.
Their flowers were extremely large and full, and the substance
of the petals and their rich coloring exceeded anything we had
ever seen before.

The floor of the rain forest, dim and moist, was rich in
mosses and ferns. Along the many rivulets and lesser streams
that flow silently between the bases of the tree trunks this
ground-cover grew to waist height. When the watercourses
crossed small, rarely occuring, treeless meadows their banks
were heavy with *Gunnera*. From creeping, rootlike stems embedded in the soaking, acid soil its immense leaves rose from
six to eight feet and carried a six-foot, circular blade. One day
when we came across a peculiarly gigantic mass of Gunneras I
constituted myself movie director and tried to put on a show
for the camera that the Prince was operating. Just as in the tropical rain forest, so in a temperate one it is unwise to go across
country without guides. Since on that day we proposed to work
into uninhabited areas south of Lago Todos los Santos, we engaged two Indians who claimed to know their way about. These
two brought along two assistants, and so we made quite a party.

My scenario called, first of all, for the shooting of a wall of
giant *Gunnera* leaves, followed by a slow panoraming of the
camera to show the character, extent, and density of this amazing brookside vegetation. I had hidden the Indians behind the
wall. They were supposed, when notified by a shout, to thrash
about and produce an exceeding and mysterious agitation of the
giant leaves. At a second shout they were supposed to break
through the leafy wall and advance on the dead run toward the
camera. Covered to below the knees with their typical, blue-
black ponchos that were decorated with elaborate geometrical
designs in white, the guides, it seemed to me, would make unusual subjects for the screen.

Although of an habitually stolid and even sullen race I
thought that our Indians became a trifle inspired and even enthusiastic after their instructions had been elaborately and re-

peatedly explained to them. The sequel indicated that I was mistaken. Probably they were only registering amusement or amazement at the vigorous pantomime I had to put on to explain their act. At any rate my first shout produced no result. The Gunneras did not move, nor did any signs of activity follow subsequent shouts and loud-voiced inquiries. Finally I looked around and there were the Indians in a little group behind the camera, silently watching us. We thereupon went to work and ultimately succeeded in getting them to hide behind the Gunneras once more. When all was in readiness I shouted, with what was left of my voice. We waited patiently, and then, with an almost imperceptible movement of the leafy wall, four heads close together appeared for an instant and promptly disappeared again. Then and there I decided that my training and experience did not fit me to become a successful impressario.

Near the *Gunnera*-bordered meadow, and someday to become an extension of it, stood an acre or two of dead and dying trees. Some had fallen and were fast rotting on the saturated soil. Over their decaying tissues the small, round leaves of a variety of *Nertera depressa* made a smooth, green carpet set with thousands of bright, reddish orange droplets. I used to see this species, years ago, grown in a two-inch pot and sometimes called "bead plant," in the Christmas windows of some of the California florists. The minute leaves were almost completely hidden by tiny, round, pale-orange fruits that had a transparent, glassy, beadlike quality. By comparison, this south-Chilean plant was a giant, with larger, almost succulent, dark-green leaves and orange-coral berries almost as large as marbles. On hands and knees I hunted the ripest of these attractive fruits, smeared the seed-containing flesh on bits of newspaper, and then stuck these seed collections in my hatband to dry. Months later, in the process of packing or unpacking our Chilean collections, someone must have discarded as worthless those dirty, yellow scraps of paper and only long and diligent search discovered one of them with a few seeds still attached. Today we have a half-dozen plants growing vigorously from this seed. I am impatiently awaiting their flowering and fruiting to see whether these California-grown Nerteras will show the abnormally large beads that ornamented the parent plants I found in that far-off Chilean rain forest.

In Chile there are two kinds of "honey." In most restaurants in the central section and in the north, they offer *miel de palma* which, as we have seen, is obtained from the sweet sap of *Jubaea spectabilis,* the Chilean palm. In the south a true honey, *miel de abeja,* is served. It is a pale-yellow, viscous, slightly grainy substance ready to be spread like peanut butter, and possesses a flavor to which a kiss should be blown. Its delicious taste and scent are derived from the aromatic nectar of *el muermo, Eucryphia cordifolia.* This tree, one of the most beautiful in all Chile, grows to a height of one hundred feet. We saw single specimens in open parts of the rain forest and they almost always had a columnar form, with heavy branches clothing the trunk nearly to the ground. Late in the summer this massive column is covered with goblets of snow, lovely fragrant cups like miniature white roses. They swarm with bees and other insects. On a still, warm, sunny day a cheerful humming always announces your approach to this *Eucryphia.*

In addition to the copihue, that splendid climbing lily that we first saw near the falls of the Rio Pilmaiquen, there are a number of vines in the wet forests of southern Chile. The ornamental value of some of them has long been appreciated, but they are rarely, if ever, grown in California. As contrasted with the copihue that blooms rather near the ground, such a vine as *Mitraria coccinea* usually flowers unseen, high up on the trunk of a forest tree where thin shafts of light penetrate the leafy canopy above. This climber is called *la botellita,* referring to the flasklike shape of its reddish vermilion flowers. Often we were aware of its presence overhead only by fallen petals at the foot of the tree which it had climbed.

There are a few isolated areas near the Chilean lakes where relics or remnants of the Magellanic floras, now eight hundred miles to the south, are to be found. Since we were on the spot it seemed too bad not to explore at least one of these remarkable and little-known islands of Antarctic plants, and accumulate additional evidence bearing upon the geologic history of the lower west coast of South America as revealed by the present-day distribution of its vegetation. In the coastal cordillera near Osorno is a long, moisture-laden three-thousand-foot-high plateau where one finds species that really belong only near the tip of the continent, and along with them, typical rain forest plants altered in form and structure by increased altitude.

In 1935, Florence, the Prince, and I attempted to reach this unique collecting ground. We started by automobile and were to continue on horseback. It had been raining intermittently all the day before and when we got under way the first stretch of country road was sloppy. As the hilly country approached the rain became continually heavier. The car skidded badly, even on the easy curves, and, without chains, appeared to have little chance of negotiating the increasingly high ranges, over the first of which we were slowly passing. The rain beat through the cracked and poorly fitted side curtains, and gusts of wind blew muddy wheel spray into our faces. The car began to slip and slide on the heavy grades, and by the time we topped this first rise the chófer had to stop so that all the water in the radiator should not boil away. In order to get a bit of exercise and because nothing could be worse than the cold, wet inside of the car, I opened a door and crawled under the curtain out into the pouring, driving rain. Then I started to walk downgrade on the slippery grass that bordered the sea of mud into which the surface of the road had disappeared. Just beyond the crest I saw a horse standing beside the green pathway and beside it a large bundle of some sort. Nearer approach revealed this bundle to be a south-Chilean huaso in his best regimentals, curled up sound asleep almost under the hoofs of his fine horse. He had pulled his gaily decorated, heavy woolen poncho over his head, drawn his knees up under his chin, laid his broad-brimmed, low-crowned, black hat to one side, and let nature take its course. Apparently the effects of too much alcohol, acquired in near-by Osorno, had overtaken him on his way home, and, being a hardy soul and relying upon his poncho and leather leggings to turn most of the deluge of rain, he decided to sleep off his jag on the spot. As I stepped off the grass into the muddy road the horse slowly turned his head and watched me pass, but, aside from skin twitchings where rivers of water splashed down from the ponderous sheepskin saddle, no part of his rain-soaked body showed a sign of movement.

I walked far enough down the grade to see that a lake had collected in the first hollow. Beyond it were other lakes. The hills were misty with the rain that showed no sign of abating its intensity. Obviously we could not get much further without danger of stalling the automobile, and the *fundo,* or farm, where horses could be obtained was still far away. I therefore ordered a retreat, and while the chófer hunted a spot where he could turn around we went out into the dripping forest and managed to collect enough so that our abortive expedition was not a total loss.

At a slightly drier season and a better one for flowers and seeds John, in 1939, managed more successfully to get into the Cordillera de la Costa. After two attempts and a lot of exceedingly hard going he reached the high plateau and the peculiar vegetation I had wanted to collect. Were space available his experiences botanical and otherwise deserve to be recounted in detail. He saw virgin forests in which the *alerce* (*Fitzroya patagonica*) grew to extreme size. This conifer, peculiar to the southern Andes and much prized for its handsome, easily worked, and lasting wood, is becoming extinct in areas where it can be profitably cut. Under its spreading branches masses of *Desfontainea spinosa* lightened the gloom of the rain forest with thousands of large red, and yellow, tubular flowers. He saw many rare plants in their most luxuriant and uncontaminated condition. There was the curious, dwarf conifer, *Dacrydium fonckii,* which grew only two feet high, in the boggiest depressions of the rain forest—an olive-green treelet with minute, scaly leaves covering the dwarf branches. Nearby was *Podocarpus chilena,* a tree that might be mistaken for a willow were it not for its brilliant red, yewlike fruits. The shadowy forest floor was here and there brightened by the reddish blossoms of *Philesia buxifolia.* Its local name, *coicopihue,* relates it to copihue, the climbing lily already mentioned more than once, and its specific name refers to its boxlike leaves that are bright-green above and grayish white below. Although its flowers are smaller than, and somewhat different in shape from, those of *Lapageria rosea,* its exceeding floriferousness and more shrubby habit recommend coicopihue as an ornamental.

In a fundo garden John saw a low, woody plant with at-

tractive, red tubular flowers. It proved to be *Latua pubiflora,*
the *palo de brujas* or witch's stick of the Araucanian Indians.
From its leaves they have from time immemorial brewed a hell-
ish concoction that, like hashish, produces mental disturbances,
violent and lasting ones. At this farm he was hospitably received and soon found himself treated like a member of the
family. At dinner one day the middle-aged, German-Chilean
proprietor recounted a part of the story of his life, most of
which had been passed in south Chile. Many years before he
had become the junior partner in this fundo, and after marry-
ing the senior's daughter ultimately became full owner. He said
that his first wife had died in her youth after bearing him several children and was succeeded by the present mistress of the
establishment who added three more members to the family.
At this point she took up the tale and laughingly referred to the
fact that in addition to his legitimate brood, her husband had
"cinquenta y tres niños afuera." The others at the table, some
of whom were apparently among the fifty-three illegitimates,
nodded vigorously and exclaimed, *"que diablo,"* *"que macho,"*
("what a devil of a fellow," "what a vigorous male,") as they
gazed proudly at the head of the mixed household. John was
thunderstruck by this revelation and had some difficulty in re-
gaining his composure and still more in visualizing his host in
the role of a dashing Don Juan.

In addition to John's successful trip through the marvel-
lously rich vegetation of the far-southern Cordillera de la Costa,
many of us saw the dominant elements of that vegetation on
both sides of the Chilean lake region. The rain forest is a never-
ending source of delight and fascination for the plant hunter.
At the beginning he must become accustomed to the ever-
present *Nothofagus,* a tree much like a European beech and
still not like it. He notes its variations—in size, and form, and
characters of the leaf—and attempts to recognize the three or
four species that are said to be present. He looks forward eagerly
to coming across his first *Drimys winteri,* winter's bark, and
hopes that the season has arrived when snowy flowers are clothing it from head to foot. With even greater anticipation he
watches for the heavy, ragged crowns of those South Andean

conifers, *Saxegothea* and *Fitzroya,* which rise solitary above the green surface of the rain forest's roof.

As an old friend he welcomes *Berberis darwinii,* but is amazed at its height and bulk, for in the shade of the moist forest this barberry grows to fifteen feet, and its orange flowers and blue-black fruits are suspended far above his head. Also familiar will be *Fuchsia magellanica,* at last far enough south to justify its specific name, and the Godetias, Epilobiums, Violas, and many more. Most of them will, however, seem a little less familiar when more carefully examined and prove to be species known only from southern Chile. Of oddities there will be a number, among them chupalla *(Fascicularia bicolor)*, the big bromeliad that lives in trees and at a distance suggests mistletoe on a scale unknown in the north.

Natural openings or clearings in the rain forest contain their own specialties. Among them we found many orchids. Most of them were large Chloreas, with pale-green petals striped with bright green; but there were also other, lowlier species, more delicate and more complicated in flower form. Rarely, and in the partial protection of low shrubs, we came across *Asarca odoratissima,* its part pale-yellow, part bright-yellow flowers, full of delicate fragrance. Soft grasses, easily crushed, tiny annuals with inconspicuous flowers, and harsh-leaved little ferns formed the cover through which the orchids and other attractive species pushed their leaves and blooms to accept all the sunlight that the short southern summer can allow them.

The Switzerland of South America will always be a lodestone and we shall never be happy until we see it again. There is so much still to be collected, so many out-of-the-way corners to be explored, and so much unraveling of variations and peculiarities of form and structure that can be attempted only on the spot where the living plants in their remarkable environment are available. In addition, next time perhaps I can manage to get in a little of what the experts claim is the finest trout fishing in the world!

Chapter XIV

DESERTS AFLOAT

IN THIS final chapter I return you from the southern limits of our Chilean wanderings in the land of lakes and rivers to the arid coasts of northern Peru, the starting point of all our west coast collecting. On and near those deserts where, at the beginning, we saw verdant meadows on the burning sands the last important collecting of the two South American expeditions was carried on. It is therefore appropriate that this account of plant hunting in the Andes should be concluded at the point where our hunting came to an end.

Travelers by sea from Panama down the west coast of South America are mystified as well as perturbed by a sudden change from stifling tropical air to chill, foggy breezes. Without warning they envelop the ship at a point about four degrees south of the Equator or opposite Point Parinas, the most westerly extension of our sister continent. Inquiry of the ship's officers discloses that this remarkable atmospheric shift occurs where the tropical waters are met by the mighty, one-hundred-mile-wide Humboldt Current. It bears not only cool waters but in addition a rich flora and fauna, everything from microscopic seaweeds to the wide-winged albatross. At the meeting place of the two zones of ocean temperature the marine organisms characteristic of both give up the ghost, and in a wide graveyard a feast is spread for sharks and other predatory denizens of the deep. This famous current of northward-flowing cool water establishes by its name an undying monument to the eager, tireless scientist, Alexander von Humboldt, who visited Peru in 1802.

As we have already discovered, the Humboldt Current provides western Peru with an air-conditioned climate, a cool and dry one. The average annual temperature at Lima is sixty-six degrees. By contrast that of Bahia at the same latitude, but on the other side of the continent, is eighty degrees. The upwelling of cold water from the tremendous depths of the Pacific along the west coast has a part in the cooling and drying proc-

399

ess. As it blows over the cold Humboldt Current humid air is chilled and condensed to form rain and fogs. The latter are often wafted inland to support "meadows on the desert," but rains rarely fall on the land because the rapidly warming air takes up moisture rather than discharges it.

In the months of January, February, and March a warm ocean current flows south along the coast from the equatorial regions. Since this current makes its appearance more or less during the Christmas season it is called *El Niño,* the Christ child. Where the Humboldt Current deviates westward toward the Galapagos Islands, El Niño wedges itself in along the coast. As it moves southward it seems to deflect the Humboldt Current still farther out to sea. This landward intrusion of El Niño occurs each year, but only rarely does this warm current extend southward far enough to affect the climate of the coasts of northern and north central Peru. But when it does, then come torrential rains that flood the deserts and melt the adobe houses of coastal towns. In recent times rains have descended upon the arid Peruvian coast at intervals of seven years. In 1911, 1918, 1925, 1932, there were periods of heavy rainfall, with 1925 the year of heaviest rains. Those who find in sun spots a satisfying explanation for almost every climatic variation have no difficulty in pointing out the basis for the periodic extension of *El Niño* beyond its apparently normal southern boundary. Certainly there were abundant predictions that 1939, the seventh year from 1932, would see rains in the northern desert of Peru. These predictions came true to such a degree that not only "the rains descended" but in addition "the floods came."

During March the Lima newspapers carried accounts of high water in the north. Roads had been washed out, bridges had gone down the rivers, mud houses were fast disintegrating, and each day the rains increased in violence. I had heard stories of the vegetation that clothed the desert in former rainy years— of head-high grasses, of the sandy, wind-swept dunes transformed into a rolling sea of green. It looked as though the coast of Peru, for once at least, was going to do something for us, and something quite exceptional in the way of vegetation. It was too good an opportunity to overlook and so I asked Harvey and Bob to head north again. Incidentally I wanted to know something

Naked guides lead the botánicos over a ford of the flooded Piura
Capparis (shrubs) and *Nolana* bloom in the Piura desert during floods

Bob and Ing. Favre botanizing on lush "deserts afloat" near Paita

The muddy canal of a desert city meets many needs—Chiclayo, Peru

more about the tobacco varieties that were being grown commercially near Tumbes, at the coastal frontier of Peru and
Ecuador. On the morning of March 28, Florence and I saw the
two botánicos off for Piura, at the Faucett airfield in Lima. We
remained in headquarters to dry the plants and seeds which they
were instructed to send to Lima by air express as fast as collected.

North as far as Trujillo, across the coastal strip over which
they had already traveled both on land and in the air, there was
little change in the desert landscape that was so well known to
them. They saw the same sandy wastes, the same green oases
where diminishing rivers crossed the coastal plains to the sea,
the same tan hills slowly rising to a misty, blue-green background. Beyond this previous farthest north Harvey and Bob
began to look down from eight thousand feet upon "deserts
afloat." Spread out below them was a wide, level plain across
which the first foothills floated in a hazy distance more than
seventy-five miles to the east. Toward the coast, on this Desert
of Sechura, there were broad expanses of water. To the north
the swollen, yellow Rios Piura and Chira spread their overflow
into great, shallow, clear-blue lakes. Everywhere was a startling
confusion of sands and waters.

Northward from Chiclayo over a still arid portion of the
desert the picture gradually changed. Imperceptibly the monotonous yellow and brown plains began to become more and
more stippled with dark dots. At first this stippling was light
and then gradually it became deeper and almost continuous.
Each stipple represented the position on the sands of a shrub or
small tree. Most of them were algarroba (Prosopis), but some
were Acacia and Capparis. If a brief rainy season occurs they
bring forth leaves; otherwise they wait until a year when there
is sufficient moisture to produce foliage. The roots strike deep,
as much as twenty-five feet, until they make contact with the
water table. Competition for available water is so great that
these desert "trees" cannot grow close together and survive; and
so from the air the general effect of their distribution is that of
groves or orchards with the individual plants spaced at fairly
equal distances one from the other. To the east and north the
stippling graded into a denser vegetation, which they knew was

the rainy-green shrubland, and it in turn dissolved into the evergreen shrubland. In the farthest distance, inland, were the blue-green ridges covered with the forests of the Ecuadorean jungle.

The landing field at Piura was a shock, not because it was any rougher than other Peruvian coastal landing fields had been, but because it was overgrown with a dense stand of grass and weeds. Unless you have actually seen the north Peruvian coastal strip in its intense aridity no words can picture the contrast in its appearance produced by the heavy vegetation that follows the sabbatical downpours of rain. At Piura the landing field actually had to be mowed with a scythe if planes were to be brought down safely. During the years over which the Faucett Air Line had been operating along the Peruvian coast such a condition had never before existed.

From the air, and at a considerable distance, they had seen that the Piura and Chira rivers were out of their banks, but had no conception of the volume of water that was running in them. The Piura was a deep menacing flood, flowing exceedingly fast and full of sand and debris. The soft banks were constantly crumbling as the river cut deeper down into its channel, and then pushed out to undermine its feebly constraining margins. Later on Harvey flew over the Rio Chira. Only four sections of the steel highway bridge could be seen, the other three had been torn out and washed downstream. Traveling on the same plane was the engineer who had built the bridge. It was his contribution to the Pan-American Highway. According to his statement the bridge piers went down thirty-six feet and rested on sandstone. Most of this coastal zone is composed of sandstone, clays, and stratified conglomerate that was uplifted from the sea bottom in relatively recent times, geologically speaking. It is said that these deposits carry evidence that periodic floods occurred in Peru in the far distant past.

The Peruvian Government maintains an agricultural Experiment Station between Piura and Paita, the next considerable settlement northward on the coast. This station could not be reached by the regular road, now under water, but the botánicos managed to get there by following a devious route connecting a series of haciendas lying on higher ground. Ingeniero

Julio Favre, who was in charge, showed them his experimental fields, and later took them to some of the regions where the rain flora appeared to best advantage. Apparently the heavy rains were not uniformly distributed, and the vegetation that followed them was likewise variable in distribution. Plant growth in the area between Piura and Paita was particularly rank. Grasses and herbs made a veritable jungle, difficult to walk through. The number of species involved was not large, some fifteen or twenty being responsible for the larger share of the vegetation. The seeds of these plants must have maintained their viability over periods of at least seven years because in the intervals between heavy rains it was rare to see any vestige of green on the desert. As they tore their way through rank growths of mallows, morning glory, Nolanas, and other fast-growing herbs it was only an occasional sandy opening that reminded them that this was one of the driest deserts on the earth's surface. Even cacti cannot exist on those exposed, sandy wastes. Cacti are shallow-rooted plants and only appear on the eastern foothills where a little moisture is condensed on the soil surface almost every year.

There are two common but very interesting plants that laugh at dry years on the desert, even though they are not deep-rooted. When the rains come they luxuriate and spread wide mats of green on the sands. When it is dry they simply retire underground. One is called *yuca de caballo* (*Proboscidea altheifolia*). It develops a large storage root, usually three or four inches in diameter and over a foot long, which retains moisture and food so efficiently that the plant will survive for several, perhaps many, years without putting leaf and stem above ground. As its name indicates it is relished by horses. Burros and goats also fancy it. Like pigs rooting for truffles all three paw the earth in likely spots to dig out the roots of yuca de caballo. Travelers in the desert when overtaken by thirst are said to emulate their four-footed friends and to obtain some relief by chewing the succulent roots. The other plant whose underground storage organs permit it to defy a limited amount of total aridity is known as *yuca de montaña* (*Apodanthera biflora*) because its roots can, in a pinch, be substituted for the true *yuca* (*Manihot*).

On the north coast the most important native desert food supply for animals is the algarroba. When Harvey and Bob were there these small trees had matured an abundant crop of long green pods. They have a sweetish taste and are sometimes, but rarely, used for human consumption. For animals they take the place of corn, oats, and hay, and in fact constitute a complete diet, either fresh or dried. All over the desert the harvesting of these pods was in full swing. Sacks of them were carried in to Piura on the backs of men and beasts. Free-ranging burros and herds of goats were making the most of this year of plenty and eating their fill. As was to be expected the goats were the most consistent and effective gorgers and all but climbed some of the trees whose limbs were lowest.

The oddest sight of all was the impromptu agricultural operations in the environs of Piura. At the first evidence that this was to be a year of rains, patches of maize, beans, squash, melons, and even cotton had been planted on depressions in the desert floor where water would be likely to accumulate. Each of these scattered desert plantations had to be fenced against the invading hordes of goats and burros. Fences were improvised from any material that came to hand, mostly brush struck in the ground, and the plantations had little regularity of outline. Normally the extreme north coast of Peru is hot as well as dry, and the addition of moisture had turned the desert into a gigantic hothouse where the hurriedly planted crops were growing at a great rate. There seemed to be no doubt that they would achieve a mature cotton crop, because in 1932, a less favorable year, the desert cotton planters had considerable success.

The flora of the rainy desert showed a great sameness, and it was not long before they felt that they had collected most of the relatively few species which had sprung up in the Piura area as a result of the abnormally heavy rains. It was therefore decided that Bob should go still further north along the coast, while Harvey went eastward into the foothills, so that a thorough canvass of the vegetation of "deserts afloat" might, if possible, be made. The problem of coastal travel was relatively easy but to get across the flooded deserts to the east was not so simple. Ingeniero Favre helped by putting Harvey in touch with a friend who not only gave advice as to routes but also offered to provide introductions to hacienda managers at Pabur, Serran, Canchaque. It would be a day inland by truck to the first stop, another day by mule to Serran, and then another day on muleback to Canchaque.

Bob's diary gives an amusing account of their efforts to leave Piura:

"Wednesday. Harvey found that there was a truck going inland to Pabur this very afternoon. I was not so lucky and cannot get a truck to Talara until tomorrow. So after lunch I bade Harvey farewell and then trotted off to the Faucett office to express a bundle of wet plants by next morning's plane to Lima, for Harper to dry. Settled down for a dull wait only hoping that my truck would be sure to go, and not put off its start until day after tomorrow or later. After dinner, went to the movie house and sat down and pulled my feet under me to keep the fleas from traveling up from the floor. When the light came on after the first reel, imagine my surprise when I turned around and there sat the supposedly departed Harvey E. Stork, Ph.D., in person! His truck had traveled all over the town to pick up a little cargo here, and another passenger there, checked out at the guardia civil, and at last made a start toward the eastern hills. After a half hour the chófer drove more and more slowly and finally stopped. He then addressed himself to the passengers and, with many gestures and torrents of adjectives, called attention to what he said were rain clouds ahead, to the early approach of nightfall, to the dangers of automobiling in general and in particular, and ended by expressing a desire to turn back and wait until early the next morning when a fresh start would be made. Five of the passengers were insistent that he go ahead. On the other hand, a Chinese merchant, convoying boxes of "made in China" goods, and one other passenger agreed with the chófer. The majority being against him he was forced to start on again, but after a couple of miles he lost his nerve completely and without a word turned around and headed at top speed for Piura.

"Thursday. After bidding Stork another good-bye at 9:30 —he was supposed to leave at 7:00—I caught my own truck, Talara bound, and we went through the usual procedure of touring around town, gassing up, drumming up more passengers and, finally, visiting the guardia civil. Of course, we had to make a last stop on the business street. Whom should I see but Harvey! We then engaged in a third, but not final, farewell because my truck made another aimless swing around the town and I had a chance to shout a few parting wisecracks at Harvey whose conveyance, when last I saw it, actually looked as though it was getting under way!

"Instead of heading directly north toward Talara we went west over the new, oiled road to Paita; since, according to report, the direct road to Talara was washed out. A good, warm morning, but windy enough to be cool in our speedy, uncovered truck. In about an hour we were in Paita. It seemed a friendly little town, nestled beside a natural harbor but one which is too shallow to allow the close approach of ships. Then we turned north to follow a coast road that wasn't a road at all. Just as the bumping, banging ride had reached a peak of misery for the passengers, a short but snappy thunder shower added the more than final touch. In thirty seconds I was soaked to the skin.

"The desert floor, like that near Piura, was sprinkled with shrubs and low trees and a few flowering plants. An hour and a half after leaving Paita we dropped down the steep cliffs bordering the Rio Chira. Since the bridge was mostly out of sight downstream, we had to cross the soupy waters on an extremely doubtful-looking lighter, similar in design, but not in size or strength, to those used in unloading freighters along this coast. The trip across the Chira flood waters was exciting. The lighter was so overloaded with passengers and cargo that the brown water kept slopping over the sides. This flood water was heavily charged with coarse sand. Too often big logs and uprooted trees came shooting by. A few days ago, this same lighter swamped and five passengers were drowned. They didn't have a chance because, in the water, your clothes almost immediately become sand-laden.

"On the other side we had to wait three hours for the Talara bus to flounder through muddy roads and pick us up. Then it took a long time to get to Talara because the new road —part of the Pan-American highway—was apparently built in the notion that it never rains along this coast and so is mostly washed away. After climbing out of the Chira river valley the vegetation increased immediately and the rolling sand hills were absolutely covered with a luxuriant growth of grasses and herbs. In places they were from hip to shoulder high. Is it possible that this is the absolute desert we saw not so long ago? The bus ran north to the foothills before turning west to Talara. These foothills, also, are covered with an exciting green flora and I am keen to get my hands on it."

Unfortunately Bob did not have much chance to collect in the green fields the heavy rains had left behind. The reason is revealed by the entries in his diary that refer to the next few days:

"Monday. Talara. I planned to drive on north to Tumbes for a day or so but find that the roads are completely washed out. Could fly, but there are only two planes a week, Tuesday and Friday, so that's out and I still have a day's collecting to do here and I don't have to join Harvey in Piura until Friday. Hence, plan to fly south Wednesday and put in a day's collecting at a hacienda north of Piura.

"Tuesday. Talara. The weather is so hot that I consume untold quarts of water and fear that the results are something akin to the 'Rocky Mountain trots.' At any rate I felt quite in the trotting mood all day. Spent six hours working along the bluffs east and south of town and still no indication of *Nicotiana,* although managed to pick up a few plants not found before.

"Wednesday. Talara. What a night! Sleep out of the question on account of I was so busy. Violently sick at my stomach and had binding cramps all night. Was supposed to take the plane at 7:30 but knew that I couldn't remain away from a convenience the thirty minutes necessary to reach Piura and, as I am ahead of schedule, decided to rest up today and take tomorrow's plane.

"After a makeshift breakfast I went to the hospital of the American Petroleum Company in the hope of getting something that would stop my bellyache and the other thing. The American doctor suggested that I take the amoebic dysentery test. I agreed, although I feel sure that my condition is the result of too much hot weather plus too much ice water. Dropped by the Faucett office to arrange for reservations for tomorrow's plane and found there was nothing doing, so made arrangements to drive back. Spent the rest of the day trotting.

"Thursday. Talara Hospital. Another bad night. The doctor informs me that I have picked up a lot of amoebae and should start taking treatment at once. The treatment consists of five daily injections of emetin, a special diet, then ten days of rest accompanied by pills. A Grace Santa boat is going south on Monday, so by taking my first injection today I can have the fifth Monday and finish treatment in Lima. After sending telegrams to Harvey and Harper, I moved my belongings from the hotel to the hospital."

After four days in the excellent Talara hospital Bob was well enough to get aboard the *Santa Clara* on its way to Callao. After a week of rest, diet, and pills in Lima he was as chipper as ever. Some weeks later, when he and the others left Peru on the homeward voyage, he was entirely free from amoebae.

Harvey's route to Hacienda Pabur led through algarroba-covered terrain into territory that normally receives more and more rain as one goes eastward, until some twenty-five miles inland some rain falls each year. With a little moisture the columnar cacti could live, along with algarroba and other small trees and shrubs, which together began to form an increasingly dense shrubland. Most conspicuous was *overal, Cordia rotundifolia,* a common shrub bearing masses of bright yellow flowers. At the base of the foothills *gualtecas,* or *Bombax* trees, began to appear. They are relatives of the cotton plant and their seed pods are full of a brown wool. The trunks are smooth and spindle-shaped with the greatest diameter halfway up. Another dominant tree was *Bursera graveolens,* called *palo santo.* It closely resembled *Bursera gummifera,* which in Central America is called by the natives "naked Indian," and by the Jamaican Negroes, "birch," because it has a brown papery bark. Below these taller trees were smaller tree species, then shrubs, and finally a very dense stand of annual plants, the latter making it difficult to detour around the ponds of water that stood in the single-track truck road.

Pabur is situated on the river, and as they came nearer

their destination the roar of the water could be heard a mile and more away. Boulders were rolling along just under the surface, trees and shrubs whirled by on the yellow flood, and the riverbanks were constantly crumbling. In fact the banks had eroded so far back that some of the shacks occupied by peons employed on the hacienda were endangered. The road passed an old, spreading algarroba that had lost its moorings and was toppling over. It was only a question of hours until the angry current would work under the landside roots sufficiently to start the poor tree downstream to the Pacific. The unbridled power of this wild river whose banks were utterly powerless to restrain or direct its flow was immensely impressive.

Don Augusto, local manager of the hacienda, was not at home but was scheduled to get in at any time. When he had not returned at midnight Harvey carried to bed the certainty that all chance of getting mules and making an early start toward Serran was gone. That evening and well on into the night the rain came down in torrents. There was some thunder and lightning. Listening to a continuous near cloudburst pounding on the roof and to the increasing roar of the mad river it was hard to believe that during most of the year this region was a dry, brown, dead desert except where parts of valleys could be irrigated to produce some cotton and rice.

In the small hours of the morning Don Augusto and his ingeniero returned. They had worked most of the night to extricate their Ford truck from a mudhole. At breakfast they were excusably tired and cross. Don Augusto was impolitely positive that a trip to Serran would be impossible because the road was either washed out or under water. He made it clear that no one in his right mind could even think of making such a trip.

During the afternoon the rain somewhat decreased in intensity, and Harvey started out to begin a search for *Nicotiana, tabac cimmaron,* reported to be growing somewhere across the river. A big dugout canoe looked safe enough. Four men paddled and two poled but their competition with the current was not very successful, and the party was lucky to make a landing only a quarter of a mile downstream. Then the boatman walked along the bank and towed the canoe upstream for a considerable distance, so that when ready to return they would be able to land the dugout at the starting place on the other side of the river. Ashore, Harvey soon found that the going was too bad to make collecting profitable. However, he stuck to it long enough to assure himself that there was no tobacco near the river. His pertinacity so far as collecting was concerned must have impressed Don Augusto, who worked himself into a state of sufficient enthusiasm to order Miguel, his leading arriero, to get ready three of the hacienda's best mules for an early morning start toward Serran and Canchaque.

Next day Harvey and Miguel spent ten hours in the saddle, on roads and trails through the brushland that consisted of a continuous alternation of mudholes and small lakes. Every now and then they had to leave the flooded track and strike across country through a tangle of shrubs and annual vegetation. Canchaque is excellent orange country and several trucks bringing out ripe fruit had bogged down. The approach to each of these stranded trucks was signaled by quantities of orange skins, remnants of a feast which every passerby had enjoyed. At Palo Blanco the road, for a quarter of a mile, led through a lake of shallow water. The mules were *muy fuerte,* but toward the end of that grueling day were only with much violent persuasion forced into a lope. Finally they rode into Hacienda Serran. A few moments later the heavens opened. This time there was no question that it was a cloudburst and a first-class one.

The hacendado, Don Félix, and his ingeniero, Don Miguel, gave Harvey a hearty welcome. It was their opinion, however, that a trip farther on toward Canchaque was impossible on account of the high stage of the Rio Pate and the Rio Piura, both of which would have to be crossed. After another night of downpour one of the river men was sent out to the Pate to ascertain its condition. He returned to say that no man or beast could possibly cross. Making the best of it Harvey settled down to collecting in the hills behind the hacienda. From these hills he could see the broad yellow flood in the valley and was willing to agree with the reports of its impassability.

The town of Serran, home of the peons who work on the near-by hacienda, consisted of a miscellaneous collection of scattered huts and cottages. Goats roamed on every hand, great herds of them, and their smell not only rose to high heaven

but spread far and wide over the land. Pigs continually went
in and out of the shacks and were just as continually being
chased out, along with chickens, ducks, and dogs. Apparently
it had never occurred to anybody to fence them out. Under such
circumstances children never think of small animals as household pets but only as animate objects to be yelled at, chased,
kicked, beaten with sticks, and pelted with stones. Hammocks
graced every cottage, hammocks inside and hammocks outside,
and men and women everywhere lolled in them. Everyone
seemed to have hammockitis. All the towns along the road to
the east were the same and all of them advertised their proximity by the penetrating aroma of goat. The people were swarthy
brown, almost black. There seemed to be Negro blood about,
or perhaps it was the hot sun.

The church at Serran consisted of a shed built on a prominent mound near the edge of the town. It had a thatch roof, and
barbed-wire side walls as a protection against goats and burros.
A heavy cross of hewn timbers stood under the roof and on it
were crossed bones and skulls, wisps of wilted flowers, and
crudely carved figures. At long intervals an itinerant *cura* arrives, stops a day or two to baptize, and also to read the marriage service for those who had committed matrimony in the
interim.

Conversation at the hacienda turned to the government's
recent refusal to send a schoolteacher to Serran. It had been
based on the report that there were not enough children to
justify public instruction. Harvey suggested that there must be
over a hundred children in the neighborhood, a number sufficient to require the presence of at least one teacher. But Harvey was entirely mistaken. There weren't over a hundred; indeed, there were exactly six—the children of the hacendado
and of his ingeniero. For, of course, the ragamuffin offspring of
the peons gamboling with the goats in the village street did not
figure in anyone's plans for formal instruction. Theirs was to
be the ultraprogressive education of the great out-of-doors.

At various points along the road Harvey was continually
being mistaken for one of the long-awaited highway engineers.
The almost impassable condition of the road, following the
heaviest rains in many years, had brought numerous petitions to

the provincial officials in Piura asking that "the government do something about it." Two engineers had been sent inland to make a report. They had disappeared somewhere along the way, and no one had heard from them. On the second morning of Harvey's stay at Serran they appeared at the hacienda with the story that they had found the rains and roads not to their liking and so had laid up for a couple of days at a small town off the main route. When things did not get better they had come ahead.

Early the next morning, when the engineers examined the river, they thought there were indications that it had started to fall, and announced their intention of trying to cross. They invited Harvey, with Miguel and the mules, to join them. Several other travelers had accumulated at Serran, and when they rode out of town anxious citizens and complacent goats stared after a small cavalcade of eleven mules carrying riders and freight. Two black river boys who were to help in the crossing trotted alongside. On nearing the river the party rode upstream for about a mile through dense shrubland to a point where the river fanned out into several wide channels. The two naked river guides then waded out to get the feel of the current and to search with their feet for the shallowest spots. When they had determined the proper course to steer each took a mule on a long rope and led him across. The mules went cautiously and at each step felt carefully for safe footing. The current was strong in the middle of the channels, but nowhere quite deep enough to make the mules swim. The crossing continued until all the animals and their riders or cargoes had safely reached the opposite shore. Then, on the tops of their heads, the river boys carried across those portions of the cargoes that had to be kept perfectly dry.

The next river was not as wide as the Pate had been and was crossed without difficulty. During the remainder of the journey the road was in many places under water and in hilly terrain was often washing away. Along the river valleys it had been built on shelves above the streams. In places these shelves were entirely gone, and then the cavalcade had to take to the slippery hills and flounder about in the dense undergrowth.

Canchaque, which they finally reached after a long punish-

ing day, lies at an altitude of about thirty-seven hundred feet.
It proved to be a rather inviting mountain town where the
visitor is utterly detached from the outside world and finds employment only in communing with wild nature and studying the
peaceful life of simple villagers. But let him visit Canchaque
in the dry season only. When they arrived the town was *muy
triste*. The oranges were rotting on the trees in the informal
groves scattered in the town's environs. Trucks had ceased to
ply over the mountain road down to the coast, and such few
staple foods as the townspeople had come to depend upon from
below were getting scarce. Worst of all there was legitimate
doubt whether the road would ever be rebuilt, so completely
had the floods obliterated much of a roadway that has taken
many years to build. The first citizen of Canchaque was a
Señor Aguila. In his house travelers found posada. There they
found the largest general store. There, too, was the office of the
alcalde, he himself serving in that august capacity. Since he was
the alcalde his brow was knit. He was plainly worried. The
people demanded that something "be done about our sad
plight." While they did not exactly blame him for their misfortunes they had a definite notion that a leader ought to lead.

On the night of Harvey's arrival a meeting of prominent
townsmen was convened in Aguila's house to discuss with the
government engineers the increasingly serious emergency. All
that the experts could do was to give estimates of the length of
time required to re-establish highway communication with the
outside world when the rains had finally stopped. This was very
cold comfort, because it appeared that the rains were never
going to stop. The streets were brown floods, thatched roofs had
become so sodden that they sagged, and little streams were penetrating them to make the insides of houses almost as wet as their
outsides. The better-built residences, provided with tile roofs,
were none too dry. People went about wearing drenched clothes
and long, wet faces.

Even light-hearted Miguel, Harvey's arriero, succumbed to
the universal pessimism and for three days could think of nothing but getting home to Pabur before the road should become
impassable even for mules. He kept reminding himself, Harvey,
and anyone else who would listen that he had a wife and three

children and that they must be considered as well as the desires
of the botánico. He painted a sad, but still somewhat exciting,
picture of the river leaving its banks near Serran and washing
his shack and contained family down to the ocean. When a
Peruvian peon is really gloomy he challenges the world's cham-
pion pessimist. During the first day of his lamentations Harvey
persuaded him to stay on with the promise of extra pay. On
the second day even this inducement had no appeal, and Harvey
was forced to become exceedingly hard-boiled and to threaten
dire consequences if there were any signs of desertion. On the
third morning Miguel looked so excessively sad that Harvey
purchased a large bottle of pisco and directed him to drown his
sorrows and homesickness with some cronies he had picked up
in the town.

Looking northward from Canchaque a mountainside, some
five miles away, showed a white, vertical streak—the foaming
waters of a great waterfall. A local dignitary, named Simon, was
recommended to Harvey as one who, for a consideration, would
act as guide to the region near the falls. Next morning they
started out. After crossing the Canchaque river, a narrow mountain torrent at that point, the path led through orange groves,
over a turbulent tributary stream, and then began to climb
rather abruptly toward the level of the falls. It was no path,
but just a mud slide, up which they progressed by grabbing
such shrubs and small trees as were still firmly anchored in the
softening clay and sand. Finally it appeared necessary to cross
a deep ravine. But its sides had already begun to slide and in
the bottom there was a moving mass of mud, carrying boulders,
shrubs, small trees—the whole rolling down the narrow valley
like a lava flow. At sight of this strange phenomenon Simon
became extremely agitated and demanded that they return to
Canchaque as quickly as possible. Such a terrible thing he had
never seen in his life and these awful rains would probably
continue until all Peru turned into mud and flowed into the
sea. To make matters worse the clouds thickened at noon, and
soon a drizzle started that grew into a steady downpour and
finally assumed cloudburst proportions. There was nothing to
do but hasten back. Before they reached the town the press full

of soggy plants was so wet that the paper folders were fast returning to their pristine pulp stage.

Although he had not, of course, communicated the proposal to Don Augusto at Hacienda Serran, nor to Miguel, Harvey had from the beginning hoped to push on still further inland beyond Canchaque to the city of Huancabamba. He had written me to this effect and I received the letter in Lima on the same morning that, through the grapevine, I heard rumors of a severe outbreak of bubonic plague in the Huancabamba region. Imagine my state of mind, particularly as there appeared to be nothing that I could do to warn Harvey of what he was getting into. Because of the floods all telegraph lines were down and no messages could be sent from the coast up into the back country through which he was traveling. No one could suggest a method by which I could make contact with Harvey. Finally I discovered that the "plague squad" was leaving that afternoon by airplane for Huancabamba, or as near the city as a landing field could be found. By pulling some wires I succeeded in having one of the doctors on the squad take a message to Huancabamba. It was then to be carried by an Indian runner down the trail to meet Harvey. This sounded like a very long chance, but it was the best I could do. Until a reassuring telegram from him arrived five days later Florence and I went about our tasks as normally as possible. According to our settled policy in such emergencies we did not refer to what might be happening to Harvey in the north Peruvian mountains, but thoughts of him and his position were constantly in our minds.

What had actually happened was this. On the day after the futile collecting expedition to the falls the rain came down in a continuous torrent, Miguel's hangover made him dangerously nasty and positive that the time had come to desert, and all reports indicated that the road to Huancabamba was thoroughly washed out. Nevertheless Harvey was determined to wait another day even if he had to sit on Miguel's head to keep him from disappearing. Early in the afternoon word went about that a messenger was looking for the botánico norteamericano. After some exploring of grog shops Harvey finally located a drunken Indian who handed over my message about bubonic in Huancabamba. In another hour the mules were being loaded for the return to Serran.

On the way up the principal burden of one of the pack animals had been two sacks of algarroba pods for mule feed. By this time the sacks were empty and Miguel, seeing an opportunity for a little business on the side, had filled them with Canchaque oranges. He asked Harvey's permission to transport them back to Pabur, where they would command a scarcity price. Harvey agreed, but had a distinct feeling that rough roads and detours through the brushland would reduce the oranges to juice and pulp long before Miguel's market was reached.

The return journey to Serran was wet, muddy, slow, but without mishap except for one baptizing of a plant press in a flooded river. It slid from a mule's back as he sprang up the riverbank and, by good luck, fell into shallow water near the shore rather than into the current that would have swept it away. The rivers had lowered considerably and the crossings were not difficult. In Serran a supply of algarroba pods was bought so that the mules might eat, and after a night's rest the journey to Pabur was resumed.

Harvey insisted upon an early start from Serran, because he wanted to collect the flora of the *Bombax* forest through which they would be traveling and still arrive in Pabur by daylight. It was a fine morning with sunshine for a change and bird notes in the air. Bird life was abundant along their route and they saw many beautifully plumaged varieties. The piping note of a singer called *chilalo* was with them all the way down to Pabur. Its nests were built of mud, grass, and pebbles plastered together on the ends of slender twigs of the algarroba trees. They were more or less globose, about eight inches in diameter, and looked like small termite nests. Strong winds did not dislodge them, nor did continuous rainfall disintegrate them.

The road was terrible, much worse than it had been on the way up. The mules needed rest at frequent intervals, and then there was opportunity to collect specimens. Despite rests and slow travel in general the animals tired rapidly, and it was noon before Harvey and Miguel reached Buenos Aires, one of the goat hamlets along the road. It must have received its name before the goats arrived! They bought more algarroba pods for the mules and in one of the thatched huts were served with what passed for luncheon.

In the afternoon the animals poked along more and more slowly. Even a strong mule tires fast on a slippery road where mud has to be fought every inch of the way. It soon began to look as though darkness would overtake them before they reached Pabur. While they might do the last stretch of road after dark it was doubtful whether, without some daylight, they could hope to cross the great lake of river overflow near Palo Blanco, unless the water had gone down considerably since they had navigated it some days before. Miguel, with a sort of whistling-in-the-dark courage, kept saying that they would make it easily. They met a traveler who had come from Pabur that day. He claimed that the lake was a foot deeper than before and that it was becoming continually more difficult and dangerous to cross the rising expanse of water. The sky began to be heavily overcast, and it grew darker rapidly. Then the mosquitoes came out in full force and Harvey knew that this was bad malaria country. He put on a raincoat, hung leafy branches over his bare knees, and, with another branch, attempted to fan the mosquitoes from his face and neck. By the time they reached a small settlement a mile or so from the lake the darkness was almost complete.

Their voices and the splashing and wallowing of their mules on the muddy road brought most of the citizens to the doors of their shacks. Inquiry gave most positive assurance that it was dangerous to cross the lake in the daytime and that at night it was definitely impossible. A garrulous old man invited them to stop with him. He boasted of having the largest house in the settlement and that to him always came the good fortune of entertaining travelers when night had overtaken them in the neighborhood. So to Pablo's establishment they went.

It consisted of a crude corral containing two cows and some pigs, and an attached shack. They turned the mules into the corral and laid out an algarroba-pod supper for them. The pigs grunted a welcome and watched for a chance to squeeze into the house, as Harvey, Miguel, and Pablo shook off the muck of the corral on its threshold.

At this point Harvey's diary must be quoted: "Two flicker-ing candles revealed a low room, partially divided by a bamboo partition. A dozen chickens had draped themselves for the night on poles along the walls. Two ducks waddled about and quacked vigorously in response to the general excitement that had pervaded the household at the advent of visitors. With difficulty two large, lanky hounds and a small, dirty, white cur were quieted. Pablo's wife, son, and daughter busied them-selves with preparing hot water for our tea. I shared my canned beef and 'dog biscuits' with the family, and they contributed hominy from a big, black kettle.

"They were very curious concerning us; whence had we come and where were we going? Miguel, tired as he was, rose to the occasion. In his best oratorical manner he did all that he could to impress his audience with the importance of our mis-sion, and I had only to listen in order to learn what a remark-able scientist I was and how I had come all the way from the *Estados Unidos* to visit this particular region where one found such plants as no other corner of the globe contained. Indeed, I learned that we had in our collection many specimens that would command sums upwards of hundreds of soles in the United States. The family proved, however, to be much more interested in our two sacks. Miguel had thrown them in a corner and piled the other baggage over them, hoping that they would not be noticed and thus become the object of an orange raid. But Pablo was suspicious. He asked point-blank what was in the sacks. Miguel replied that they contained some of the sam-ples of plants that the gringo had gathered to take back to the Estados Unidos.

"While I was still taking inventory of the various forms of animate nature that had congregated in this Noah's Ark I began to take council with myself concerning what might be done to secure a peaceful night's sleep. To make the situation almost ludicrous, a red deer sauntered out from the back room, blinked her large dark eyes at all the commotion, and retreated to her corner. She had been captured as a fawn and adopted as a member of the household.

"The old couple offered me their bed, but I declined, with no reluctance. It was merely a wooden platform covered with a cowhide that had been tanned with the hair. Miguel made his bed on the saddle blankets. After considering various alternatives I brushed clean a space on the floor, laid out my sleeping bag, and improvised some uprights to support my mosquito tent. I knew malaria too well from first-hand experience, and was taking no more chances than were necessary. My activities had the greatest interest for the family. In fact a neighbor was called in to enjoy the show. I finally retired beneath the mosquito netting, all of the spectators lending a hand to tuck the edge of the net well under the sleeping bag. Then they stood about viewing the body, as it were, and discussing at great length the advantages and disadvantages of sleeping bags and mosquito tents. Laid out to public view in that fashion, with a candle eerily flickering at my feet and another at my head, I began to realize how old Pizarro must feel as the tourists file by his dessicated form lying in the glass cage in the cathedral in Lima.

"Morning came, and, with it, evidence that Pablo knew that our sacks contained oranges. How he had found out during the night Miguel and I could not imagine, because the protective layer of baggage had not been disturbed. He announced that he knew how to make excellent *punche,* the 'u' pronounced with a very broad sound. From an Englishman he had learned the trick. It was particularly excellent before breakfast. Thereupon he produced a tall tin can, for which he had whittled a crude, wooden plunger. Into this he would have to put some orange juice and some milk. The milk was in the corral. Perhaps we might have some oranges; no? This was directed at Miguel who, with a look of resignation overspreading his dark features, proceeded to untie one of the sacks. For the milk, Pablo produced a kettle and sent his wife out to do a little milking. It was not exactly milking time in our sense of the term, but milking time for these people was simply an occasion upon which they needed milk.

"The milk and orange juice were put into the churn and the dasher worked up and down until an emulsion resulted. Then Pablo produced a bottle with a spot of pisco left in the bottom. With a generous sweep of his arm he dashed it into the emulsion, put on an elaborate stirring act, and finally dealt

the punche into three calabash shells. We drank and pronounced it good. Pablo then insisted that more punche was
indicated and gave me no rest until I had sent Miguel out to
the local drunkery for a bottle of pisco. Thereafter we made
free with the punche. The family must have canvassed the settlement's henhouses, because we actually had an abundance of
fried eggs for breakfast. Following the meal, Pablo decided that
more punche was indicated. After a while Miguel and I found
ourselves thoroughly fortified for the crossing of the *laguna* at
Palo Blanco. When we finally said good-bye, Pablo was still
at the churn and it was a question whether he or the pisco
would hold out the longer.

"Arrived at the lake, it was necessary to swim the mules
and so we had to find porters who would carry our baggage
over a route that was not so deeply inundated but where the
mules could not go. They, sensing that home was nearby, actually broke into a trot. Miguel was delighted with the small
fortune—three dollars U. S.—that I bestowed upon him, and
was exceedingly rejoiced to find both his family and his shack
still intact. I presume that for many days he was the center of
attraction at the Hacienda Pabur, and that his account of our
trip was better embroidered at each succeeding recital."

From Pabur Harvey's coastward journey was uneventful,
but he was thankful to reach comparatively dry ground once
more. At Piura the news of Bob's hospitalization awaited him.
He caught the next plane for Talara where he stayed a day or
two, to cheer up the invalid and assure himself that he was
being well cared for. Then he flew south to Lima and began
the final packing that preceded the homeward voyage, then only
a few weeks off.

On the whole this expedition to northern Peru for botanizing on "deserts afloat" did not pay so much in the way of
exciting dividends as we all had expected, for the combination
of amoebae and high water precluded extensive collecting.
Nevertheless the plants that we had received by air from the
north, and had succeeded in drying, gave an adequate picture
of the vegetation that grows on the sabbatically floating deserts.
To obtain such evidence was the primary objective of the last
Peruvian assignment.

At its close Florence and I said good-bye, on the dock at
Callao, to Harvey, Bob, John, and Walter who, after eight
months, were at last reassembled, to begin their homeward
voyage. A week later we ourselves said good-bye, for the second
time, to the west coast of South America.

INDEX